LAND SURV

G000016762

THE M. & E. HANDBOOK SERIES

LAND SURVEYING

RAMSAY J. P. WILSON, B.Sc., F.R.I.C.S.

*Principal Lecturer in Land Surveying at the
Polytechnic of the South Bank*

MACDONALD AND EVANS

MACDONALD & EVANS LTD.
Estover, Plymouth PL6 7PZ

First published 1971
Reprinted 1973
Reprinted 1974
Reprinted 1975
Reprinted 1976
Second edition 1977

©

MACDONALD AND EVANS LIMITED
1977

ISBN: 0 7121 1242 1

*Printed in Great Britain by Richard Clay (The Chaucer Press) Ltd,
Bungay, Suffolk*

PREFACE TO THE FIRST EDITION

THIS **HANDBOOK** has three aims: to provide a set of study and reference notes for all students preparing for professional and degree examinations and for the National Certificates and Diplomas in land surveying; to serve as a practical reference book for students, graduates and others who are occasionally called upon to undertake some site surveying or setting out; and to remove the mystique so often attached to the processes of land surveying and the manipulation of surveying instruments.

Method of study. Each chapter covers its subject from the simplest approach to the higher standards of application. Not all land surveying syllabuses will include the full range of work which is covered in this book or even in the individual chapters. The extent of any particular syllabus should be established by reference to the syllabus itself and, as these are usually imprecise, by reference to past papers and by consultation with lecturers or tutors. Those parts of the book which are not relevant to a particular syllabus must not be overlooked, however. *Further reading* in any subject is always essential and careful study of the **HANDBOOK** itself, apart from other sources, will help to complete the picture of the whole and will prove invaluable in the understanding of the particular sections.

Progress Tests at the end of each chapter are designed to assist the student in assessing his absorption of the chapter content. Test questions should first be answered *in writing*, and the student should check frequently with the text to see that the answers are correct. Later, by trying to answer the questions without having to refer to the text, the Progress Tests will assist in revision. Progress Test questions which are marked with an asterisk (*) are answered in Appendix IV. The student should attempt the question first and turn to the answer only to check his result. In addition, there are examination questions in Appendix II, which are reprinted by kind permission of the various examining bodies referred to.

Practical work. Although it is just possible to pass an elementary written examination in land surveying without any practical experience at all, this is not recommended! Land surveying is a *practical* subject and every opportunity should be taken to use all types of surveying instrument, especially the theodolite and level. For this reason the use of instruments is described in detail in this book. For good examination answers it is always better to imagine and describe actual handling processes rather than to try and remember a list of instructions, the significance of which may not be fully understood without sufficient practical experience.

Finally, those who expect to handle survey work under site conditions can only do so successfully with experience. The waste of time and the errors caused by lack of appreciation of the basic principles of surveying are of all too frequent occurrence on site work. Correct reference to the HANDBOOK can prevent such happenings and assist the individual in achieving the training and experience required.

March, 1971   R.J.P.W.

PREFACE TO THE SECOND EDITION

MOST basic land surveying processes are traditional and remain unaltered with time, but modern instrumentation and computer techniques have promoted great changes in some aspects of surveying in recent years.

The HANDBOOK is not intended as a treatise in advanced surveying, but to maintain its established position of providing a practical reference some recent changes in certain aspects of surveying have been included.

The use of electronic calculators has been almost universally accepted, and this fact has been incorporated in the consideration of simple calculations, the old-fashioned hand calculating machine having been virtually superseded. Logarithms, however, are still considered to be important in basic training in computation methods, and a sound knowledge of their application is invaluable, especially when batteries run down!

There are improvements in the services provided by the

Ordnance Survey which have come into effect since the previous edition, mainly in the field of Advanced Revision Information using modern reproduction techniques, including the production of maps by computer. Reference to these modern services is now included in Chapter V.

The vernier theodolite is still worthy of consideration in its own right and as an aid to the understanding of optical reading instruments. Chapter VI has been rearranged so that greater weight is given to the handling of modern instruments.

As forecast in the first edition, tremendous advances have been made in the range of Electro-magnetic distance measurement (EDM) instruments now available. Though the basic principles of such measurement remains unchanged, new instruments are electronically operated with push-button simplicity and the manufacturers' range of EDM equipment offers a bewildering variety of electronic advantages. In the limited space available an attempt has been made to give the student some idea of what he will expect to find in various fields of operation today and how such instruments have affected the provision of both plane and geodetic control.

As in the first edition, space limits the inclusion of the derivation of some formulae, but the student may obtain these as necessary from *further reading*, and it is expected that appropriate derivations would be covered in class by lecturers. The range of such formulae has been extended in this edition to cater for the more advanced student.

Finally it is noted that as the National Diplomas and Certificates are being phased out, this HANDBOOK will cover in the main the syllabuses of all the various Land Surveying modules being prepared under the control of the Technician Education Council.

March 1977 R.J.P.W.

NOTICE TO LECTURERS

Many lecturers are now using HANDBOOKS as working texts to save time otherwise wasted by students in protracted note-taking. The purpose of the series is to meet practical teaching requirements as far as possible, and lecturers are cordially invited to forward comments or criticisms to the publishers for consideration.

CONTENTS

LIST OF PLATES

The following plates are to be found between pages 194 and 195

LAND SURVEYING

CHAPTER I

MAPS AND PLANS

REPRESENTATION OF THE LAND

1. Definition of surveying. The dictionary defines surveying as *"taking a general view of; by observation and measurement determining the boundaries, size, position, quantity, condition, value, etc., of land, estates, buildings, farms, mines, etc."* This definition covers the work of the valuation surveyor, the quantity surveyor, the building surveyor, the mining surveyor and so forth, as well as the *land surveyor*. However, in every case there is a common, basic approach to the work, which ends with the *presentation* of the survey data in a suitable form.

2. The process of surveying. Surveying falls into three easily recognisable stages:

(a) *"Taking a general view."* This part of the definition is important as it indicates the need to obtain an overall picture of what is required before any type of survey work is undertaken. In land surveying this is achieved during the *reconnaissance* (*see* **3**).

(b) *"Observation and measurement."* This part of the definition denotes the next stage of any survey, which in land surveying constitutes the *measurement*, to determine the relative position and sizes of natural and artificial features on the land (*see* **4**).

(c) *Presentation.* In any survey the data collected must be presented in a form which allows the information to be clearly interpreted and understood by others. This presentation may take the form of written reports, bills of quantities, data sheets, drawings, etc., and in land surveying maps and plans showing the features on the ground in graphic miniature (*see* **7**). These three stages in the process of land surveying will be examined in greater detail.

1

3. Reconnaissance. The reconnaissance prior to a survey may be considered as being divided into three parts:

(*a*) *Decide on the purpose of the survey.* It is first necessary to understand the purpose of the survey before deciding on its method of treatment. There are four main branches of land surveying, although these separations tend to overlap to varying degrees:

(*i*) *Geodetic surveys.* These are surveys, generally carried out on a national basis, which provide survey stations, precisely located, large distances apart. Account is taken of the curvature of the earth and the accurate measurements used form part of the science of *geodesy* in which the size and shape of the earth are examined. Geodetic survey stations are used as control points to position both *topographical* and *cadastral* surveys when necessary.

(*ii*) *Topographical surveys.* These are surveys where the physical features of the earth are measured and maps and plans prepared to show their relative position both horizontally and vertically. Depending on the extent under survey these may consist of either *geodetic* type surveys or *plane* surveys, where no account is taken of the earth's curvature.

(*iii*) *Cadastral surveys.* These are surveys undertaken to define and record the boundaries of properties, legislative areas and even countries. In some cases cadastral surveys may be almost entirely topographic, where features define boundaries. In others, accurately surveyed *beacons* or *markers* define boundary corner or line points and little account may be taken of the topographical features. Again, geodetic principles may have to be applied, such as in the survey of the thirty-eighth parallel dividing North and South Korea, but much of this work consists of plane surveying.

(*iv*) *Engineering or site surveys.* These are surveys undertaken to provide special information for construction projects. They are essentially large-scale topographic surveys, supplying details for particular engineering schemes, and could include the *setting out* of works on the ground. These are usually plane surveys, but on large projects, such as motorways and pipe-lines, some geodetic control may be necessary.

(*b*) *Determine the accuracy to which measurements are required.* This depends on the best method of presenting the survey information, the scale of such maps or plans as are required and the degree of accuracy needed for any setting out which may be necessary.

(c) *Establish the method of measurement that is needed*. This is part of the reconnaissance stage and involves deciding on the most suitable station positions.

4. Measurement. Two forms of measurement are required in land surveying:

(a) *Linear*. The measurement of the *distance* between points on the surface of the earth.

(b) *Angular*. The measure of the *angle* between survey lines or between a reference direction or line and a survey line in either a horizontal or vertical plane.

One or other or both of these forms of measurement are used in the *four* basic methods of land surveying, which are *chain surveying* (II), *triangulation* (VII and VIII), *traversing* (IX) and *levelling* (X).

NOTE: Surveying from aerial photographs is omitted from this list because, although it forms a major part of land surveying today, it is not an entity in itself. Air survey has to be controlled by ground survey methods and is thus an extension of traditional techniques and cannot entirely supersede them.

5. Control and checking. Two common principles apply to all methods of surveying:

(a) The first principle is to lay down an overall system of stations, the positions of which are fixed to a fairly high degree of accuracy. This is known as *control*. The survey of detail between these control points may then be carried out by less elaborate methods. Errors which inevitably arise are then contained within the framework of the control points and can be adjusted to it. Thus they have no chance of building up or accumulating throughout the whole survey. This is known as *working from the whole to the part*. If this system were not adopted and a survey were made to expand outwards it would be found that small errors would build up so quickly that the survey would become unmanageable and impossible to plot properly.

(b) The second principle is that all survey work must be *checked*. All measurements must be taken in such a way that any error will be apparent before the survey is completed.

6. Units of measurement. The metre is now the standard unit of linear measure, the change to the metric from the Imperial system taking place in stages in Great Britain between the years 1968 and 1975.

(a) *Système International d'Unités (S.I. units).* These have been accepted by international agreement. The base unit of length is the metre, which is defined as "the length equal to 1 650 763·73 wavelengths in vacuum of the radiation corresponding to the transition between the levels $2p_{10}$ and $5d_5$ (the orange line in the spectrum) of the krypton-86 atom."

NOTE: Originally the metre was intended to represent one ten-millionth part of the distance from the equator to the poles. It is now differently defined and, in addition, subsequent measures of the earth's meridian quadrant show that the calculated distance on which the metre was based was inaccurate.

(b) *Linear measurement.* The traditional units of centimetre, decimetre, etc., are now discarded in practice. The kilometre, metre and millimetre only are used in linear measurement.

$$1 \text{ kilometre (km)} = 1000 \text{ metres (m)}$$
$$1 \text{ metre} \qquad = 1000 \text{ millimetres (mm)}$$

NOTE

(*i*) To avoid the need for continually writing m or mm the convention is to show measurements in metres with a decimal point, and to show measurements in millimetres with no decimal point. Where kilometres are used the km must be added.

(*ii*) As most metric countries use the comma as the decimal marker it should no longer be used as a thousand marker as before. However, the Decimal Currency Board prefer the comma to be retained to reduce the possibility of fraud. Either a space or a comma is therefore acceptable as a thousand marker, but in computing it is preferable to use the space to prevent confusion with the continental decimal system.

(c) *Area measurement.* The units used in practice for the measure of areas are the following:

The square kilometre (km²)
The hectare (ha)
The square metre (m²)

1 km² = 1 000 000 m² = 100 ha
1 ha = 10 000 m² = 100 m × 100 m

(d) *Conversion.* The following systems apply:

(i) To convert feet to metres multiply by 0·3048 exactly.

(ii) To convert square feet to square metres multiply by 0·0929 or 0·092 903 04 to gain the exact figure.

(iii) To convert acres to hectares multiply by 0·4047 or 0·404 685 64 for complete accuracy.

7. Presentation. The presentation of the measurements made in land surveying is in the form of maps, plans or diagrams with the information recorded in a suitable manner on the drawings by scale representation, by the use of conventional signs and by the tabulation of notes and measured and calculated data. The most suitable method of representing the information depends on the nature of the survey work.

On *small-scale surveys* where conventional signs will describe many features, detailed measurements of such features are unnecessary. In *large-scale work*, on the other hand, where a precise building outline can be drawn to scale, accurate measurements must be taken of all features which will be shown on the drawing. However, in large-scale work some important features, such as stop valves, cannot always be drawn to scale and only measurements to define their position need be taken.

In *engineering surveys* it is often necessary to take and record measurements which are not required for a topographic representation. Critical distances between abutments, bridge clearances and so on, which cannot be scaled with sufficient accuracy, may have to be specifically shown.

The ability to present survey data in the best possible way can only come with experience, the study and interpretation of existing drawings, and the understanding of the main principle that drawings must be clear and easily read and that every line or feature shown should be capable of ready interpretation.

8. Maps and plans. The difference between maps and plans is that on *maps* the scale is too small to allow every feature to be properly represented to scale. Thus conventional symbols are used to represent features which would otherwise be too small to be recognised. The art of designing suitable symbols has been developed by the Ordnance Survey to a high degree and students should become accustomed to the use of Ordnance Survey maps generally and the interpretation of the symbols used.

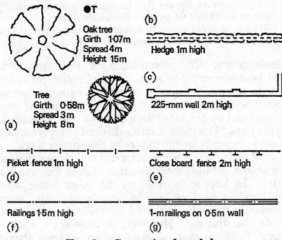

Fig. 1.—*Conventional symbols*

Some of the symbols or methods used in field notes and on plans to represent ground features. These are produced either in black on transparent sheets from which copies are made or in coloured inks on paper for presentation work.

(a) Methods of showing trees in plan. The spread and section through the trunk should be plotted to scale and the description and size must be recorded. The outline can be in green and the branches in light brown and sienna.

(b) A hedge; the root line is shown in black and the outline in green.

(c) A wall.

(d) Any light, open fence.

(e) A close board or corrugated iron fence.

(f) Iron railings or a chain link fence.

(g) Railings on top of a wall.

Plans, on the other hand, show all features on the ground correctly to scale. Figure 1 indicates some common methods of illustrating features on plans and in field books, which are readily understandable. Different organisations will have slightly different conventions for representing detail on plans, and the best are those forms which are simple and clear and cannot be misinterpreted.

9. Relief. So far only the representation of the relative displacement of features in a horizontal plane has been considered. However, points on the ground are also displaced in height, which must also be represented on plans.

(*a*) *Pictorial.* On early plans relief was roughly shown by illustrations. A pictorial view of hills and mountains as seen by the surveyor was the obvious way of indicating their existence, but this was unsatisfactory for two reasons:

(*i*) It was not possible to maintain any scale in height.
(*ii*) The pictures obscured the areas of plan behind them.

(*b*) *Hachuring.* An improvement on the pictorial representation was the use of hachuring to show relief. This too is a pictorial form of showing hills, but in a plan view. It consists of wavy lines drawn down the slopes, the lines being thicker and stronger on steeper slopes. This is similar to the conventional symbol traditionally used to indicate embankments and which appears on Ordnance Survey maps. The Ordnance Survey symbol for cliffs, known as *cliff marking*, is also a form of hachuring still in use.

(*c*) *Hill shading.* Another form of hachuring, which is easier to interpret, is hill shading. This is drawn to represent hills as if light were shining on them and forming shadows. Hill shading, in coloured tints which do not obscure other detail, is used to great effect by the Ordnance Survey in their tourist maps.

(*d*) *Contour lines.* The present method of indicating relief is by means of contour lines. A contour line on a map represents a line joining points of equal height on the ground. From such lines the general shape of the ground represented in plan may be easily read. Contour lines are further examined in V and XIII.

MEASUREMENT FROM MAPS AND PLANS

10. Scale. The scale of a map or plan is the ratio of ground length to the map or plan length. Thus a scale of 1:1000 indicates that one metre on the paper represents 1000 m on the ground, or that one inch on the paper represents 1000 in. or 83 ft 4 in. on the ground. Such a scale is termed a *natural scale* and can be used with any units of measure.

(*a*) *Imperial scales.* Under the old Imperial system scale was often represented by a length in inches on paper being equivalent to a distance in some other unit on the ground, *e.g.* 1 in. = 66 ft, or 6 in. = 1 mile. These scales may be represented as fractions, thus:

$$1 \text{ in.} = 66 \text{ ft or } 66 \times 12 \text{ in.}$$
$$= 792 \text{ in.}$$
$$\therefore \text{ scale } = 1/792$$

This fraction is called the *representative fraction* or R.F. of this scale.

Similarly, 6 in. = 1 mile
$$\therefore 6 \text{ in.} = 5280 \times 12 \text{ in.}$$
$$\therefore 1 \text{ in.} = 10\,560 \text{ in.}$$
$$\therefore \text{ scale } = 1/10\,560, \text{ the R.F. of this scale.}$$

Both of these are representative fractions, but they are not natural or preferred scales.

(*b*) *Metric scales.* The preferred scales for use with the metric system are as follows:

(*i*) *Small-scale maps:*	1:1 000 000
	1:500 000
	1:200 000
	1:100 000 (1/126 720 = $\frac{1}{2}$ in. to 1 mile)
	1:50 000 (1/63 360 = 1 in. to 1 mile)
	1:25 000
	1:20 000
(*ii*) *Large-scale maps:*	1:10 000 (1/10 560 = 6 in. to 1 mile)
	1:5000
	1:2500 (about 25 in. to 1 mile)
	1:2000
	1:1250 (about 50 in. to 1 mile)
	1:1000
(*iii*) *Site plans:*	1:500
	1:200 (1/192 = 1 in. to 16 ft)
	1:100 (1/96 = 1 in. to 8 ft)
	1:50 (1/48 = 1 in. to 4 ft)

(iv) Detail plans: 1:20 (1/24 = 1 in. to 2 ft)
1:10 (1/12 = 1 in. to 1 ft)
1:5
1:1 (full size)

NOTE: Drawings to scales other than to those shown above are no longer expected to be produced.

(c) Scale bars. Another method of indicating scale is by means of a scale bar, illustrated in Fig. 2. This method has two advantages:

(i) It provides a ready means of measurement from maps and plans when a scale is not available.

(ii) If the material on which the drawing is printed is distorted the scale bar will alter accordingly, so that scaling will still remain reasonably accurate.

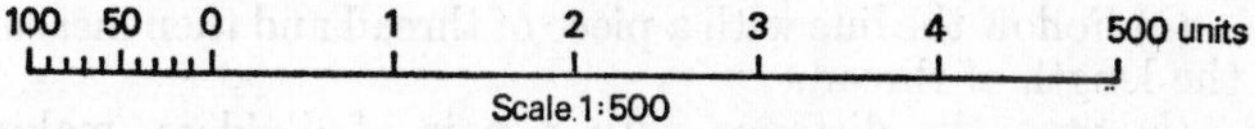

100 50   0   1   2   3   4   500 units

Scale 1:500

FIG. 2.—*A scale bar*

This is a scale bar, which may be reproduced on drawings to provide a ready means of scaling distance. It is not reproduced as here at a true scale.

11. The diagonal scale. This is a form of scale which allows measurement to a higher degree of accuracy than on a normal

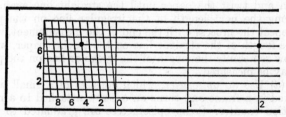

FIG. 3.—*A 1:50 diagonal scale*

This illustrates how a reading of 2·47 m is obtained directly instead of having to estimate the final figure.

scale. Instead of estimating the distance between small graduations a *diagonal* is extended upwards to provide an enlargement of the space as illustrated in Fig. 3. A pair of dividers is used to pick off or set a distance. The reading between the dots indicated is 2·47 m on this 1:50 scale, the second decimal place being read directly instead of being estimated between the fourth and fifth graduation only along the bottom line, as on the normal scale.

12. Measuring distance from the survey plot. In order to obtain the distance between two points represented on a map or plan the procedure is simply to mark off the distance between the points with a pair of dividers or with the straight edge of a piece of paper and transfer it to the scale bar or diagonal scale and read off the distance. If a scale graduated to the scale of the map is available the distance may be read off directly.

It is sometimes necessary to measure distances along a road, a boundary or other irregular line, known as *curvilinear distances*, and then one of these methods may be used:

(a) Follow the line with a piece of thread and then measure the length of thread.

(b) Step the distance with a pair of dividers, making allowances for minor bends. Count the number of steps and step off the same number along a scale.

(c) Using tracing paper and two pins, draw a straight line on the paper and place a pin through the beginning of the line and the point where the measurement begins. Twist the paper until the line falls along the first bit on the plan. Where it begins to deviate from the straight line, place the second pin and twist the paper until the straight line again lies along the next length of the irregular line on the plan. Repeat the process until the end of the measurement, when the length of the straight line on the tracing paper, which now represents the length of the irregular line on the plan, may be measured.

(d) Use an *opisometer*, which consists of a small wheel fixed in a frame and turns on a screw attached to a revolution counter. Some opisometers are graduated to read directly to set scales. Others are run along a scale bar until the revolution counter returns to zero, when the distance traversed can be read off the scale.

13. Orientation. Apart from being able to measure distance by scaling from a map, it is also important to be able to establish *direction*. The direction of any line drawn between two points can only be obtained by measuring the angle the line makes with some fixed reference direction. Every map or plan, therefore, will indicate the direction of this reference, which by convention usually points towards the top of the sheet, and which may be one of the following:

(a) The direction of True North.

(b) The direction of magnetic north.

(c) The direction of any arbitrary line between two features on the drawing.

By measuring the angle formed between the line, the direction of which is required, and a line parallel to the reference direction, the *bearing* of that line is obtained.

NOTE: When a map or plan is rotated so that it points in the direction of its reference direction it is said to be *oriented* or *orientated*. *Orient* means *east* as early maps were drawn with the east towards the top instead of north.

14. Measuring areas from the survey plot. Areas can be calculated from the survey plot in three ways:

(a) By dividing the plot into *geometrical figures* and calculating the area of each from scaled dimensions (*see* **15**).

(b) By scaling *ordinates* across the figure and calculating the area by Simpson's rule or the trapezoidal rule (*see* **16**).

(c) By using a *planimeter*, which allows the area to be obtained mechanically from reading off a graduated measuring unit (*see* **17**).

15. Measuring areas from geometrical figures. The methods of measuring areas from geometrical figures are as follows:

(a) *Triangles*. Divide the plot into triangles, following the irregular boundaries with "give-and-take" straight lines to provide a rectilinear area equal to the irregularly bounded area. Scale the base and perpendicular of each triangle formed and calculate each area from the formula $\frac{1}{2}$ base × height.

(b) *Squares*. By placing squared tracing paper over the plot and counting the squares it contains the area can be obtained. Some squares will only be partially filled, and these can be dealt with in one of three ways, depending on the area of the plot and the size of squares used:

(i) The areas of partially filled squares can be judged fractionally by eye.

(*ii*) They can be scaled off into triangles as in (*a*) above.

(*iii*) The number of partially filled squares can be counted and divided by two. By assuming that this is the number of wholly filled squares an accurate result can be obtained, provided the squares used are comparatively small.

NOTE: A useful overlay for large-scale Ordnance sheets can be formed from squares scaled with 10-m sides. Every 100 squares, *i.e.* squares of 100-m sides, are accented, each of these representing 1 ha in extent.

(*c*) *Parallel strips.* The area can be obtained from a measure of parallel strips. Place tracing paper over the plot, the paper being ruled in parallel strips and the distance between them being some whole number of metres to suit the scale and the irregularities of the plot. Midway between each pair of lines a mid-ordinate is drawn and the area of each strip is calculated by multiplying the length of each mid-ordinate from one side of the plot to the other by the constant distance between the lines.

For example, if d is the distance between the lines and O_1, O_2, etc., are the lengths of each mid-ordinate scaled across the plot, then the area $= (O_1 \times d) + (O_2 \times d) + (O_3 \times d) + \ldots$. Therefore the total area $= d(O_1 + O_2 + O_3 + \ldots)$, the common distance apart multiplied by the sum of the lengths of each strip.

16. Measuring areas from ordinates. A line is described axially through the area and at equal distances along it per-

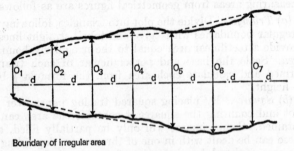

Boundary of irregular area

FIG. 4.—*Area calculation from ordinates*

These may be drawn as shown, the scaled dimensions being used for the area calculation using the trapezoidal or Simpson's rule.

pendicular ordinates are drawn and their lengths scaled, as illustrated in Fig. 4.

(a) *The trapezoidal rule*. This rule assumes that the short lengths of boundary between the ordinates are straight lines, so that the area is divided into a series of trapezoids. If d = the common distance between the ordinates and O_1, O_2, $O_3 \ldots O_n$ = the scaled ordinate lengths, then:

The area of the first trapezoid $= \dfrac{O_1 + O_2}{2} \times d$

The area of the second trapezoid $= \dfrac{O_2 + O_3}{2} \times d$

The area of the last trapezoid $= \dfrac{O_{(n-1)} + O_n}{2} \times d$

Summing up, the total area $=$

$$d\left(\frac{O_1}{2} + O_2 + O_3 + \ldots + O_{(n-1)} + \frac{O_n}{2}\right)$$

The total area therefore equals the common distance apart multiplied by the sum of half the first and last ordinates, plus all the others.

NOTE: Where the length of either the first or last ordinate happens to be zero it must still be included, or otherwise the area of the first—or last—trapezoid, which is then in fact a triangle, will be omitted.

(b) *Simpson's rule*. This rule assumes that the short lengths of boundary between alternate ordinates are parabolic curves. Referring to Fig. 4 again, the area of such a segment is $\frac{2}{3}(p \times 2d)$, where p is the mid-ordinate of the segment. The total mid-ordinate for both segments on either side of the axial line is the difference between the whole mid-ordinate, O_2, and the mean of the two end ordinates of the two sections,

$$\frac{O_1 + O_3}{2}$$

The area of each pair of sections can then be calculated, forming as it does the area of a trapezoid plus two parabolic segments.

Area of the first two sections

$$= \frac{O_1 + O_3}{2} \cdot 2d + \frac{2}{3}\left(O_2 - \frac{O_1 + O_3}{2}\right) \cdot 2d$$

$$= 2d\left(\frac{O_1 + O_3}{2} - \frac{2}{3} \cdot \frac{O_1 + O_3}{2} + \frac{2}{3} \cdot O_2\right)$$

$$= 2d\left(\frac{1}{3} \cdot \frac{O_1 + O_3}{2} + \frac{4}{6} \cdot O_2\right)$$

$$= \frac{d}{3}(O_1 + O_3) + \frac{4d}{3} \cdot O_2$$

$$= \frac{d}{3}(O_1 + 4 \cdot O_2 + O_3)$$

Area of next two sections

$$= \frac{O_3 + O_5}{2} \cdot 2d + \frac{2}{3}\left(O_4 - \frac{O_3 + O_5}{2}\right) \cdot 2d$$

$$= \frac{d}{3}(O_3 + 4 \cdot O_4 + O_5)$$

and so on until the last pair of sections, ending with the nth ordinate, the area of which

$$= \frac{d}{3}(O_{(n-2)} + 4 \cdot O_{(n-1)} + O_n)$$

Summing up, the total area $= \frac{d}{3}(O_1 + 4 \cdot O_2 + 2 \cdot O_3 + 4 \cdot O_4 + \ldots + 2 \cdot O_{(n-2)} + 4 \cdot O_{(n-1)} + O_n)$

This expression illustrates *Simpson's rule*, which states that the area equals one-third the common distance apart multiplied by the sum of the first and last ordinates, plus twice the sum of the other odd ordinates, plus four times the sum of the even ordinates.

NOTE

(i) Simpson's rule requires an even number of divisions of the area, *i.e.* the total number of ordinates must be odd.

(ii) Memorise the sequence of the multipliers, thus:

1, 4, 1, or
1, 4, 2, 4, 1, or
1, 4, 2, 4, 2, 4, 2, . . ., 2, 4, 1

(*iii*) To calculate an area with an even number of ordinates by Simpson's rule, omit the final ordinate, calculate, then add back the last sectional area calculated as a simple trapezium.

SPECIMEN QUESTION

A strip of land is 960 m long. This length is marked off into eight equal intervals and the consecutive breadths are scaled off at the ends of the intervals as follows:

5, 13, 15, 18, 20, 24, 12, 6 and 5

Find the area in hectares by:

    (*a*) the trapezoidal rule and
    (*b*) Simpson's rule.

SOLUTION

(*a*) *By the trapezoidal rule:*

$$\text{Each interval} = \frac{960}{8} \qquad = \underline{120 \text{ m}}$$

Half sum of first and last ordinates =   5
Sum of remaining ordinates = 108

$$\text{Total} = \overline{113} \text{ m}$$

$$\begin{aligned}
\text{Area} &= 120 \times 113 \\
&= 13\ 560 \text{ m}^2 \\
&= 1 \cdot 356 \text{ ha}
\end{aligned}$$

(*b*) *By Simpson's rule:*

Sum of first and last ordinates =   10 m
Twice the sum of all other odd ordinates ($2(15 + 20 + 12)$) = 94
Four times the sum of all even ordinates ($4(13 + 18 + 24 + 6)$) = 244

$$\text{Total} = \overline{348} \text{ m}$$

$$\begin{aligned}
\text{Area} &= \frac{120}{3} \times 348 \\
&= 13\ 920 \text{ m}^2 \\
&= 1 \cdot 392 \text{ ha}
\end{aligned}$$

17. Measuring areas by the planimeter. This instrument is used to measure areas mechanically on plans. The Stanley Allbrit planimeter is illustrated in Fig. 5 and consists of the following parts:

(a) *The tracer arm*, which is attached at one end to the measuring unit, which may be fixed or on a movable carriage, and at the other end supports the *tracer point* for tracing the circumference of the area to be measured.

(b) *The pole arm*, which rotates about a needle-pointed weight or *pole block*. The other end of the pole arm is

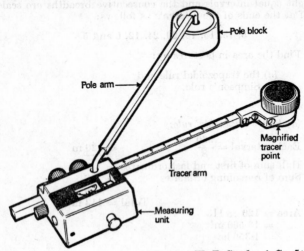

[*Courtesy W. F. Stanley & Co. Ltd.*

FIG. 5.—*The Stanley Allbrit planimeter*

finished in a small sphere which rests in a socket on the carriage.

(c) *The measuring unit*, which consists of a hard steel measuring wheel attached to a drum graduated into tenths and hundredths and geared to a revolution counter. A vernier index against the drum allows readings to be taken directly to one-thousandth of a revolution of the measuring wheel.

NOTE: Fixed-arm planimeters are set to read directly in either square inches or square centimetres only. Sliding-arm planimeters are supplied with tables giving vernier settings of the carriage on the tracer arm to suit various scales.

18. Using the planimeter. The planimeter can be used in two ways, but whichever method is adopted the pole block is placed on the paper in such a way that the tracer arm remains as close as possible to 90° with the pole arm. Also the tracer point must easily reach every part of the circumference of the area.

(a) *Methods of use.* The two methods are the following:

(i) With the pole block placed *outside* the area to be measured (the usual and more convenient method).

(ii) With the pole block placed *inside* the area to be measured (used for areas too large to be measured conveniently by the method in (i)).

(b) *Operation.* The procedure is as follows:

(i) Having fixed the pole block suitably, place the tracing point on a mark on the outline and read the vernier.

(ii) Follow the outline carefully with the tracing point in a clockwise direction returning to the starting point. Read the vernier again.

(iii) The difference between the two readings is proportional to the area measured.

(iv) Repeat the process until at least three consistent readings are obtained and take the mean.

(v) If the block is outside the figure simply multiply the result by the scale factor to produce the area.

(c) *The zero circle.* If the pole block is inside the figure an area will be swept out by the pole arm which does not register on the wheel. This is known as the *zero circle.* Tabulated constants are supplied with the instrument which represents the area of the zero circle in terms of wheel revolutions. It is necessary to establish whether the area measured is greater or less than that of the zero circle. This is done by noting whether, in circumscribing in a *clockwise* direction, the measuring wheel makes an overall forward or backward movement.

(i) If the instrument records a forward movement, the constant should be *added* to the reading before calculating the area.

(ii) If the instrument records a backward movement, the reading should be *subtracted* from the constant before calculating the area.

NOTE

(i) The planimeter does not measure the *length* of the line followed by the tracer point. It measures the *area* swept out by the line of the tracer arm as it moves across the figure.

(*ii*) When planimeter readings increase past the ninth graduation the next reading will be 0, but must obviously be read as 10.

SPECIMEN QUESTION

(*a*) *Using a fixed-arm planimeter with pole block outside the figure.* The following readings were recorded on a fixed-arm planimeter, where one revolution of the measuring wheel represented 100 cm² when measuring an irregular area on a plot to a scale of 1 : 500. What was the ground area?

Initial reading	Final reading	Difference
0·160	2·173	2·013
2·173	4·188	2·015
4·190	6·204	2·014

SOLUTION

The mean reading is 2·014.

Each revolution = 100 cm², therefore the area on the plot = 201·4 cm².

At a scale of 1 : 500, 1 cm² = $\dfrac{250\ 000}{10\ 000}$ = 25 m² on the ground.

Therefore area on ground = 201·4 × 25 m²
                     = 5035 m²
                     = 0·504 ha

(*b*) *Using a movable-arm planimeter with pole block inside the figure.* In measuring an irregular area on a 1 : 2500-scale plot the planimeter carriage was set such that one revolution of the wheel represented 5 ha. The constant of the instrument at this setting was 26·102. What was the area measured if the mean of three readings taken was 7·341 and it was noted that the initial readings were greater than the final reading each time?

SOLUTION

The instrument recorded a backward movement, therefore the area measured was less than the area of the zero circle. The reading must therefore be subtracted from the constant.

Constant   26·102
Less Reading   7·341
               ‾‾‾‾‾
               18·761
Therefore area = 18·761 × 5 ha
                = 93·805 ha

19. Plan distortion. If measurements are made on plans with a scale and the plans are known to have shrunk or stretched, allowance will have to be made for the alteration in scale, if the amount of distortion is known. This is a problem which seldom arises today, except in examinations, because of the inclusion of scale bars (*see* **10** (*c*)) and because of the use of stable drawing materials, such as plastic sheets. The assumption must also be made that any distortion is even throughout the area, which, however, is unlikely.

SPECIMEN QUESTION

A plan plotted to a scale of 1:2500 was found to have *shrunk* causing a line plotted 300 mm long to now measure 296 mm. A distance was measured on the plan and found to be 198 mm long. What is the true distance on the ground?

SOLUTION

The scale is no longer 1:2500 but:

$$1:2500 \times \frac{300}{296} = 1:2534$$

Therefore the line 198 mm long represents:

$$198 \times 2534 = 501\ 732 \text{ mm}$$
$$= 501 \cdot 7 \text{ m}$$

SPECIMEN QUESTION

A plan plotted to a scale of 1:500 was found to have *stretched* by 1 per cent. A line scaled on the plan produced a distance of 227·5 m. What was the true distance?

SOLUTION

The scale is no longer 1:500 but:

$$1:500 \times \frac{100}{101} = 1:495$$

The scaled distance should be:

$$227 \cdot 5 \times \frac{100}{101} = 225 \cdot 25 \text{ m}$$

20. Areas on distorted plans. If an area is measured on a plan and found to be 532 mm² and the scale is 1:1250, then the area on the ground is:

$$\frac{532 \times (1250)^2}{(1000)^2} = 831 \cdot 25 \text{ m}^2$$
$$= 0 \cdot 083 \text{ ha}$$

In dealing with areas the scale has been squared, so too must the correction to the scale be squared. Thus if the measure of 532 mm² was made on a plan stretched by 1 per cent, the true area would be:

$$\frac{532 \times (1250)^2 \times (100)^2}{(1000)^2 \times (101)^2} = 814.87 \text{ m}^2$$

$$= 0.081 \text{ ha}$$

NOTE: In all calculations relating to distorted plans the scale is multiplied by a factor which is the original length or 100 per cent and *divided* by the altered length or increase or decrease in percentage. The factor must be *squared* for area calculations.

PROGRESS TEST 1

1. What are the three steps in the performance of any type of survey? (1–2)

2. What are the three points to be established prior to undertaking a land survey? (3)

3. What forms of measurement are required in land surveying? (4)

4. What are the four main branches of land surveying? (4)

5. What is meant by the term "control"? (5)

6. What are the units of linear and area measurement in the metric system? (6)

7. The end result of most land surveys is either a map or a plan. What is the difference between the two? (8)

8. *Relief* is the configuration of the earth's surface. How was this represented on early maps and how is it shown today? (9)

9. What are the three ways in which scale may be shown on existing maps? (10)

10. Describe the methods of scaling straight and curvilinear distances off a map. (12)

11. What is meant by the term "the bearing" of a line drawn on a map and how may it be obtained? (13)

12. Describe three methods of obtaining the area of an irregular-shaped plot of ground drawn on a plan using geometric figures only. (15)

*13. The plot of a narrow strip of ground drawn to a scale of 1:500 was measured and found to be 77 mm long. The length was divided into seven equal sections and the ordinates at the beginning and end of each section were measured as follows:

2, 9, 13, 16, 12, 8, 10 and 0 mm

Calculate the area of the ground in square metres by:

    (a) the trapezoidal rule and
    (b) Simpson's rule. (16)

14. Describe the construction and use of the planimeter. (17, 18)

*15. The following readings were taken with a planimeter of an irregular area plotted to a scale of 1:500 with the pole block placed inside the figure:

Initial reading	Final reading
2·928	6·040
6·041	9·155
9·155	2·271

The carriage was set so that one revolution of the wheel represented 0·2 ha at this scale. The planimeter constant is 26·503 at this setting. What is the area on the ground? (18)

*16. A plan plotted to a scale of 1:1000 was found to have shrunk causing a line plotted 256 mm long to now measure 253 mm. An area measured on the plan was found to be 278 mm². What is the true area on the ground? (19, 20)

CHAPTER II

CHAIN SURVEYING

LINEAR MEASUREMENTS

1. Methods of making linear measurements. There are three main methods of making linear measurements:

(a) *By direct measurement*, in which a chain, tape or steel band is used, and which is discussed in this chapter.

(b) *By optical means* (tacheometry), which is dealt with in XII.

(c) *By electro-magnetic distance measurement* (EDM), which is considered in VII.

2. Direct measurement. The method of making a direct measurement depends largely on the accuracy required. It is a waste of time and money to take very accurate measurements when only low accuracy is required. Conversely it is useless to try and achieve high accuracy with a chain or plastic tape.

Under ideal conditions the greatest accuracy that can be expected from a chain or plastic tape is 1/2000, but in practice 1/500 or less will probably be achieved. A steel tape is generally more convenient and should be used if any reasonable accuracy is required.

3. Ranging rods. When measuring between two points it is obviously the straight-line length between them that is required. This presents no difficulty when the distance is less than the length of the tape, chain or band being used. It is simply drawn out straight between the points and the distance read off.

On long lines it is necessary to define the straight line by means of *ranging rods* to control the tape's position. These are poles of circular section about 25 mm in diameter and 2 m long. They have pointed iron shoes at one end for pushing into the ground and are painted red, black and white in bands each 500 mm wide, and so they can also be used for measurement. The process of placing ranging rods on the straight line between two points is known as *ranging*. The term ranging must not be confused with *chaining*, which denotes the measurement of the line.

4. Ranging by eye. The process of ranging a line by eye is carried out as follows:

(*a*) Plant ranging rods at each end of the line to be ranged and plumb them both vertical.

(*b*) Squat down behind one terminal rod to get a low line of sight, lining up the sides of the two rods.

(*c*) Find an assistant to hold a ranging rod approximately on the line just short of a tape length, standing off the line himself. The rod is held lightly between thumb and forefinger, high up, to hang vertically.

(*d*) Signal a shift to the left or right to the assistant until the sides of the three rods line up.

(*e*) Check that the opposite sides also line up.

(*f*) Signal for the rod to be placed after any necessary final adjustment. The assistant then marks the line by forcing the ranging rod into the ground. Check for verticality and see whether any final adjustments are required.

5. Chaining (with chains). Chaining is the process of the direct measurement of a line, although not necessarily with a *chain*. Three kinds of chain are used for measurement:

(*a*) *The Gunter's chain.* This is 66 ft long and is divided into 100 links, each 0·66 ft or 7·92 in. long.

(*b*) *The engineer's chain.* This is 100 ft long and is divided into 100 links, each 1 ft long.

(*c*) *The metric chain.* This is usually 20 m long and is divided into 100 links, each 200 mm long. A metric link is always 200 mm long and a 30-m chain will therefore contain 150 links.

NOTE

(*i*) The chain is a seventeenth-century development of the rope as a means of measurement. Although it is strong the links tend to stretch and it is heavy and clumsy to handle.

(*ii*) The chain was the best means of measuring for many years, but it is now generally superseded by the steel band, glass fibre or plastic tape. Because of its relative cheapness and toughness the chain is still used as a surveying instrument, but predominantly in colleges of education.

(*iii*) The term "chaining" persists in common usage even though the chaining may be undertaken with a *steel band*.

6. Chaining (with bands and tapes). Metric bands and tapes may be of any length from 15 to 100 m or even more. Linen, glass fibre and plastic tapes should be marked with 10-mm graduations with the metre figure repeated every 100 mm. Owing to the instability of the material 1-mm divisions are of little value. Steel tapes and bands should be marked with 5-mm graduations with the metre figure repeated every 100 mm as before. The first and last metres only of steel tapes are graduated in millimetres.

NOTE

(*i*) A steel band is a robust steel tape, 30 m or more in length, held on an open steel winding frame instead of being contained inside a leather or plastic winding case.

(*ii*) The terms *taping* or *banding* are often used in preference to *chaining*.

7. Measurement on sloping ground. The earth is represented on a map or plan as a projection on a flat, horizontal surface. Measurements scaled off a map or plan are *horizontal distances* and the lengths used in the preparation of the maps and plans must likewise be horizontal. All measured distances on sloping ground in land surveying must therefore be reduced to the horizontal before being used in calculating or plotting. This reduction to the horizontal may be achieved in two ways:

(*a*) *Directly*, by step chaining (*see* **8**).

(*b*) *Indirectly*, by calculating the horizontal equivalent of the measured slope distance (*see* **9**).

8. Step chaining. This consists of stretching the chain or tape horizontally in the air clear of the sloping ground and plumbing the raised end down to the ground as illustrated in Fig. 6 (*a*), thus forming a series of *steps*. The sum of the lengths of the individual horizontal steps gives the overall horizontal lengths of the sloping line.

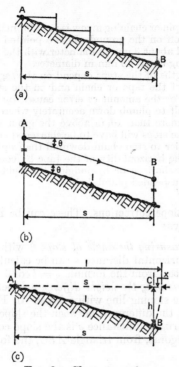

FIG. 6.—*Slope corrections*

(*a*) The process of step chaining.

(*b*) The method of measuring the angle of slope with a clinometer.

(*c*) The slope correction, which is evaluated in terms of the height difference *h* and the measured slope length *l*.

The raised end of the tape may be plumbed down to the ground in three ways:

(*a*) By a ranging rod, which is held vertically.

(*b*) By a drop-arrow, which is a chain pin with a lump of lead near the point. It is dropped from the tape graduation and sticks into the ground vertically below the end of the horizontal measurement.

(*c*) By a plumb-bob, which is the most accurate method.

NOTE

(*i*) A chain pin or chaining arrow is used for marking measured lengths off on the ground. It is a pointed steel pin 0·4 m long and about 3 mm in diameter with the top bent into a small ring about 40 mm in diameter.

(*ii*) The lengths of the steps depend on the sag caused by the weight of the tape or chain and on the steepness of the slope. For the amount of error caused by sag, *see* **17**. It is difficult to plumb down accurately where the end of the tape is more than 1·5 m above the ground, and on steep slopes the steps will have to be shortened accordingly.

(*iii*) It is easier to step chain downhill than uphill.

(*iv*) Judge the horizontality of the tape by comparing it with a distant horizon or by judging the right-angle it forms with a suspended plumb-bob.

9. Indirect slope corrections. These can be made in either one of two ways:

(*a*) *By measuring the angle of slope* θ with a clinometer, when the horizontal distance s can be calculated from the slope distance l from the formula $s = l \cos \theta$ (*see* Fig. 6 (*b*)).

(*b*) *By measuring the height difference h* between the end points of the sloping line with a level. In Fig. 6 (*c*) it can be seen that the difference between the slope measurement l and the horizontal distance s is the slope correction x.

By Pythagoras, from triangle ABC, the following can be deduced:

$$l^2 = s^2 + h^2$$
$$\text{but } s = (l - x)$$
$$\therefore l^2 = (l - x)^2 + h^2$$
$$\therefore l^2 = l^2 - 2lx + x^2 + h^2$$
$$\therefore 2lx = h^2 + x^2$$
$$\therefore x = \frac{h^2}{2l} + \frac{x^2}{2l}$$

However, $\frac{x^2}{2l}$ is small enough to be neglected completely:

$$\therefore \text{ slope correction } x = \frac{h^2}{2l}$$

10. Clinometers. Clinometers are used to measure *angles of inclination*. In Fig. 6 (*b*) the angle of slope of the tape is required, but as the tape is lying on the ground the angle of slope of a line parallel to the tape is measured instead. This is done by holding the clinometer against a ranging rod at one end of the line and sighting to a ranging rod at the other. The second ranging rod is viewed at the same height above the ground as the clinometer is being held at the first one. In this way the angle of the line of sight parallel to the slope of the tape is obtained. The two most common types of clinometer are the following:

(a) *The abney level*. This instrument is illustrated in Fig. 7. It consists of a rectangular, telescopic tube, without lenses, about 125 mm long with a graduated arc attached. A small bubble is fixed to the vernier arm and once the image of the bubble is seen reflected in the eyepiece the angle of the line of sight can be read off with the aid of the reading glass. The

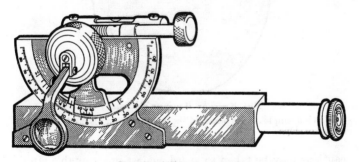

FIG. 7.—*The abney level*

This is a clinometer used for measuring angles of slope.

vernier allows readings to be taken to 10 minutes of arc. Although the abney level does give a horizontal line of sight with a zero reading, it is not really a level at all and must not be confused with the true levels described in X.

(b) *The Watkins clinometer*. This instrument is a small disc about 60 mm in diameter, as illustrated in Fig. 8. A weighted ring inside the disc can be made to hang free and by sighting across this graduated ring angles of slope can be read off. It is less accurate than the abney level, angles being read by estimation to quarters of a degree of arc only.

11. Errors in measurement. There are twelve sources of error in making direct linear measurements (*see* **12**) and these must be examined for their cause and effect so that pre-

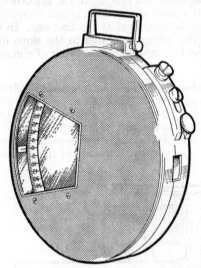

FIG. 8.—*The Watkins clinometer*

This is a simple device based on the pendulum, and is used to measure angles of slope.

cautions may be taken to guard against unacceptable errors. Errors may be of three kinds:

(*a*) *Systematic or cumulative errors.* These errors exist in any survey measurement and each additional measurement increases the effect of the error. Such errors, which may be either positive or negative, can have an appreciable effect, but this effect can be reduced as required by taking suitable field precautions or by correcting the observed measurements.

(*b*) *Compensating or accidental errors.* Although every precaution may be taken certain unavoidable errors always exist in any measurement. Such errors are generally of less importance than systematic errors. As they are sometimes positive and sometimes negative they tend to cancel each other out in the long run.

(c) *Gross errors.* These errors arise from mistakes, carelessness or lack of experience. They are quite random and allowance cannot be made for them.

12. Sources of error.

(a) *Systematic, cumulative or constant errors.* The six sources of this type of error (*see* 13–18) are the following:

(i) Wrong length of tape (cumulative positive or negative).
(ii) Poor ranging (cumulative positive).
(iii) Poor straightening (cumulative positive).
(iv) Slope (cumulative positive).
(v) Sag (cumulative positive).
(vi) Temperature variation (cumulative positive or negative).

(b) *Compensating, accidental or random errors.* There are two sources (*see* 19, 20) of this type of error:

(i) Holding and marking (compensating).
(ii) Variation in tension (compensating).

(c) *Gross errors.* The four sources of mistakes (*see* 21) are the following:

(i) Displacement of arrows or station marks.
(ii) Miscounting tape lengths.
(iii) Misreading the tape.
(iv) Wrong booking.

13. Wrong length of tape. This is the most serious source of error, particularly with a chain because of its tendency to stretch. Chains and fibre tapes should be tested frequently. Steel bands need testing less often, but should always be tested for precise work or after any repairs.

Measurements made with a tape found to be in error can be corrected using the formula:

$$\frac{\text{True distance}}{\text{Measured distance}} = \frac{\text{Actual length of tape/chain}}{\text{Nominal length of tape/chain}}$$

Where area calculations have been made from measurements which are in error they can be corrected using the formula:

$$\frac{\text{True area}}{\text{Measured area}} = \frac{(\text{Actual length of tape/chain})^2}{(\text{Nominal length of tape/chain})^2}$$

NOTE

   (i) To obtain an accuracy of 1/5000, a 30-m band may be in error by $\pm 0 \cdot 006$ m.

   (ii) If the tape is too long, the measured distance is too short and the correction must be added.

   (iii) If the tape is too short, the measured distance is too great and the correction must be subtracted.

SPECIMEN QUESTION

After completing a survey the 30-m band used was checked and found to be 30·023 m long.

(a) What is the length of the line AB observed to be 125·510 m long?

SOLUTION

$$\text{True distance} = 125 \cdot 510 \times \frac{30 \cdot 023}{30 \cdot 000}$$
$$= 125 \cdot 606 \text{ m}$$

(b) The area of the site was calculated from the observed measurements at 1·762 ha. What is the true area?

SOLUTION

$$\text{True area} = 1 \cdot 762 \times \left(\frac{30 \cdot 023}{30 \cdot 000}\right)^2$$
$$= 1 \cdot 765 \text{ ha}$$

14. Poor ranging. This gives rise to a relatively small error. If a whole tape length deviates a distance d from the ranged straight the error in length is $d^2/2l$, where l is the length of the tape. (Compare this with **9** (b), where the divergence is in a vertical instead of a horizontal plane.)

NOTE

   (i) Very refined ranging is unnecessary if the distance only is required, but any offset measurements taken at right-angles to the line of the tape will be in error by the amount the tape lies off the correct line.

   (ii) To obtain an accuracy of 1/5000 one end of a 30-m tape may be 0·6 m off line.

15. Poor straightening. This is similar to **14**, but if both ends of the tape are on the correct line and the centre is off by a distance d, the effect is greater, being $\dfrac{2d^2}{l}$, or twice the error arising in each half of the tape.

NOTE: To obtain an accuracy of 1/5000, the centre of a 30-m tape may lie 0·3 m off line.

16. Slope. Although the effect of slope is similar to that in **14**, but in the vertical plane, it can be the source of quite large errors.

NOTE: To obtain an accuracy of 1/5000, one end of a 30-m tape may be 0·6 m higher or lower than the other end or the angle of slope may be θ where sin θ = 0·6/30, *i.e.* θ = 1° 9′, the maximum angle of slope which may be ignored in order to maintain this accuracy.

17. Sag. When a tape is suspended, as in step chaining, or when measuring over rough ground, the unsupported part will *sag* giving an observed reading which will be too great. The amount of error caused by sag is proportional to:

$$\left[\frac{\text{Weight of tape}}{\text{Tension on tape}} \right]^2$$

and increases as the cube of the suspended length (*see* **VII, 11**).

NOTE: To obtain an accuracy of 1/5000, the centre of a 30-m tape should not be allowed to sag by more than 0·3 m.

18. Temperature variation. The effect of temperature variation is negligible in work where a chain is used. For precise work with a steel band temperature corrections must be made (*see* **VII, 9**).

$$\text{The error} = l \times c \times t$$

where l = measured length,

c = coefficient of expansion (0·000 011 per °C for steel) and

t = temperature difference from standard.

NOTE: To obtain an accuracy of 1/5000, the temperature should not vary from standard (*see* **VII, 9**) by more than 18°C when taping with a steel band.

19. Holding and marking. When a tape zero is held against a point and the length is marked with a chain pin or read off against another point errors will always occur. Provided reasonable care is taken these errors will be small and will tend to compensate each other. When an untrained man holds the tape zero or marks, always to the same side of the point, the overall error will tend to increase and this must be guarded against.

20. Variation in tension. The tension applied to a tape should be the same as that applied when testing it against a standard. Variations in tension are bound to occur, even when using a spring balance, but the resulting errors are small and tend to compensate each other. If the tape is consistently pulled too hard or too lightly, a cumulative error will arise and this must be guarded against, particularly when using linen or plastic tapes.

21. Gross errors. The four main gross errors are as follows:

(a) *Displacement of arrows or station marks.* If an arrow or ranging rod has been accidentally removed or knocked over it may be replaced wrongly. This can occur frequently when children are about and this must be guarded against. On roads and pavements where nails are used as station marks there may be other similar marks placed by others. Care must be taken that the wrong station is not used.

(b) *Miscounting tape lengths.* This can be prevented in the measurement of long lines by the surveyor starting the measurement with, say, ten arrows. Each arrow placed represents one tape length measured. By checking the count of arrows with the assistant following up the tape zero and collecting used arrows, a check can be made. On paved areas the tape lengths should be numbered in chalk, the assistant checking the sequence. Gross errors still occur, but may be located by scaling from a large-scale map of the area if available.

(c) *Misreading the tape.* The chain has tags or tallies every metre with distinctive tallies at 5 and 10 m. As the tallies in each half of the chain are the same it is easy to confuse the 7- and 8-m tallies with the 12- and 13-m tallies unless care is taken in noting the position of the distinctive central tally.

In reading a tape a common source of error is to concentrate on the decimals and then to note the metres wrongly. Some tapes are metre marked every 100 mm and the metre reading should be automatically checked against at least two of these. This is especially necessary when the tape is dirty or rusty.

(*d*) *Wrong booking.* If an assistant calls out readings to the surveyor, he should read them back out loud to confirm the readings booked. Care must be taken not to interchange figures.

PRINCIPLES OF CHAIN SURVEYING

22. Introduction. This is the process of surveying an area using linear measurements only. Although it is the earliest form of surveying it is a method still used for small surveys today. Its operations are often applied in the survey of detail in traverse surveys and it forms the foundation upon which many modern surveying techniques are built. For these reasons a thorough understanding of chain surveying is necessary. Also many students have to perform a complete chain survey as part of their professional examinations. Its basic principles may be illustrated as follows:

(*a*) Take the case of an area of ground with *three straight boundaries AB, BC* and *CA.* If these three sides are measured this simple survey can be plotted in the following way:

(*i*) First the line *AB*, say, is drawn to scale on paper to form a base line.

(*ii*) The length *AC* is set to the same scale on a pair of compasses and an arc of radius *AC* is drawn.

(*iii*) Similarly an arc of radius *BC* is drawn to intersect the first.

(*iv*) Point *C* is represented by the intersection of the arcs, and the three points *A, B* and *C* are then plotted in the same relative position on the ground.

(*b*) Where an area of ground is bounded by *more than three straight sides* and if these lengths only are measured an infinite number of figures can be drawn with these dimensions. Therefore the survey must be so arranged that the area can be plotted by triangles as described in (*a*). For example, with a four-sided figure one of the diagonals must also be measured. This diagonal is first scaled on to the plotting sheet and the two triangles can be constructed on either side of it.

23. Check or proof lines. The process described in 22 allows the survey to be plotted, but if any mistakes were made in a measurement or in the scaling then the plot would be wrong and would not properly represent the area of land surveyed.

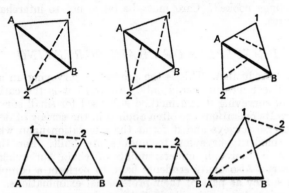

Fig. 9.—*Check measurements used in chain surveying*
Six common methods of checking chained triangles are shown.

To prevent this occurrence *check* or *proof lines* must also be measured to check or prove that the plotted figure is correct.

In the case of the simple triangle *ABC*, if another measurement from *C* to some point on the base *AB* were also measured and this distance were found to scale correctly on the plot, it would prove that no errors existed in the plotted figure. Similarly in the four-sided figure, if the other diagonal were measured and it also scaled correctly it would check or prove that both triangles had been correctly plotted. Figure 9 illustrates six common methods of applying check measurements. In each case the base *AB* is first scaled on the plot and the triangles *hung* on to this longest line, the points being plotted in the numerical sequence shown.

NOTE

(*i*) Check lines need not necessarily start from the corners of the figure. As long as the points along the line from which they start are known and can be plotted they may be positioned as required.

(*ii*) Check lines must not be short in comparison with the lines which they prove, or otherwise the check may not be adequate.

(*iii*) To confirm whether all proper checks have been applied always consider each plotted line in turn and see whether, if it had been plotted, say, 10 m longer, where this error would have shown up against another measurement. If these extra 10 m would merely alter the plotted position of a point without also altering the length of some other measured line, checking is inadequate and additional measurements must be made.

24. Offsets. So far chain-surveying principles have only been applied to areas of land with straight boundaries. As most

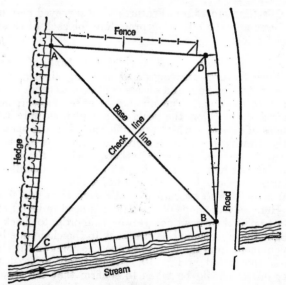

FIG. 10.—*A chained network showing offsets*

These are used to locate the position of natural features relative to the survey lines.

boundaries are irregular the method of surveying their positions is first to lay down a network of triangles which can be plotted and checked. From these survey lines *offsets* are measured, being perpendicular measurements from the chain lines to points of detail, as illustrated in Fig. 10.

Perpendicularity may be obtained in one of the following ways, depending on the accuracy required:

(*a*) By judging with the eye the right-angle formed between the two tapes.

(*b*) By swinging the offset tape to obtain the shortest measurement.

(*c*) By setting out the right-angle with the optical square (*see* **39**).

(*d*) By using the isosceles triangle construction described in **40**(*b*).

25. Offsetting procedure. Features to be surveyed may take three forms and the offsetting procedure for each of these is described below:

(*a*) *Irregular features such as hedge lines, banks of streams, etc.* Such features are considered as being divided into a series of straight lines and offsets are taken to each point of change of direction. The number of offset measurements required depends on the scale of the plot as only those changes of direction which are sufficiently large to show up on the drawing need be measured to. Also, less offsets are needed for surveying vague outlines, such as the edge of scrub land or marshy ground, than for a more definite but still irregular boundary such as a hedge line.

(*b*) *Straight features such as walls, kerb lines and fences, etc.* Here only the ends of the straights need to be offset in order to plot their position. However, in order to check the straight the ends should be tied back to the chain line by a measurement from the feature to another point on the chain line as illustrated in Fig. 10. Alternatively at least two other offsets should be taken to confirm that the straight does run through these plotted points. If only one extra offset were taken and the straight did not plot on all three there would be no indication of which offset was in error.

(*c*) *Curved features such as kerb lines on bends of roads, railway lines, etc.* Here offsets are measured at regular intervals, noting in the field that the feature forms a curve.

The spacing of the offsets should be such that they plot about 30 mm apart on the drawing.

26. Accuracy of measurement. Assuming that it is just possible to plot to an accuracy of 0·2 mm, depending on the scale, this will represent a length on the ground which is incapable of being plotted. Measurement in the field need not therefore be more refined than this. The following table illustrates the degree of relationship between the refinement needed in measurement and the various scales:

Scale of plot	Unplottable length (m)	In practice measure to (in metres):
1/5000	1·00	1·00
1/2500	0·50	0·50
1/2000	0·40	0·10
1/1250	0·25	0·10
1/1000	0·20	0·10
1/500	0·10	0·10
1/200	0·04	0·01
1/100	0·02	0·01
1/50	0·01	0·01

NOTE

(*i*) It is often easier to measure to a greater refinement than is actually necessary because at a scale of, say, 1/200, it is simpler to read to the second decimal place than to be concerned with the nearest 0·04 m each time.

(*ii*) For a plot to a scale of 1/1000 there is no need to read the tape more accurately than to 0·1 m. However, if there is any possibility that any part of the survey may have to be re-plotted to a larger scale then reading accuracy should be increased to 0·01 m.

(*iii*) Only at scales larger than 1/50 is it necessary to measure in millimetres.

27. Maximum length of offset. This depends on the following:

(*a*) The accuracy needed in plotting any particular feature; *e.g.* a wall corner should be more precisely defined than the rough outline of a tree.

(*b*) The method of setting out the offset perpendicular to the chain line.

(*c*) The scale of the survey plot.

The maximum allowable length may be calculated for any particular survey. Offsets are generally estimated at right-angles by eye, but when the right-angle is accurately set out the only limit to its length is in the accuracy of the angle. Normally offsets will not exceed 30 m.

Offsets are estimated usually within 2° of the perpendicular. The greater its length the greater will its deviation become from the perpendicular line which is used in plotting the position of the point offset. If this deviation on the ground is too small to be plotted no inaccuracy occurs. When an offset is so long that its deviation from the perpendicular causes an error large enough to be plotted, then it is in excess of its maximum allowable length.

SPECIMEN QUESTION

On a particular survey it was estimated that perpendicularity for offsetting purposes could only be guaranteed to an accuracy of 2°. Determine the maximum allowable length of offset if the survey is to be plotted at a scale of 1/500.

SOLUTION

At a scale of 1/500, assuming a plotting accuracy of 0·2 mm, the unplottable length on the ground, represented by 0·2 mm on paper, $= 500 \times 0·2 = 100$ mm. Therefore, where $x =$ the unknown offset length:

$$\sin 2° = \frac{100}{x} \text{ or}$$
$$x = \frac{0·1}{\sin 2°} \text{ m}$$
$$= \frac{0·1}{0·0349}$$
$$= 2·86 \text{ m, or 3 m for practical purposes.}$$

FIELD WORK

28. Reconnaissance. The value of the reconnaissance prior to any survey must never be underestimated. It is important that the surveyor should walk all over the site to obtain a picture in his mind of the whole area while deciding the most suitable way of carrying out the work economically in time and energy. Any existing map or plan covering the ground is a useful aid during this recce. At the same time, while deciding on the best layout, the surveyor will prepare a *sketch plan* showing the lines chosen to form the framework of the survey.

29. Choice of stations. During the reconnaissance the following seven points must be borne in mind as the criteria to provide the best arrangement of survey lines:

(a) *Few survey lines.* The number of survey lines should be kept to a minimum, but these must be sufficient for the survey to be plotted and checked.

(b) *Long base line.* If at all possible a long line should be positioned right across the site to form a base on which to build the triangles.

(c) *Well-conditioned triangles.* No triangle should contain an angle less than 30° or greater than 150°. Preferably the arcs used for plotting should intersect as close to 90° as possible in order to provide a sharp definition of the station point.

(d) *Check lines.* Every part of the survey should be provided with check lines (*see* **23**), but they should be positioned in such a way that they can be used for offsetting too, in order to save any unnecessary duplication of lines.

(e) *Obstacles.* There are means of overcoming obstacles (*see* **41–43**), but the use of these constructions generally indicates a poor reconnaissance. Equally, steep slopes and rough ground are obstacles and the need for step chaining (*see* **8**) and slope or sag corrections (*see* **9** and **17**) should be avoided as far as possible. Remember also the obstacles caused by pedestrian and vehicular traffic.

(f) *Short offsets.* Lines should be kept close to the features to be offset, preferably within 2 m, so that an offset measuring rod, operated by one person, can be used instead of a tape, which needs two people.

(g) *Extension lines.* It is often convenient to position a station on the extension of a check line or a triangle side. Such points can be plotted without the need for intersecting arcs, as illustrated in Fig. 9.

30. Station marking.

(a) *Requirements.* Survey stations should be marked in such a way that they fulfil the following requirements:

(*i*) They must be easily and quickly found during the survey.

(*ii*) They should not be readily disturbed by others.

(*iii*) They should be fairly permanent so that they will be available later.

(*b*) *Construction of stations.* Survey stations may take some of the following forms:

(*i*) For rough work of comparatively low accuracy the hole made by a ranging rod is sufficient. The hole can be marked by a twig for later location. Obviously such a station will not last for long.

(*ii*) In soft ground wooden pegs about 0·5 m long, hammered nearly flush, are used. For greater accuracy a nail defining the station may be driven into the peg.

(*iii*) In streets and other paved areas pipe nails or galvanised, large-headed, felt nails are hammered down and chalk marked or painted to make them conspicuous during the survey. To increase accuracy the nail heads may be punch marked to define the station point. In concrete a chiselled cross or 5-mm drilled hole may be made, also conspicuously coloured.

(*iv*) In precise work or where greater permanence is required the stations may consist of steel or alloy pegs or pipes embedded in concrete monoliths.

(*c*) *Witnessing.* As stations are placed they should be witnessed. This consists of making an outline sketch of the immediate area around the station, showing existing permanent features, the position of the station, and its description and designation. Measurements are then made from at least three surrounding features to the station point and recorded on the sketch. These sketches will enable the stations to be found again at a much later date, even by others, and should the mark be destroyed it may be replaced and checked from the witness measurements.

31. Field notes. Field notes for a chain survey are made in a notebook usually with a double red line ruled up the middle of each page. Booking takes place as illustrated in Fig. 11. In addition the following eight items of information will be included to complete the field record:

(*a*) The *name* and *location* of the survey.

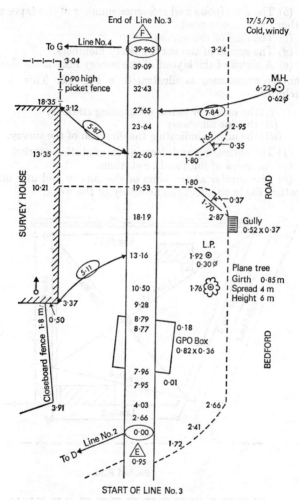

FIG. 11.—*An example of line booking*

This is the method used for recording the offset distances measured in the field.

(b) The *description* and reference number of the tapes and other instruments used.

(c) The *date* of the survey.

(d) The *names* of the survey party members.

(e) A *sketch* of the layout of the survey lines made during the reconnaissance as illustrated in Fig. 12. This sketch includes:

    (*i*) the names or letters designating stations;

    (*ii*) the line numbers;

    (*iii*) the arrows indicating the direction of the survey.

(f) The *witnessing* and description of station marks.

(g) An *index* of lines and/or stations.

(h) The *weather* at the time of the survey and any other feature likely to affect the accuracy of the work.

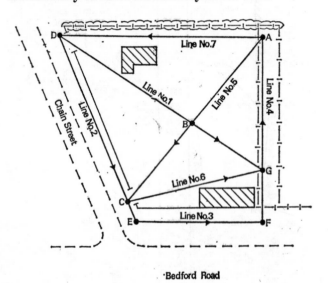

Fig. 12.—*A chain survey*

The survey shows a good layout of survey lines, properly checked, and how the ground features are related to them so that their positions may be plotted.

32. The procedure for taking field notes. The following points should be remembered:

(a) Booking must be accurate and clear. Do not sketch detail ahead of measurements and exaggerate the size of complicated features. The notes should be recorded as if another person would be doing the plotting.

(b) It is easier to find the correct booking page while plotting if the lines are numbered consecutively, with a note of the line number of the sketch. Alternatively lines may be labelled by the stations through which they pass.

(c) Sketches must be clear with no doubt about the point to which the offset is taken.

(d) The chainage runs continuously from one end of each survey line to the other with an arrow drawn on the sketch to show the direction of survey. It is usual to ring the chainage of stations as these measurements are extracted first to enable the framework of lines to be plotted.

(e) Only tie lines and cross measurements are sketched in the field book—offset lines are not. The offset distance is recorded clearly beside the point to which the measurement was taken and not beside the chain line.

(f) Always take running dimensions around buildings to pick up detail and to check plotting and measure tie lines between salient features to provide additional plotting checks.

(g) Take care not to book in centimetres. The correct booking is, say, "0·95." This is not the same as 950 mm, which implies an accuracy of measurement to one milli- metre, but which is a convention sometimes adopted. A booking of 95 strictly means 95 mm. Do not therefore forget the zero, which indicates the proper measurement; write either 950 or more properly 0·95.

(h) Leave nothing to memory; include explanatory notes on details such as street names, house numbers and names, ancient lights, the girth, spread, height and kind of tree, types of pavement boxes, etc.

(i) Use an H or 2H pencil. Harder pencils are too faint and tear damp paper and softer pencils tend to smudge.

NOTE: Suggested symbols for representing different features are illustrated in Fig. 1.

33. Running the survey line. This consists of chaining the line and the survey or picking up nearby detail. It includes the following procedure:

(a) The tape or chain is ranged along the survey line by pulling and whipping it straight, past the ranging rod marking the line, and the forward arrow or mark is then placed while it is still under tension.

(b) The tape is left lying on the ground, the surveyor returning to the zero end to assist in offsetting.

(c) The zero of the offsetting tape or offset rod is held against the features to the right or left of the line while the offset tape or rod is held at right-angles to the tape on the chain line and the chainage and offset distances are recorded.

(d) The chainages along the line at which fences, streams, kerbs and other survey lines intersect the chain line are also recorded.

(e) Offset measurements must be horizontal and should be booked in order of their chainage.

34. Plotting the survey. The chain survey network of lines is first plotted in pencil as follows:

(a) *Base line*. The base line is positioned on the drawing sheet in such a way that the whole area will be contained within the limits of the paper. Its full length is then scaled off, including the position of any line stations along it.

(b) *Triangles*. The length of one of the lines to the first point to be plotted is extracted from the field book and set to scale on a beam compass and the arc is drawn. Similarly the second arc length is set on the beam compass and the arc intersection drawn to give the plot of the first point. The position of the check line is drawn in. It is scaled and confirmed to agree with the field measurement. Each triangle is plotted and checked in the same way, and any points lying on the extension of lines are scaled, plotted and checked by means of a further scaled dimension. When the whole framework has been plotted, make sure that no check measurements have been omitted and that no plotting errors exist.

(c) *Offsets*. Offset measurements can then be plotted in one of two ways:

(*i*) The running chainage along the lines can be scaled off along the main lines on the plot and light pencil lines are drawn perpendicular to them, along which the offset distances are scaled.

(*ii*) A proprietory offset scale can be used. This is a short scale graduated outwards from its centre to enable offsets on either side of the survey line to be plotted. A long scale is laid on the paper parallel to the survey line so that the offset scale can slide along it with its zero coinciding all the time with the survey line while the chainage of the edge of the offset scale can be read off the long scale.

(*d*) *Detail drawing.* As the offsets are plotted they are joined up in pencil to correspond with the features noted in the field book. Tie lines must be scaled to check the plotted positions of points as they arise.

(*e*) *Fair drawing.* Once the pencil plot has been completed and checked the chain survey network of lines, but not the offset or tie lines, is inked in in red and the fair drawing completed as described in IX, **51**.

OVERCOMING FIELD PROBLEMS

35. The survey of woods, lakes and narrow strips. Where the network of survey lines cannot be contained within the area being surveyed owing to obstructing features, such as woods or lakes, the following procedure, illustrated in Fig. 13, must be adopted:

(*a*) The network of lines is set out to surround the area in the manner shown.

(*b*) The base line *AB* is first scaled and plotted.

(*c*) From the shorter base *AC*, *E* is plotted and the line extended to *F*.

(*d*) From the new base *EF*, *G* is plotted and the line extended to *X*.

(*e*) From the base *DB*, *H* is plotted and the line *BH* is also extended to *X*.

(*f*) The two separately plotted positions of *X* should co-incide to prove the accuracy of the plot.

NOTE

(*i*) To localise any errors which may arise each triangle should be provided with a proof line.

(*ii*) Any error in the plotting of a point such as *E* is increased
as the line is produced towards *F*. To minimise such errors
the corner triangles must be as large as possible.

The same principle can be applied to the survey of *narrow
strips of land* as illustrated in Fig. 14, although nowadays this

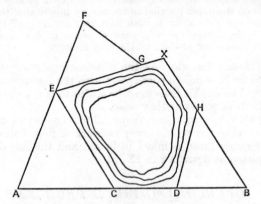

FIG. 13.—*Survey of a small lake*

The method is shown of how to set out the chain lines to surround the
area to be surveyed in such a way that the lines can be plotted and the
plotting can be checked.

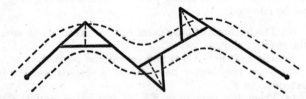

FIG. 14.—*Survey of a narrow strip of land*

The method of setting out chain lines in order to survey a narrow,
winding strip of land is shown.

work would normally be undertaken by a theodolite traverse.
The use of chained triangles is simply the linear method of
plotting the angles between the lines. The triangles should be
checked as usual, but there is no check on the lines between
them unless they are measured twice.

36. The cross staff. An instrument which allows a right-angle to be set out with reasonable accuracy can help in overcoming many field problems. The *cross staff* is a simple device which does this. Two forms are illustrated in Fig. 15. One is a frame with sighting slits at right-angles, the other, in the form of a cylinder, is slightly more refined and has additional slits enabling angles of 45° to be set out as well. Both types are

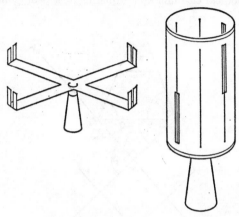

Fig. 15.—*Two kinds of cross staff*

These are used for setting out right-angles in chain surveying.

mounted on short ranging rods when in use. These instruments are traditional pieces of equipment, although now more or less superseded by prism squares (*see* **38**).

37. The optical square. This is an advance on the cross staff and is based on the principle that a ray of light reflected from two mirrors is deviated by twice the angle between the mirrors. The instrument consists of a hollow metal disc about 50 mm in diameter and about 20 mm thick. It contains two mirrors inclined at 45°, one of which is capable of fine adjustment.

The instrument is used to set out a right-angle to a line by holding it firmly against a ranging rod on the line and sighting into its peephole, through the unsilvered half of one of its mirrors, at a rod ranged along the line. Another ranging rod is

then placed at the side of the line and adjusted until its reflected image is seen to coincide with the direct view of the rod
on the main line. This rod is then on the perpendicular to the
main line from the position of the optical square.

38. The prism square. This is the modern development of
the optical square. Instead of two inclined mirrors, which require periodical cleaning and adjustment, a pentagonal prism

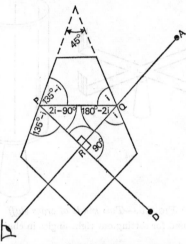

FIG. 16.—*The method of operation of the prism square*

This is used for setting out right-angles between survey lines.

is used to provide the reflecting surfaces as indicated in Fig. 16.
Its principle of operation is the same as for the optical square
except that the instrument cannot be adjusted as the prism
angle cannot be altered. Also the object directly sighted is
viewed above and below the prism holder and not through it
as in the previous instrument.

Its principle of operation is shown in Fig. 16. It can be
shown that the angle formed between the two lines of sight to
A and D, when the image of D is coincident with the direct
view of A, can only be 90°. This is always so, even if the ray
of light from D does not enter the prism normal to its face.

If the angle at Q between the reflecting surface and the

incident ray is i, then by the laws of reflection the angle between this surface and the reflected ray will also be i. Therefore the angle $PQR = 180° - 2i$. It follows that the equivalent angles at P are each $135° - i$ as shown because the prism
angle is $45°$. The angle RPQ will be $180° - 2(135° - i)$
$= 2i - 90°$. Therefore angle QRP, the angle of intersection of
two rays, will be $180° - (2i - 90°) - (180° - 2i) = 90°$,
which is independent of the value of i.

39. The double-prism square or line ranger.

An obvious
development of the prism square would be to place two
pentagonal prisms on top of one another so that a right-angle

FIG. 17.—*The double-prism square*

This is used for setting out right-angles from both sides of a chain line
at the same time. It is also used for ranging a line.

could be set out on both sides of a survey line at the same time.
This would be achieved by obtaining coincidence of the two
images from either side with the direct view. This instrument,
illustrated in Fig. 17, is the double-prism square, often simply
called an *optical square* because it supersedes the other instruments mentioned developed for setting out right-angles.

Obviously when images of ranging rods on either side of the
instrument are in coincidence the instrument will be on the
straight line between them. Thus this optical square can be
used as a *line ranger*. By walking across a survey line the
terminals of which are marked, this instrument will be ranged
on that line when the images of the terminal rods are coincident across both prisms.

40. Chain survey constructions. In order to overcome obstacles using chain survey techniques the construction of right-angles and parallels is often necessary. There are several ways in which this can be done. The main methods for setting out angles without using an instrument are illustrated in Fig. 18.

(a) *To erect a perpendicular from a point on the chain line* (*see* Fig. 18 (a)):

Use the 3:4:5 ratio triangle. From A measure 12 m to C. Holding the tape zero at A and the 30-m graduation at C, hold the 9-m graduation beside the 15-m graduation, pulling

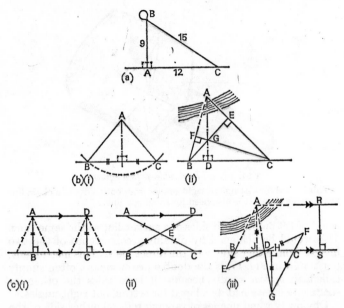

FIG. 18.—*Chain surveying constructions*

(a) Methods of erecting a perpendicular from a point on the chain line.
(b) Methods of erecting a perpendicular to a chain line from a point off the line with (i) the point accessible and (ii) the point inaccessible.
(c) Methods of running a parallel to a chain line through a given point with (i) and (ii) the point accessible and (iii) the point inaccessible.

both sections taught. The intersection of the tape lengths is the position of B, perpendicular to A on the chain line. This method leaves a 6-m loop at B, which is necessary when using a steel tape as it cannot be sharply bent at B.

(b) *To erect a perpendicular to a chain line from a point off the chain line (see Fig. 18 (b)):*

(i) *With the point accessible.* With the tape zero at A swing the tape in an arc to cut the chain line at B and C. The midpoint between B and C is the foot of the perpendicular.

(ii) *With the point inaccessible.* Select points B and C on the chain line. Range lines BA and CA and erect perpendiculars BE and CF using the above method. Range in their intersection at G. AG produced to D on the chain line is the required perpendicular.

(c) *To run a line parallel to a chain line through a given point (see Fig. 18 (c)):*

(i) *With the point accessible.* From A drop a perpendicular to the chain line at B. Measure AB and at C erect a perpendicular making the length CD equal to AB. AD is then the required parallel.

(ii) An alternative method is to measure from A to a suitable point C on the chain line and then to mark its midpoint E. Choose a suitable point B, measure BE and produce it an equal distance to D. AD is then the required parallel.

(iii) *With the point inaccessible.* Mark suitable points B, D and C on the chain line such that $BD = DC$. Produce AB to E, measure ED and produce it an equal distance to F. FC has now been constructed parallel to AE. Produce FC to G, which is also on AD produced. Triangle DFG has now been constructed congruent to triangle ADE and the now accessible perpendicular GH can be constructed and measured. It is equal to the perpendicular AJ, which can now be constructed at S, providing the required parallel AR.

41. Obstacles obstructing ranging but not chaining.

(a) *When both ends are visible from intermediate points on the line.* In Fig. 19 (a), A and B are terminal points of a survey line. This line cannot be ranged directly because of the rising ground, but by taking up positions at C_1 and D_1, approximately on the line, both terminal stations can be seen from both points. From C_1, D_1 is ranged to D_2 on line to B. D_2 then ranges C_1 to C_2 on line to A. C_2 then ranges

D_2 again on line to B until the position is reached where from C D can be seen to be on line to B, and from D C can be seen to be on line to A, when the whole line is properly ranged.

(b) *When both ends are not visible from any intermediate*

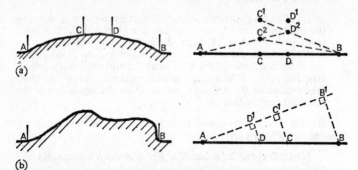

FIG. 19.—*Obstacles obstructing ranging but not chaining*

(a) Where both ends are visible from intermediate points on line.
(b) Where both ends are not visible from any intermediate point.

point. When it is impossible to adopt the method in (a) the line may be ranged by means of the *random line* (*see* Fig. 19 (b)). Here a line AB' is set out clear of the obstruction in such a way that a perpendicular from B may be dropped to the random line at B'. AB' and $B'B$ are measured and from the similar triangles the perpendicular distance from C' to C can be calculated if the distance AC' is known. Similarly when AD' is known:

$$D'D = \frac{AD' \cdot BB'}{AB'}$$

NOTE: The right-angles must be erected on the ranged random line AB'; they cannot be set out on AB because it is not yet set out.

42. Obstacles obstructing chaining but not ranging.

(a) *Obstacles which can be chained around* (*e.g.* a pond):

(i) Figure 20 (a) (i) illustrates a solution without setting out a right-angle. The line AB is ranged, but the measurement of

AB cannot be taken directly. A point C is set out clear of the obstruction and D and E are placed midway along the lines AC and CB respectively. ED is measured and twice this distance gives the length of AB. Other ratios for similar triangles such as $1:3$ instead of $1:2$ may be used depending on surrounding obstructions.

(*ii*) Figure 20 (*a*) (*ii*) illustrates the solution of the same

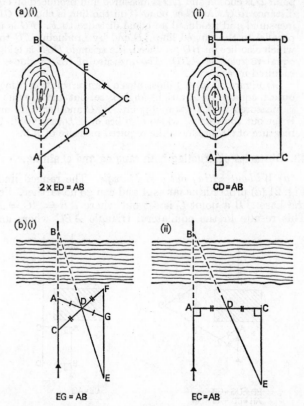

Fig. 20.—*Obstacles obstructing chaining but not ranging*

(*a*) Obstacles which can be chained round (*i*) without setting out a right-angle and (*ii*) setting out a right-angle.

(*b*) Obstacles which cannot be chained round (*i*) without setting out a right-angle and (*ii*) setting out a right-angle.

problem using an optical square. Right-angles are set off the line at *A* and *B*, and *C* and *D* are marked such that *AC* = *BD*. *CD* is measured to give the length of *AB*.

(*b*) *Obstacles which cannot be chained around* (*e.g.* a river):

(*i*) Figure 20 (*b*) (*i*) illustrates the solution where *AB* is the part of the ranged line which cannot be measured. A suitable point *D* is chosen and *AD* is measured and produced an equal distance to *G*. Another point *C* on the line is chosen, *CD* is measured and produced an equal distance to *F*. *FG* is now parallel to the ranged line *AB* and by producing *FG* to *E*, which also lies on *BD* produced, the triangle *DGE* is laid out equal to triangle *ABD*. The measure of *GE* produces the required measure of *AB*.

(*ii*) Figure 20 (*b*) (*ii*) illustrates a similar solution using an optical square. At *A* a right-angle is set out and the line *AC* is measured with *D* its mid-point. At *C* another right-angle is set out towards *E*, which also lies on *BD* produced. The measure of *CE* produces the required measure of *AB*.

43. Obstacles obstructing both ranging and chaining.

(*a*) *Without setting out a right-angle*. The ranged line in Fig. 21 (*a*) proceeds as far as *A* and can go no farther. From the base *AB* a point *C* is set out where *AB* = *AC* = *BC*. This results in the equilateral triangle *ABC* where angle

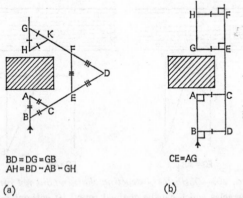

$$BD = DG = GB$$
$$AH = BD - AB - GH$$

$$CE = AG$$

(a)   (b)

FIG. 21.—*Obstacles obstructing both ranging and chaining*

(*a*) Without setting out a right-angle.
(*b*) Setting out a right-angle.

$ABC = 60°$. The line BC is produced to D clear of the obstruction and another equilateral triangle is constructed as before. The line DF is then produced to G such that $BD = DG$, so that the triangle BDG is also equilateral. G now lies on the extension of AB, but the direction of the line cannot be established until the third equilateral triangle GHK is set out. Once this is done HG produced provides the extension of the line AB on the other side of the building. The obstructed length $AH = BD - (AB + GH)$ because $BD = DG = GB$ by construction.

(b) *Setting out right-angles.* Again the ranged line ends at A and can go no farther (*see* Fig. 21 (*b*)). At A a right-angle is set out. C is placed clear of the obstruction. Going back to a point B another right-angle is set out and D is placed such that $AC = BD$. DC is now parallel to the line AB and can be extended past the obstruction to E and F. At both these points right-angles are set out to G and H such that $EG = FH = AC = BD$. GH produced provides the extension of the line AB on the other side of the obstacle and the measured length of EC equals the obstructed length AG.

NOTE

   (*i*) The diagonals AD and BC and GF and HE are sometimes measured to prove the accuracy of the setting out of the right-angles.

   (*ii*) The construction in (*b*) must not be confused with that in Fig. 20 (*a*) (*ii*) where the line is ranged direct. The line AC is too short for a right-angle set out at C to provide an accurate extension of the direction of AB.

   (*iii*) Right-angles are only set out at A and B and E and F. By construction there are right-angles at all other points, but right-angles cannot be set out at G and H because the line does not exist until these points are established.

PROGRESS TEST 2

1. What are the three main methods used in making linear measurements? (1)

2. What is the difference between ranging and chaining? (3–6)

3. Describe the differences between metric and Imperial chains. (5)

4. How are metric tapes and bands graduated? (6)

5. Explain why slope measurements should be reduced to the

horizontal and give three methods by which this may be achieved. (7–9)

6. Describe the construction and use of the abney level and Watkins clinometer. **(10)**

7. What are the three kinds of error which arise in measurements and what is the effect of each? **(11)**

8. Give examples of twelve sources of error and describe their likely effect. **(12–21)**

*9. A base line known to be precisely 100·000 m long was measured with a nominal 20-m tape. The observed length of the base was found to be 99·925 m. What is the actual length of the tape? **(13)**

*10. The tape used in question 9 above was used in the measurements to provide a calculated area of 3·162 ha. What is the true area? **(13)**

*11. What is the greatest slope that can be ignored while undertaking a survey to an accuracy of 1/3000? **(9, 16)**

12. Describe the offsetting procedure to be adopted in surveying (a) irregular features, (b) straight features and (c) curved features. **(25)**

*13. To what degree of accuracy need measurements be taken when surveying an area to be plotted at a scale of 1/1250? **(26)**

*14. Determine the maximum allowable length of offset that may be used on a survey to be plotted to a scale of 1/200, assuming that perpendicularity of offsets can be guaranteed to within 2°. **(27)**

15. What criteria must be borne in mind during a reconnaissance in order to provide the best arrangement of survey lines? **(29)**

16. Survey stations should be marked in such a way that they fulfil certain requirements. Describe four forms of station mark and show how they comply with these requirements. **(30)**

17. What are the nine items of information that should be included in a field book in order to complete the field record? **(31)**

18. Describe in detail the process of running a survey line. **(33)**

19. Describe in detail how you would plot a chain survey. **(34)**

20. Explain the method of surveying the outline of a wooded area by chain surveying. **(35)**

21. Give detailed descriptions of the construction and use of (a) the cross staff, (b) the optical square, (c) the prism square and (d) the line ranger. **(36–39)**

22. Describe how to erect a perpendicular without using an optical square (a) from a point on a chain line and (b) to a chain line from a point off it. **(40)**

23. Describe two methods of ranging an obstructed line and explain the circumstances when they would be used. **(41)**

CHAPTER III

COMPASS SURVEYING

MAGNETISM AND THE COMPASS

1. Compass surveying. If two lines are required to be plotted in chain surveying, the third line to form the triangle must also be measured. However, if the bearings of the two lines are known they can be plotted by scaling the angle they make with a reference direction without the need for making further linear measurements.

By setting up a *compass* at the intersection of the lines and by observing their *magnetic bearings* their directions may be plotted. This process may be extended through successive lines, forming a *compass traverse*, which enables a complete network of survey lines to be plotted without the need for a base line or check lines.

If the series of lines closes back on to the starting point, the work may be checked because the plotted figure must also close back on to its starting point.

Compass surveys are mainly used for the rapid filling in of detail in larger surveys and for exploratory work and not for accurate, large-scale plans. Compasses do not provide a very accurate determination of the bearing of a line as the compass needle aligns itself to the earth's magnetic field, which does not provide a constant reference direction.

2. Magnetic bearings. The magnetic bearing of a survey line is the angle between the direction of the line and the direction of the magnetic meridian at the beginning of the line.

3. Magnetic meridian. The magnetic meridian at any place is the direction obtained by observing the position of a freely supported magnetised needle when it comes to rest uninfluenced by local attracting forces.

Magnetic meridians run roughly north–south and follow the varying trend of the earth's magnetic field. The direction of a magnetic meridian does not coincide with the true or geographical meridian, which gives the direction to the true North Pole, except in certain places. The angle between the direction of the magnetic meridian and the true meridian at any point is called the *angle of declination*.

4. Isogonals. As the magnetic poles are several hundreds of miles from the geographical poles and as the magnetic meridians are not straight lines the angle of declination varies from place to place. Lines on a map joining places of equal declination are known as *isogonals*, *isogons* or *isogonic lines*. The isogonic line of zero declination, along which the direction of a compass indicates True North, is known as an *agonic* line.

5. Variation of declination. The positions of the magnetic poles are not fixed and the north magnetic pole tends to wander more than the south. This causes alterations in the positions of the isogonic lines and new isogonic charts have to be prepared from time to time. The angle of declination at any point is therefore not constant, but is subject to the following variations:

(a) Secular variation (*see* **6**).
(b) Diurnal variation (*see* **7**).
(c) Periodic variations (*see* **8**).
(d) Irregular variations (*see* **9**).

6. Secular variation. This causes the largest variation in magnetic declination. It is a slow, continuous swing with a cycle of about 400 to 500 years. For example, in 1657 the magnetic meridian at Greenwich coincided with the direction of True North. Then the magnetic declination increased westwards until 1819, reaching a maximum of about $24\frac{1}{2}°$. It is now decreasing again, its value in 1967 being about $8\frac{1}{2}°$ west of True North, decreasing by about $\frac{1}{2}°$ every six years. Because of this large movement the date, the declination and the approximate rate of annual change should be given for any magnetic orientation of a survey.

7. Diurnal variation. This is a swing of the needle about its mean daily position. In some parts of the world this swing can amount to as much as 12', which is equivalent to a lateral movement of one metre at the end of a line 285 m long.

8. Periodic variations. Accurate observations show that the magnetic meridian undergoes minor variations during the following periods:

(a) *Twenty-seven days,* the time the inner core of the sun takes to perform a complete revolution.

(b) *The lunar month.*

(c) *A year.*

(d) *Eleven years,* the period of maximum sunspot activity.

These variations seldom amount to more than about a minute of arc and are thus small enough to be ignored in ordinary compass observations.

9. Irregular variations. These are caused by magnetic storms which can produce sudden variations of up to 5°. However, these variations seldom amount to more than 1°.

10. The prismatic compass. The prismatic compass is illustrated in Plate 1 and shown diagrammatically in section in Fig. 22. It consists of a non-magnetic metal case with a glass top and contains the following features:

(a) *The pivot,* which is made of hardened steel ground to a fine tip.

(b) *The jewel,* usually of agate or sapphire and recessed to rest on it, which is supported by the pivot.

(c) *The needle,* made of magnetised steel, which is attached to the jewel.

(d) *The compass card* or *ring,* graduated like a protractor from 0° to 360° in a clockwise direction, which is attached to the needle.

(e) *A spring brake,* which is operated by the brake pin for damping the oscillations of the needle and card.

(f) *A lifting lever,* which is for raising the card and needle off the pivot when not in use.

To the outside of the casing is attached the following:

(a) *The eye vane* and *prism,* which can be slid in a groove in the casing to focus on the card readings. The prism has convex sides to act as a lens and to magnify the card graduations. The prism, from which this instrument's name is derived, allows greater accuracy of reading.

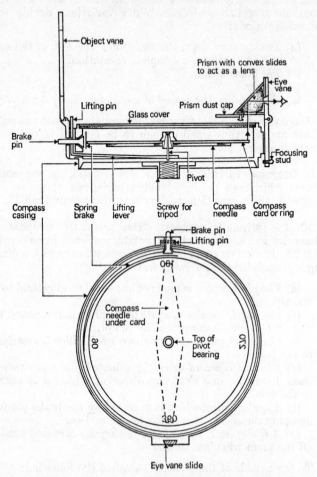

FIG. 22.—*Diagrammatic sketch of the prismatic compass*

Liquid forms are also available, which are similar but exclude the lifting lever and spring brake as their duties are carried out by the liquid, which also carries part of the weight of the needle and card.

Compasses without prisms are less refined and are not used in surveying.

(b) The slit forming the eye vane allows compass readings to be taken through the prism at the same time as sighting an object with *the object vane*. This contains a sighting wire which appears to extend down and forms an index against which the compass bearings to an object are read.

(c) When the object vane is closed down flat it depresses the *lifting pin*, which activates the lifting lever.

11. Liquid compasses. The suspension of the needle and compass dial in liquid gives it a steady action, allows quick damping of the oscillations and relieves the weight on the pivot point. Liquid compasses therefore have no brake pin or lifting lever, but require an airtight cover glass. However, bubbles would tend to form under changes of temperature in a sealed case and to prevent this the liquid compass box has a corrugated, nickel-silver bottom, which expands and contracts with the liquid, which in modern compasses is a form of purified alcohol. Liquid compasses are usually prismatic (*see* **10**).

12. Compass refinements. The following refinements have been made to compasses in recent years:

(a) When the compass needle lies in the meridian, the observer is actually reading the south end of the card, but in fact a correct zero reading is obtained. The graduations have been moved round the card to allow for the reading to take place diametrically opposite the actual direction required.

(b) As the prism lens produces an inverted image the figuring on the compass card is usually reversed so that the figures themselves are seen the right way up when viewed through the prism.

(c) The compass must be held level while observing, and to enable steeply inclined sights to be made an adjustable mirror may be attached to the object vane to reflect the image of the object.

(d) For sun observations dark glasses can be fitted to swing across the eye vane to protect the eyes.

13. Accuracy. The small, hand-held, service pattern, prismatic compasses have 1° graduations. The larger surveying compasses are graduated to half degrees, which only allow readings to be taken to quarter degrees by estimation. Such readings cannot be relied on closer than about 10′ and permit an accuracy of only 1/344. Even this degree of accuracy depends on the following factors:

(a) *The sensitivity of the needle suspension.* Excessive friction may be due to incorrect materials in the pivot or jewel, flaws in their surfaces, a faulty profile or excessive weight of the needle or card.

(b) *The alignment of the needle and graduations with the sight vanes.* The magnetic axis of the needle should coincide with its mechanical axis. Also the pivot must be aligned exactly between the eye and object vanes and be in the precise centre of the circle of graduations.

(c) *Diurnal variation.* This kind of variation (*see* 7) can be large enough to influence compass bearings, but its effect on any one observation cannot be gauged.

(d) *Local magnetic attraction.* Local attraction, disturbances in the earth's magnetic field or metal in the vicinity of the compass will affect the needle's correct alignment along the magnetic meridian at the point of observation.

FIELD WORK

14. Compass traversing. In theodolite traversing bearings are obtained by applying the observed angles from an initial adopted bearing at the start of the traverse (*see* IX). In compass traversing every bearing may be observed directly from the magnetic meridian established at each station by the floating needle.

(a) *The advantages of compass traversing:*

(i) The equipment is light and easy to carry.

(ii) Observations can be made comparatively quickly.

(iii) Each bearing taken is independent of previous observations, so errors do not accumulate.

(b) *The disadvantages of compass traversing:*

(i) Readings can be very inaccurate. They can at best only give an accuracy of about 1/344 (*see* 13), so that the scope of compass traversing is very limited.

(ii) Precautions have always to be taken against the effects of local magnetic attraction.

15. Reconnaissance. A reconnaissance prior to a compass survey is necessary to provide suitable station positions. The points to be borne in mind are similar to the requirements of a theodolite traverse (*see* IX, **16**) except for the following:

(*a*) *Stations* should be kept away from metal posts or fences, electric sub-stations or other sources of local magnetism which disturb the earth's magnetic field.

(*b*) *Short traverse legs* need not be avoided because any errors will not be carried forward with compass observations.

(*c*) *Grazing rays* will only cause errors less than the inherent compass inaccuracy.

(*d*) *Stable ground* at stations is not so important with light or hand-held equipment of low-order accuracy.

NOTE: Owing to the inaccuracy of the angular measure, no great refinement is needed for the linear measurements. In many instances even pacing the lines will provide an adequate measure of length. The number of paces, for, say, 20 m, should be checked against a tape laid out over the type of terrain to be covered.

16. Observations. Once the stations have been set out the compass is either held in the hand or set up on its tripod over a station and roughly levelled to allow the needle to swing free. The case is rotated until the back station is sighted and the reading recorded when the card is still. The case is then rotated again to sight to the forward station and the next reading recorded.

Moving on to the forward station the same process is repeated with an initial observation being made on to the back station from which observations have just been made. This bearing should differ from the first by 180° because the bearing of a straight line from one end differs from its bearing from the other end by this amount. If these two observed bearings do not differ by 180° and the needle is freely suspended there must be some local attraction affecting the direction of the magnetic meridian at either one of these stations.

17. Local attraction. The effect of local attraction is illustrated in Fig. 23. It may be described as follows:

(*a*) The bearing of AB is 50°. If the direction of the magnetic meridian (MN) at B were parallel to its direction at A, the bearing of BA would be $50° + 180° = 230°$.

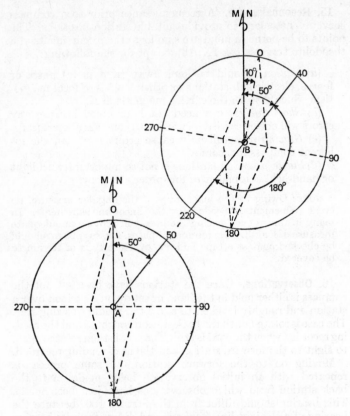

FIG. 23.—*The effect of local attraction on compass readings*

This effect is shown where the compass card has been swung through an angle of 10° at one end of a survey line.

(b) In the illustration the needle is deflected to a direction 10° east of the parallel, therefore the expected reading of 230° back to A is reduced by 10° to 220°. As the card has shifted round 10°, all readings from B will be affected by this amount.

(c) From these two observations it is not known at which station the local attraction exists; *either* all observations from A must be decreased by $10°$ *or* all observations from B must be increased by $10°$ so that the reference directions at each point are parallel.

18. The elimination of local attraction.
From the above it can be seen that the two principles involved in eliminating the effects of local attraction are as follows:

(*a*) The same correction must be applied to each forward bearing observed from any one station.

(*b*) The back and forward directions of any one line, after correction, must differ by just $180°$.

19. Reduction of observations.
In order to eliminate the effects of local attraction the field observations are reduced in the following way. The table is the reduced field sheet of the closed compass traverse illustrated in Fig. 24:

Line	Length (m)	Observed bearing	Correction	Final bearing
AE		$137°$	$-6\frac{1}{4}°$	$130\frac{3}{4}°$
AB	85	$60\frac{1}{2}°$	$-6\frac{1}{4}°$	$54\frac{1}{4}°$
BA		$230\frac{1}{4}°$	$+4°$	$234\frac{1}{4}°$
BC	91	$358°$	$+4°$	$2°$
CB		$182°$	$0°$	$182°$
CD	154	$148\frac{1}{4}°$	$0°$	$148\frac{1}{4}°$
DC		$328\frac{1}{4}°$	$0°$	$328\frac{1}{4}°$
DE	119	$219°$	$0°$	$219°$
ED		$44\frac{1}{2}°$	$-5\frac{1}{2}°$	$39°$
EA	98	$316\frac{1}{4}°$	$-5\frac{1}{2}°$	$310\frac{3}{4}°$

NOTE

(*i*) The bearing of each line is observed twice.

(*ii*) The first letter in each line designation indicates the station from which the observations were made.

(*iii*) Only in the case of line CD do the back and forward directions differ by $180°$.

(*iv*) Assume that both stations C and D are free from local attraction, so no corrections are needed for any observations from either C or D and the observed bearings can be recorded as final bearings.

(*v*) As $DE = 219°$, ED must $= 39°$ ($180°$ different). Therefore ED and all readings from E must be corrected by $-5\frac{1}{2}°$. Therefore $EA = 316\frac{1}{4}° - 5\frac{1}{2}° = 310\frac{3}{4}°$, the final bearing.

(vi) As $EA = 310\frac{3}{4}°$, AE must $= 130\frac{3}{4}°$, but $137°$ are observed so correct this, and all observations from A, by $-6\frac{1}{4}°$. Therefore $AB = 60\frac{1}{2}° - 6\frac{1}{4}° = 54\frac{1}{4}°$, the final bearing.

(vii) As $AB = 54\frac{1}{4}°$, BA must $= 234\frac{1}{4}°$, but $230\frac{1}{4}°$ are observed so correct this, and all observations from B, by $+4°$. Therefore $BC = 358° + 4° = 2°$.

(viii) As $BC = 2°$, CB must equal $182°$, which its observed bearing, requiring no correction, does equal, thus proving the reduction correct.

20. Problems of reduction. The following points should be remembered when reducing observations:

(a) If no two readings differ by just $180°$, the corrections should be made from the mean value of the bearings of the line in which there is the least discrepancy between backsight and foresight readings, unless otherwise instructed.

(b) Bearings for correction must be observed at stations and not at intermediate points on the line. This is because the effects of local attraction can only be eliminated if the bearings of adjacent lines are observed under similar conditions.

(c) The corrections considered refer to local attraction and not to observational errors. If gross errors in observation occur the readings will not be capable of reduction. Small differences between back and forward bearings are due to minor observational errors and are meaned and not applied as corrections.

(d) If the final forward direction after adjustment does not equal the final back direction $\pm 180°$ exactly, look for errors of observation or calculation, then, if the difference is small, mean the result.

NOTE: A large error will indicate erroneous observations due perhaps to the needle sticking on the pivot or an alteration in local attracting forces between observations at a station. This can be caused by moving survey equipment during observation or the movement of metal, such as a knife, on the observer's person.

PLOTTING THE SURVEY

21. The graphical plot. After reducing the field observations the traverse is plotted, as illustrated in Fig. 24, using a *scale* and *circular protractor*. A circular protractor is more useful in survey plotting than an ordinary half-circle protractor as not only does it simplify plotting but it also helps in understanding directions and the use of bearings.

The traverse is plotted in the following way:

(*a*) Draw a line up the sheet of the plotting paper to represent the reference direction of the magnetic meridian and mark the starting point *A*.

(*b*) Place the circular protractor with its centre at *A* and the zero lined up with the reference direction. Mark on the paper against the protractor edge the corrected bearing of AB ($54\frac{1}{4}°$ in **19**).

(*c*) Remove the protractor, draw the direction of the line AB, scale the distance (85 m in **19**) and plot the position of *B*.

(*d*) The direction of BC is plotted by placing the centre of the protractor at *B* and orienting it by rotating it until its zero direction is parallel to the reference direction as before. This is achieved, in **19**, when the line AB cuts the protractor at $54\frac{1}{4}°$ on one side and at $234\frac{1}{4}°$, the bearing of BA, on the other.

(*e*) Mark the bearing BC ($2°$ in **19**) and plot *C* in the same way as *B* was plotted before.

(*f*) Continue the process, orienting the protractor at each station by lining up the back and forward direction of the previous straight line on either side of the protractor. By marking off the forward bearing of the next line each point may be scaled and plotted in sequence until the position of the first point is again plotted from the last station.

(*g*) Accuracy can be checked by examining the distance between the starting point and the position of the same point plotted after working around the figure.

22. The graphical adjustment. The figure $ABCDEA'$ as now plotted does not truly represent the actual figure on the ground because the plotted figure gives two positions for *A*, whereas only one exists on the ground. This apparent displacement of *A* is due to the build-up of error in surveying and plotting around the traverse. The total error in the figure indicated by the line AA' may be distributed back around the figure graphically in the following way:

(a) A' should be at A and must be moved the distance AA' in the direction shown. The effect of this movement will be to move the plotted position of the other points proportionally along parallel directions.

(b) Draw lines parallel to the direction of the closing error through the other plotted points.

(c) Draw a straight line and scale off the lengths of the traverse legs along it. The scale of this construction need not be the same as for the original traverse plot and is more conveniently drawn to a smaller scale.

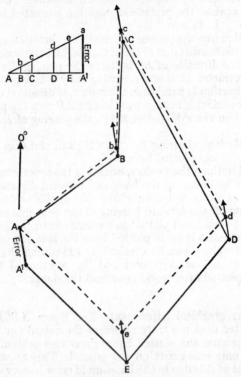

FIG. 24.—*The graphical plot and adjustment of a closed compass traverse*

This form of adjustment may be used for plotting any closed figure.

(*d*) Erect perpendiculars at each point along the line. Pick off the length of the closing error on the plot with a pair of dividers and mark it on the perpendicular erected at *A'*. Join *aA*.

(*e*) The intersection of *aA* with the perpendiculars indicates the extent of adjustment needed for each station, illustrating also the proportional build-up of error from nothing at *A* to the maximum amount at *A'*.

(*f*) The amount of error at *E*, being *eE*, is picked off the diagram and transferred to the line drawn through *E* on the plot parallel to the closing error, giving the adjusted position *e*. The other errors at each station are transferred to the plot in the same way.

(*g*) Join up the positions of the adjusted points giving the figure *AbcdeA*, which now forms the graphically adjusted traverse. This figure represents more closely the actual layout on the ground than the original plot did, prior to adjustment.

NOTE: This adjustment illustrates graphically the effect of the *Bowditch adjustment* on a calculated traverse (*see* IX, 37).

23. Completing the survey. The survey drawing may now be completed in the same way as a chain survey, except that the framework of survey lines used is the graphically adjusted plot instead of a framework of chained and checked triangles.

PROGRESS TEST 3

1. What is the difference in plotting technique between compass surveying and chain surveying? (1)

2. Define what is meant by the following terms:

    (*a*) Magnetic bearing.
    (*b*) Magnetic meridian.
    (*c*) Angle of declination.
    (*d*) Isogonals. (2–4)

3. Describe the four types of variation which affect declination. (5–9)

4. Describe the construction and use of the two kinds of prismatic compass. (10–12, 16)

5. What governs the accuracy of compass surveying and what sort of accuracy can be expected? (13)

6. Compare the advantages and disadvantages of compass traversing. (14)

7. What points should be borne in mind when undertaking the reconnaissance for a compass survey? (15)

8. What are the two principles which govern the process of eliminating the effect of local magnetic attraction? (18)

*9. Graphically plot to a scale of 1:1000 the field observations recorded in 19 and make any graphical adjustment which may be needed. What is the direction and extent of the closing error of your plot? (19–22)

*10. A rough compass traverse of a closed figure produced the following field record:

Side	Length (m)	Forward bearing	Correction	Final bearing	Back bearing	Correction	Final bearing
AB	375	25°			200½°		
BC	400	117°			297°		
CD	265	197°			27°		
DA	420	283°			97½°		

Eliminate the effects of local attraction and then plot the traverse to a scale of 1:5000 and make a graphical adjustment of the traverse plot. What is the scaled direction and length of the closing error? (19–22)

CHAPTER IV

CO-ORDINATES

RECTANGULAR PLANE CO-ORDINATES

1. Defining the position of a point. The position of a point on a plan may be defined by means of *rectangular co-ordinates*, as illustrated in Fig. 25.

Let the origin of the co-ordinate system be at O and let ON

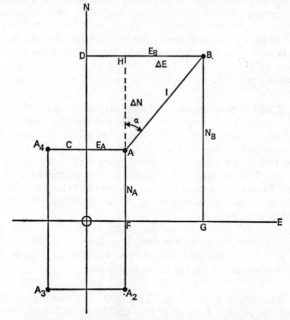

FIG. 25.—*The plane, rectangular, co-ordinate grid*

This is used as a basis for defining the relative positions of survey marks.

be a fixed reference direction and OE a direction at 90° to ON. The position of A can then be fixed relative to O by the lengths OF and OC, which by construction are also equal to CA and FA respectively. The lengths OF and OC are known as the *co-ordinates* of the point A.

The length $OF = CA$ is known as the *easting* of A (E_A) and the length $OC = FA$ is known as the *northing* of A (N_A). By convention eastings are always recorded before northings.

2. Latitudes and departures. A conventional alternative to eastings and northings is the use of the terms *latitude* and *departure*. Thus the distance $OC = N_A = $ the total latitude of A, and $OF = E_A = $ the total departure of A. By convention latitudes are always recorded before departures, the reverse of eastings and northings. When using co-ordinates it is therefore vital to note which convention is being used. Mainly owing to the influence of the Ordnance Survey, who have adopted the use of eastings and northings, the use of latitudes and departures is now less common. Should they arise it is generally simpler to interchange to the easting and northing notation before calculating.

3. X and Y co-ordinates. Mathematicians usually label the north–south axis of origin the Y-axis and the east–west axis of origin the X-axis. Most land surveyors adopt the reverse of this, eastings being Y-distances and northings X-distances. Some textbooks adopt one convention and some the other. This can lead to confusion unless it is appreciated that the term "X-axis" is merely a name and could refer to either one or the other and that any letter of the alphabet may be used to designate either axis.

Because of these anomalies, except where existing conventions are strongly established, it is simpler to use the eastings and northings convention, particularly as this is most readily understood by the general public.

4. Eastings and northings. In Fig. 25 the eastings of A are shown to be 221·2 m and the northings 473·9 m, usually recorded as A: 221·2 m E, 473·9 m N.

It is usual to choose the point of origin such that every point lies to the east and north of the axes of origin. All co-ordinates will then remain positive. Were a survey to extend into any of the other quadrants, points such as A_2, A_3 and A_4 could arise with the same numerical value of co-ordinates. In order to distinguish their positions from that of A the terms *southings* and *westings* could be used.

It is more usual to distinguish such points by a convention of signs which considers all distances west and south of the origin as negative and all distances east and north of the origin as positive, thus:

	Eastings	Northings
	(metres)	
A	$+221 \cdot 2$	$+473 \cdot 9$
A_2	$+221 \cdot 2$	$-473 \cdot 9$
A_3	$-221 \cdot 2$	$-473 \cdot 9$
A_4	$-221 \cdot 2$	$+473 \cdot 9$

NOTE: Where all co-ordinate values are positive it is usual to omit the signs of the eastings and northings. If any one co-ordinate happens to be negative then *all* signs must be shown to prevent the possibility of error.

5. Co-ordinate differences. Most surveys are more concerned with the relative position of points than with their position referred to an unmarked point of origin. In Fig. 25 point B has co-ordinates of E_B and N_B. Also:

$$HB = DB - DH$$
but $$DB = E_B \text{ and } DH = CA = E_A$$

Therefore $HB = E_B - E_A = \Delta E$, the *co-ordinate difference* in eastings between A and B.

Similarly $AH = \Delta N$, the co-ordinate difference in northings between A and B. Thus if the co-ordinates of A are known and the co-ordinate differences of the line AB are also known then the co-ordinates of B are simply obtained:

$$E_B = E_A + \Delta E$$
$$N_B = N_A + \Delta N$$

NOTE

(*i*) Co-ordinate differences are not themselves co-ordinates. Co-ordinates always refer to some common origin or point of reference only.

(*ii*) ΔE is the same as the term *departure* and ΔN is the same as the term *latitude*. The latitude and departure of a line therefore refer to the co-ordinate differences of the ends of the line. The actual co-ordinates are termed *total* latitudes and *total* departures under this convention.

6. Bearing and distance. The relative positions of A and B have been established in Fig. 25 by their co-ordinate differences. However, it was shown in I, **13**, that the relative position of points can be established by the *bearing* and *distance* between them. In Fig. 25 the bearing of the line AB is α, the angle between the direction of the line and the line AH, which is parallel to the reference direction or grid origin ON.

7. Whole circle bearings. In III it was shown how magnetic bearings are obtained from the graduations around the circumference of a circle, which gives *angular measure*. However, bearings need not necessarily refer to the magnetic meridian (*see* I, **13**).

(*a*) *The sexagesimal system.* This is the name of the traditional system where the circle is divided into four quadrants, each subdivided into 90°, giving a total of 360°. Each degree is further divided into 60′ and each minute into 60″. There are therefore $360 \times 60 = 21\ 600'$ in a full circle or $360 \times 60 \times 60 = 1\ 296\ 000''$ in a full circle.

(*b*) *The centesimal system.* This is the continental or metric system where the whole circle is divided into four quadrants as before, but each is divided into 100 *grades,* giving a total of 400^g in the whole circle. The hundredth part of a grade is known as a *centigrade* denoted by the letter ᶜ. In temperature measure °C is sometimes called *degree centigrade,* but to prevent confusion the correct term *degree Celsius* should be used. The centesimal system has not been adopted in the British metric system.

NOTE: Whole circle bearings are usually abbreviated to W.C.B.

8. Reduced bearings. A reduced bearing is the angle between the main line marking the direction to which bearings are referred (the N–S lines in Fig. 26, which need not necessarily lie in the true meridian) and the direction of the given line measured from 0° to 90° only, the shortest way east or west from the north–south line.

Referring to Fig. 26 the following comparison of bearing systems is obtained:

Direction to:	Reduced bearing	Whole circle bearing
A	N 42° E	42°
B	S 42° E	138°
C	S 42° W	222°
D	N 42° W	318°

The *quadrantal system,* which uses reduced bearings, is the method of graduating the circle, which used to be adopted in

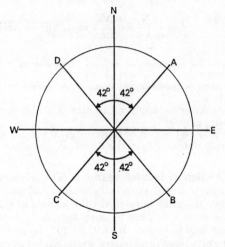

FIG. 26.—*Reduced bearings*

This diagram illustrates the direction in which reduced bearings are measured from the N–S reference line.

compasses. It is never used on theodolites, where the circle is more conveniently graduated from 0° right round to 360° on the whole circle system.

9. Formulae. The relationship between the co-ordinate differences and the bearing and distance is obtained by simple trigonometry as follows:

(a) In the triangle AHB in Fig. 25, if $l =$ the length AB and $\alpha =$ angle $H\hat{A}B$, the *bearing* of the line AB, then:

$$HB = \Delta E = l \sin \alpha \text{ and}$$
$$AH = \Delta N = l \cos \alpha$$
Therefore
$$E_B = l \sin \alpha + E_A \text{ and}$$
$$N_B = l \cos \alpha + N_A$$

(b) Conversely, if the length and bearing of AB are not known, but the co-ordinates of each point are given, then the bearing and length may be found from the following:

$$\tan \alpha = \frac{\Delta E}{\Delta N} \text{ or } \left(\frac{\text{Departure}}{\text{Latitude}}\right) \text{ and}$$

$$l = \frac{\Delta N}{\cos \alpha} = \frac{\Delta E}{\sin \alpha} = \sqrt{\Delta E^2 + \Delta N^2}$$

NOTE

(i) It is on the formulae above that all co-ordinate calculations are based.

(ii) ΔE always goes *side*ways and is produced by the *sine* of the bearing.

(iii) These formulae apply no matter in which quadrant the bearing may lie.

(iv) The sine and cosine of bearings greater than 90° may be directly obtained from their reduced bearings.

10. Application of reduced bearings. The advantage of the quadrantal system is that the sine, cosine and tangent of the bearings have the same numerical value as that of the angle, no matter in which quadrant it may lie. As tables of these functions usually only run from 0° to 90° the use of reduced bearings enables these functions of whole circle bearings greater than 90° to be obtained easily by converting first into reduced bearings.

For example:

$$\sin \ 42° = \sin \text{ N } 42° \text{ E} = +0·669\ 13$$
$$\sin 138° = \sin \text{ S } 42° \text{ E} = +0·669\ 13$$
$$\sin 222° = \sin \text{ S } 42° \text{ W} = -0·669\ 13$$
$$\sin 318° = \sin \text{ N } 42° \text{ W} = -0·669\ 13$$

The sign of the function depends on the quadrant in which the bearing lies. Referring back to Fig. 25, $\sin \alpha$ equals $\Delta E/l$, both of which are positive, so the sine is positive. The length l

is always considered to be positive, no matter in which direction it may lie, but should it lie in the third quadrant, say, then ΔE becomes negative and sin α too is negative. Similarly with the other functions, the application of signs being summarised as follows:

Point in quadrant	Bearing	sin α and ΔE	cos α and ΔN
I	0°– 90°	+	+
II	90°–180°	+	−
III	180°–270°	−	−
IV	270°–360°	−	+

11. Alternative to the reduced bearing method. Instead of using reduced bearings as the basis for establishing the sine and cosine of bearings between 90° and 360° the formulae below may be used. When accustomed to their use, this is the simpler of the two methods and would normally be adopted by surveyors. However, when calculations are only made infrequently the possibility of error is greater and it is advisable for most students to use the reduced bearing method. The formulae are as follows:

$$\sin\ (90° + \theta) = +\cos \theta : \cos\ (90° + \theta) = -\sin \theta.$$
$$\sin (180° + \theta) = -\sin \theta : \cos (180° + \theta) = -\cos \theta.$$
$$\sin (270° + \theta) = -\cos \theta : \cos (270° + \theta) = +\sin \theta.$$

CALCULATIONS

12. Co-ordinate calculation by logarithms. Given that the co-ordinates of A in metres are 206·3 E and 473·9 N, and that the length AB is 396·1 m and the bearing is 123° 37′, calculate the co-ordinates of B.

SOLUTION

		E	N
		(metres)	
	A:	206·3	473·9
log ΔE	2·518 32	+329·9	
log sin α	9·920 52		
log l	2·597 80		
log cos α	9·743 22		
log ΔN	2·341 02		−219·3
	B:	536·2	254·6

NOTE

(i) The formulae used are to be found in **9**.

(ii) To obtain the co-ordinates of B the co-ordinate differences of the line AB must first be obtained from:

$$\Delta E = l \sin \alpha \quad \text{and} \quad \Delta N = l \cos \alpha$$

(iii) To simplify the calculation the above layout has been adopted. The logarithm of the distance 396·1 m is recorded first. The logarithm sine of S 56° 23′ E, the reduced bearing equal to the W.C.B. of 123° 37′, is written above it and the logarithm cosine is written below it.

(iv) The logarithm characteristic for the sine and cosine here is 9, using the process which is adopted in practice. This is the same as $\bar{1}$, 8 being equal to $\bar{2}$, 7 to $\bar{3}$, and so on. Bars may be used in minor work if preferred.

(v) The logarithm of ΔN is obtained by adding log l to log cos α, giving the result 2·34 102 as shown.

(vi) Similarly the logarithm of ΔE is obtained by adding upwards, 2·59 780 + 9·92 052 = 2·51 832. The logarithm characteristic is really 12, but only the units are significant. This could lead to confusion in some forms of calculation, but never in ordinary land surveying co-ordinate calculations.

(vii) The antilogarithms for ΔE and ΔN are obtained and recorded in the appropriate columns.

($viii$) The signs of these values are next required. The bearing of AB, 123° 37′, lies in the second quadrant. The easting is therefore still *positive*. The northing of a second quadrant direction is *negative* as the direction is now south (*see* **10**).

(ix) Adding these co-ordinate differences algebraically, having regard for their signs, to the given co-ordinates of A gives the co-ordinates of B:

$$536 \cdot 2 \text{ E}, \quad 254 \cdot 6 \text{ N}$$

13. Co-ordinate calculation by machine. The calculation of the problem in **12** may be carried out with an electronic calculator using natural functions instead of logarithms as follows:

				E	N
				(metres)	
			A:	206·3	473·9
AB	123° 37′	+0·832 76		+329·9	−219·3
	396·1 m	−0·553 63	*B:*	536·2	254·6

NOTE

(*i*) The above layout makes the calculation clear and is similar to the traverse calculations of IX.

(*ii*) The bearing of the line *AB* is recorded with its length in metres below it.

(*iii*) Next the natural sine is extracted from tables or the calculator and recorded with the natural cosine written below it.

(*iv*) The distance 396·1 is multiplied first by the sine, the answer 329·9 being recorded below the eastings of *A*. Next the same distance setting is multiplied by the cosine and the result 219·3 is recorded below the northings of *A*.

(*v*) The signs of the ΔE and ΔN are obtained as before in 12 and the values are applied to the co-ordinates of *A* to produce the co-ordinates of *B*.

14. Length and bearing calculation by logarithms. Given the co-ordinates of *P* and *Q* as follows, calculate the length and bearing of *PQ*:

$$P: \quad 673\cdot1 \text{ E}, \ 377\cdot6 \text{ N}$$
$$Q: \quad 477\cdot8 \text{ E}, \ 106\cdot9 \text{ N}$$

SOLUTION

Subtracting the co-ordinates of *P* from *Q*:

$$\Delta E = -195\cdot3 \text{ and } \Delta N = -270\cdot7$$

and as both are negative the final bearing must lie in the third quadrant (*see* 10).

		No.	Log
$\tan \alpha = \dfrac{\Delta E}{\Delta N} = \dfrac{-195\cdot3}{-270\cdot7}$		195·3	2·290 70
		270·7	2·432 48
$\therefore \ \alpha = 35° \ 48' \ 30''$		tan α ←	9·858 22
$\therefore$ the W.C.B. $= 180° + 35° \ 48' \ 30''$			
$= 215° \ 48' \ 30''$			
$l = \dfrac{\Delta E}{\sin \alpha} = \dfrac{\Delta N}{\cos \alpha}$	195·3		2·290 70
	sin 35° 48′ 30″		9·767 21
		333·8 ←	2·523 49
		270·7	2·432 48
	cos 35° 48′ 30″		9·909 01
Length $PQ = 333\cdot8$ m, checked.		333·8 ←	2·523 47

NOTE

(*i*) To calculate the bearing from P to Q always subtract the co-ordinates of P from Q to obtain the correct sign of the co-ordinate differences.

(*ii*) To obtain the reduced bearing always divide ΔE by ΔN, never the other way round, or otherwise the complementary angle will be produced.

(*iii*) Experienced computers will always divide the smaller co-ordinate difference by the larger as this increases accuracy. This will frequently produce the complementary angle, but so long as this is appreciated and the proper reduced bearing extracted the final bearing will be correct. This method should only be used by more advanced students using the principles found in **11**.

(*iv*) The quadrant in which the reduced bearing lies is found from the signs of the co-ordinate differences as in **10**.

(*v*) The length is calculated twice as a check, using both the sine and cosine formulae as shown. The small discrepancy in the final figure of the logarithms is due to inadequacy of the fifth figure and is not a calculation error.

15. Length and bearing calculation by machine. The calculation of the problem in **14** may be carried out by an electronic calculator using natural functions as below. The calculation of the bearing and distance between co-ordinated points is known as a *join*.

P:	673·1	377·6	+0·721 463	215° 48′ 30″
Q:	477·8	106·9		
	−195·3	−270·7	−0·585 076	333·8
	(477·8)	(106·9)	−0·810 979	

NOTE

(*i*) ΔE is divided by ΔN on the calculator to give the natural tangent of the reduced bearing +0·721 463.

(*ii*) The value of this reduced bearing, 35° 48′ 30″, is obtained from the tables of tangents or calculator and the correct whole circle bearing of 215° 48′ 30″ recorded. The bearing is in the third quadrant as both co-ordinate differences are negative.

(*iii*) To calculate the distance use Pythagoras' Theorem (*see* **9** (*b*)) and solve for l using the x^2 and $\sqrt{x}$ calculator function keys.

(*iv*) To check the calculation the sine and cosine of the W.C.B.

are next extracted and recorded. As $l \sin \alpha = \Delta E$ and $l \cos \alpha = \Delta N$, multiplying the sine and cosine by the calculated distance 333·8 and adding the result algebraically to the co-ordinates of P should produce the given co-ordinates of Q. The result of this calculation is then written below in brackets. The calculation is checked if these figures agree with the given co-ordinates of Q.

16. Use of tables. The student should always study the explanation of use included in every book of tables of logarithms and natural functions. Too often such tables are inefficiently used and interpolation incorrectly carried out. The number of significant figures required in the tables may be gauged from the following:

Angles read to:	Size of table required
01′	4-figure
10″	5-figure
01″	6-figure
00·1″	7-figure

NOTE: While five-figure tables are just adequate it is usual to work with seven-figure logarithms and six- or seven-figure naturals available in *Chambers' Seven-figure Mathematical Tables,* or *Peter's Tables for Natural Values of Trigonometrical Functions.*

PLOTTING

17. The co-ordinate grid. In order to plot the position of co-ordinated points the first requirement is an accurately drawn *grid* or rectangular network of lines. Set-squares and T-squares are not sufficiently accurate for this work and the grid must be set out in the following way:

(*a*) Draw two diagonals lightly in pencil from corner to corner across the plotting sheet.

(*b*) From the centre point of intersection scale off equal distances along each diagonal. This can be more accurately carried out with a *beam compass.* The needle is placed centrally and the equal distances along each diagonal are marked off with the pencil point.

(*c*) Join the four points marked on the diagonals accurately with light pencil lines; this produces a true rectangle, which has equally bisected diagonals.

(d) The grid is now plotted on this rectangle by scaling along the top and bottom lines of the rectangle intervals of equal numbers of metres, say, 20, 50 or 100, depending on the scale. By joining these points the vertical grid lines are obtained. Similarly by scaling along the sides of the rectangle the horizontal grid lines are obtained. The squares thus formed should not exceed 300 mm in size, 100-mm squares being preferable.

(e) The origin of the grid need not be plotted as only the area of survey is relevant. The grid lines are then numbered eastwards and northwards with appropriate co-ordinate values to suit the values of the points to be plotted.

18. Plotting calculated points. There are two methods of plotting calculated points on to a co-ordinate grid:

(a) *Scaling the co-ordinates* of each point between the grid lines.

(b) *Scaling the co-ordinate differences*, the ΔE's and ΔN's, of each line from the plotted position of the previous point.

19. Plotting from co-ordinates. If the co-ordinates of a point to be plotted are 532·7 E and 373·4 N, the grid square 500 m E and 300 m N is first located. Scaling then 32·7 m east from the 500-m grid line towards the 600-m grid line a point is first marked on the 400-m N line, then again on the 300-m N line. Joining these two points with a light pencil line, the distance 73·4 m is scaled along it from the 300-m N line up towards the 400-m N line, giving the position of the point.

NOTE

(i) Scaling accuracy may be increased by picking off the distances on a diagonal scale (*see* I, **11**) with a pair of dividers.

(ii) Minor errors in the plot of any point are not carried forward to the plot of any subsequent point, which is quite independent of previous points plotted.

(iii) The work must be checked by scaling between the plotted points to confirm the known lengths between them.

(iv) The method above is preferred for plotting and is generally adopted unless computer plotting is used (*see* **22**).

20. Plotting from co-ordinate differences. This method is used when great accuracy is needed on small surveys. The initial point is plotted as in **19**, but the next point is plotted by scaling from this point the ΔE and ΔN to the next point, ignoring the grid lines. This process of using the co-ordinate differences is continued so that any plotting error in one point is carried forward to the next. If the series of points forms a closed figure the final point plotted should coincide with the initial point. Any discrepancy between them will indicate the accuracy of the plotting. Any gross plotting errors thus indicated can then be found and eliminated. A misclosure is almost inevitable and in accurate work an advantage. The final plot can be adjusted graphically if necessary, as described in III, **22**.

21. Plotting by angle and distance. Instead of using co-ordinates plotting can be done by scaling the angle and distance used to calculate the co-ordinates. The angle used may be either the bearing, the angle between the survey line and the grid lines, or the angle between survey lines. The method of plotting by angles is usually less accurate than by co-ordinates and has been described in III. It is a method seldom used if co-ordinates have in fact been calculated, but is often used when plotting points of minor detail.

(a) *Plotting with a protractor.* It is important that the line should not extend far beyond the circumference of the protractor. This is because in scaling the angle a slight plotting error will occur and the farther the line extends beyond the point defining the angle, the greater will be the error of displacement in the direction.

(b) *Plotting by tangents.* If a point at the end of a long line is to be plotted and the available protractor is such that the line will extend well beyond its perimeter, accuracy may be maintained as follows:

(i) The angle, say 21°, is set out using tables of natural tangents. From Station A a base length scaling 100 units is set out along a given line or grid line. This base length need not be to the same scale as the plot. At the end of the base X a perpendicular is erected and from the tables the tangent is scaled off along it to point Y. For 21° the tangent is 0·38 386 and, as the base length has been set out to 100 units, the perpendicular XY must be scaled at 38·39 units to give the required tangent direction.

(ii) A line is drawn between A and Y, which gives the

direction required because angle XAY has now been drawn at 21°. Station B is then plotted along the line AY at the scale of the plot at the measured distance from A.

(*iii*) The base line AX should be set out such that the actual distance on the plot of AB is less than that of AY, or otherwise errors will again arise caused by extending the line beyond Y.

22. Plotting machines. The plotting of co-ordinated points can now be accurately achieved by automatic plotting machines such as the *Zeiss Co-ordimat*. Co-ordinates are fed into this machine on punched cards, which are sensed and stored in the control. When storing is complete the drive motors of the tracing pencil start running, guiding it along an X- and Y-axis to the point determined by the co-ordinates. As soon as both the eastings and northings positions have been achieved by the motors, the circuit is broken and the tracing pencil released, marking the point. Instructions for plotting the next point are given and the machine continues automatically. Points can be plotted to an accuracy of 0·1 mm at a speed of about ten points per minute.

Other automatic functions of such machines, apart from simply plotting points accurately, are the following:

(*a*) Drawing co-ordinate grids to a precise degree not obtainable by the method outlined in **17**.

(*b*) Drawing curves and mathematical functions.

(*c*) Drawing a black or red sign around each plotted point as well as a four-digit reference number.

(*d*) Drawing contour lines.

PROGRESS TEST 4

1. Define the terms *eastings* and *northings*. **(1)**
2. What are *latitudes* and *departures* and how are they related to eastings and northings? **(2)**
3. How do the X-axis and the Y-axis fit into the co-ordinate system? **(3)**
4. What convention of co-ordinate signs is adopted in order to define the position of a point relative to a point of origin? **(4)**
5. Explain exactly the difference between a co-ordinate and a co-ordinate difference. **(5)**
6. What is the difference between whole circle bearings and reduced bearings? **(6–8)**

*7. Give the reduced bearing values of the following whole circle bearings:

$$91° \ 37' \ 40'', \quad 254° \ 21' \ 20'', \quad 354° \ 21' \ 20''$$
$$89° \ 00' \ 00'', \quad 271° \ 37' \ 40'', \quad 269° \ 00' \ 00''$$

(8)

8. What are the signs of sin α and cos α in each of the four quadrants? (10)

*9. You are given the following data:

Co-ordinates of A = 432·4 E, 611·5 N
Length of AB = 217·2 m
Bearing of AB = 311° 36′ 00″

Calculate the co-ordinates of B. (12–13)

*10. You are given the following:

A: 691·7 m E,   312·3 m N
B: 332·2 m E,   591·1 m N

Calculate the length and bearing of AB. (14–15)

*11. Three points A, B and C lie on a straight line with B between A and C. The distance BC = 211·00 m. The co-ordinates of A and B in metres are the following:

A: 610·00 E,   497·00 N
B: 331·00 E,   350·00 N

Calculate the co-ordinates of C and give the distance AC. (12–15)

*12. A straight tunnel is to be run between two points, A and B, the co-ordinates of which are listed below. It is desired to sink a shaft at D, the middle point of AB, but it is impossible to measure along AB directly. D is thus to be fixed from C, the third known point.

Station	E	(metres)	N
A	0·0		0·0
B	3014·0		256·0
C	1764·0		1398·0

Calculate the following:

(a) The co-ordinates of D.
(b) The length and bearing of CD.
(c) The angle ACD to enable D to be set out. (12–15)

13. Describe briefly the operation of an automatic plotting machine. (22)

CHAPTER V

THE ORDNANCE SURVEY

MAP PROJECTIONS

1. Definition of a map projection. A map projection is any means of representing the lines of longitude and latitude of the globe on a flat sheet of paper. The network of lines thus formed is called a *graticule*. Since it is impossible to represent the curved surface of a sphere on a plane, flat surface, there is no

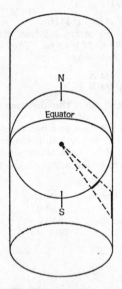

Fig. 27.—*The cylindrical projection*

The concept is illustrated where a cylinder is wrapped around the globe, in this case the line of contact being the equator.

perfect projection. However, certain projections are correct in some respects; *e.g.* scale may be correct along certain lines.

2. Mercator's projection. There are a great variety of projections, but one of the best known is *Mercator's projection* because it is used for navigational charts and in world atlases. This is classified as a *cylindrical projection*. To illustrate the form of a cylindrical projection consider wrapping a sheet of paper around the globe making a cylinder, its only contact being the line of the equator, as illustrated in Fig. 27. If a light source is placed at the centre of the globe and the lines of longitude and latitude are projected by it to the inside face of the cylinder a graticule is produced. On opening up the cylinder flat again the lines of latitude and longitude are represented by a grid formed by straight lines intersecting each other at right-angles, forming the graticule.

NOTE

(i) Scale would only be correct along the equator where the paper would be in direct contact with the globe.

(ii) As the projection moves away from the equator towards the poles, lengths on the globe are represented by increasingly longer distances on the projection, the exaggeration of the distances becoming so great as to render this perspective, cylindrical projection almost useless. For example, Greenland, 2 175 600 km^2 in extent, on Mercator's projection appears to be twice the size of the United States. The United States is actually 7 828 000 km^2 in area, over three and a half times the size of Greenland.

(iii) To control this exaggeration the spacing of the parallels of latitude is adjusted to conform with the scale increase in distance between lines of longitude, which decrease on the globe towards the poles, but remain constant on the graticule. However, there is still a substantial scale increase.

3. Orthomorphism. Orthomorphism is the property of a projection in which the scale, although varying throughout a map, is the same in all directions at a particular point, so that small areas have the correct shape. Mercator's projection, the principle of which is broadly described in 2, is calculated and plotted with the appropriate spacings of the lines of the graticule which produce this property. This property is necessary for topographical maps because it would be most disconcerting if the shape of properties on the ground were different from the shape on the map of the same areas.

(a) *The rhumb line.* Another property of this projection is that a line of constant bearing is a straight line, called a *rhumb line* or *loxodrome*, drawn across the map. For this reason navigational charts use this projection. The rhumb line course between two points is longer than a great circle, but on account of its simplicity, rhumb-line sailing is preferred, except on long voyages.

(b) *The gnomonic projection.* Great circles appear as straight lines on a gnomonic projection, in which a projection from the centre of the globe is on to a flat sheet tangential at a point. From this projection great circles can be transferred to the Mercator projection on which they will appear as a curve. A ship would then sail along chords to the great circle to prevent continuous changes of course and yet travel by nearly the shortest distance between ports. The gnomonic projection distorts areas and shapes quite considerably and is useless for reliable land representation.

4. Other projections. There are a great variety of projections which, although differing in their mathematical properties, may be classified into four main types, of which the cylindrical projection is one. Others are as follows:

(a) *Perspective projections*, in which the earth's surface is projected from a point to a tangent plane. The gnomonic projection is a perspective projection where the point of projection is at the centre of the earth.

(b) *Conical projections*, in which the earth's surface is projected from the centre to a cone seated on the globe and in contact along a parallel of latitude. The cone is then opened out flat to form the graticule.

(c) *Zenithal projections*, a special type of the conical projection, in which the apex of the cone has come down to the pole and the cone has flattened out to form a plane. This is the same as a gnomonic projection with a pole forming the tangent point.

5. The transverse Mercator. Distortions increase in magnitude the farther the Mercator projection extends on either side from its equatorial line of contact. For this reason it would be unsuitable for mapping countries any distance from the equator.

By rotating the Mercator projection through 90°, so that the cylinder touches the globe along a line of longitude instead, there is no scale error along this line of longitude origin and the errors which do occur on either side close to this line remain comparatively small. By choosing longitude origins suitable to the countries to be mapped, distortions may be kept to a minimum. This projection is most suitable for mapping and is known as the *transverse Mercator*.

This projection was first used by K. F. Gauss in 1910 and it is also known as the *Gauss conformal projection*—"conformal" because the necessary property of orthomorphism is retained by a suitable spacing of the meridians.

The Ordnance Survey of Great Britain have now adopted this projection, using longitude 2° west as the origin.

6. The Ordnance Survey application of the transverse Mercator.

By adopting the meridian 2° west as the line of contact with the cylinder, scale would be correct along the line with increasing scale distortion east and west of this line. This magnification of error, amounting to about 1/1250 in the limits of the British Isles, is cut by reducing the scale along the origin by half this amount. Thus the correct scale is obtained along parallels 180 km on either side of 2° west. The maximum scale error is then only about 1/2500, which is too small to be scaled on any one Ordnance Survey map.

NOTE

(*i*) The meridians of longitude and parallels of latitude are projected as orthogonal curves which are complex curves intersecting at right-angles, the central meridian being straight.

(*ii*) $Scale\ factor = \dfrac{\text{grid distance}}{\text{ground distance}}$, and the scale factor along the central meridian is 0·9996013. Local scale factor $\doteqdot 0\cdot9996013\ (1 + 1\cdot23E^2 \times 10^{-8})$ where E is the distance in km from the central meridian, which is 400 km E (*see* **8**).

THE NATIONAL GRID

7. Introduction. The National Grid is a form of the rectangular co-ordinate system (*see* IV) devised for the following purposes:

(*a*) *Plotting.* It forms the basis for plotting the complex curves of the graticule and the position of co-ordinated survey stations.

(*b*) *Reference.* It provides a unique reference for any

feature shown on the maps whereby such features can be located with accuracy.

(c) *Classification.* All the maps of the Ordnance Survey can be fitted into the grid system in a precise manner and the grid reference of a point shown on any one map is the same on all other maps of different scales.

8. The grid network. The grid network is based on the longitude origin of the projection, 2° west. Lines are established parallel and at right-angles to this line 100 km apart. As measurements east of the origin are considered positive and west negative (*see* IV, 4) and as this could lead to complications a *false origin* was created 400 km west of the origin. The position of this origin lies in the sea, south-west of the Scilly Isles, 400 km west of 2° W and 100 km north of latitude 49° N. As a result *all* grid co-ordinates of points in the British Isles are positive eastings and northings, no southerly or westerly measurements being involved.

9. The grid system. Figure 28 illustrates the layout of the 100-km grid lines. To prevent the need for large co-ordinate values each grid square is identified by a pair of capital letters.

The grid is first divided into major 500-km squares, each of which is identified by a letter H, J, N, O, S, T, as shown. Each major square is then divided into twenty-five 100-km squares, each of which is lettered alphabetically, starting from the top right-hand corner, omitting the letter I. Thus every 100-km square has a unique alphabetical reference; *e.g.* London lies in square TQ.

NOTE: The sequence of letters chosen to indicate the 500-km squares is the same as that indicating the 100-km squares. Conveniently, the 500-km square N covers most of the northern part of the country and 500-km square S covers most of the south.

10. Map and plan referencing. In order to provide suitable references to their various maps and plans the Ordnance Survey have devised a unique reference system. Figure 29 illustrates the 100-km grid square SP divided into 10-km squares. Such 10-km lines represent the sheet limits of the Ordnance Survey 1:25 000 maps.

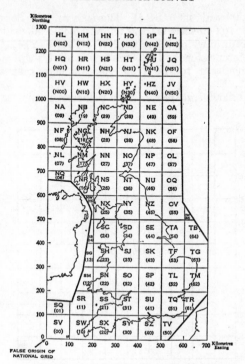

[*Crown copyright reserved*

Fig. 28.—*The National Grid*

This shows the 100-km squares and the letters used to designate them.

(*a*) 1 : 25 000-*scale maps*. Every such map is identified by
the co-ordinates of its south-west corner. As 1 : 25 000-scale
maps are always identified in terms of tens of kilometres the
map is given the reference SP 52; SP identifies the particular
100-km square in which it is located and the 5 and 2 indicate
that its south-west corner lies 50 km east and 20 km north of
the south-west corner of grid square SP.

(*b*) 1 : 10 000-*scale maps*. Maps to this scale, which will
eventually supersede the 6 in. to 1 mile or 1/10 560-scale
maps, cover an area which forms one of the quadrants of a
1 : 25 000-scale map. Figure 30 illustrates the area of a

1:25 000-scale map, SP 52. This area will also be covered by
four 1:10 000-scale maps, each of which is identified by the
quadrant in which it lies, *i.e.* NW, NE, SW or SE. To obtain
the reference for the 1:10 000- or 6-in. scale maps simply add
the quadrant to the 1:25 000-scale map reference, thus
SP 52 NE.

(*c*) 1:2500-*scale plans.* Such plans cover an area of 1 km²

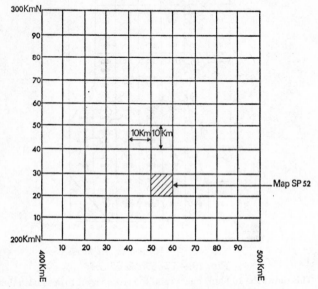

FIG. 29.—*The 100-km grid square SP*

This is also defined by the co-ordinates of its bottom left-hand corner,
400 km E and 200 km N.

as indicated in Fig. 30 and are identified by dividing the
100-km square into 1-km squares numbered from 1 to 99.
Again the grid reference of its south-west corner identifies
the particular plan, the 1:2500-scale plan, SP 5622, being
illustrated. SP again identifies the 100-km grid square and
5622 indicates that its south-west corner lies 56 km east and
22 km north of the south-west corner of the 100-km grid
square SP.

(d) 1:1250-*scale plans*. Such plans cover a quadrant of the
kilometre square covered by a 1:2500-scale plan in the same
way as a 1:10 000- or 6-in. map covers the quadrant of the
10-km grid square of a 1:25 000-scale map. Such plans are
thus also identified by their quadrant of the relevant
1:2500-scale plan.

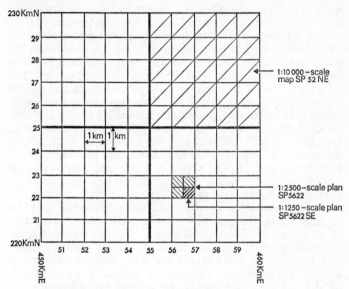

FIG. 30.—*The 10-km grid square SP 5020*

This is covered precisely by the map with the reference SP 52.

This unique map and plan referencing system may be summarised as follows:

SP 52: two letters and two numbers—the 1:25 000-scale
map.

SP 52 NE: two letters, two numbers and quadrant—
the 1:10 000 or 6-in. map.

SP 5622: two letters and four numbers—the 1:2500-scale
plan.

SP 5622 SE: two letters, four numbers and quadrant—
the 1:1250-scale plan.

NOTE: Although this reference system covers the whole of the National Grid this is no indication that maps covering the full range of scales in every grid square have been produced by the Ordnance Survey. Availability of particular maps should be confirmed by the retail agents of the Ordnance Survey.

11. Grid referencing. Every Ordnance Survey map is printed with grid lines spaced 1 km apart, but the 1:2500- and 1:1250-scale plans have grid lines at 100-m intervals.

The definition of the south-west corner of grid squares for map referencing has been described in **10**. In every case the definition is related in terms of kilometres east and north of the south-west corner of the relevant 100-km grid square. The reference SP 5622 is termed a *four-figure* reference and defines a point to the nearest kilometre. This may not be sufficiently accurate to define a specific point within this 1-km grid square. By dividing the sides of the 1-km grid into tenths or 100-m sections a point's position may be established to a greater degree of accuracy. For example, the centre point of SP 5622 is defined as SP 565225, a *six-figure* reference, indicating an easting of 56·5 km and a northing of 22·5 km. This defines a point to the nearest 100 m.

On larger-scale maps the tenth of a kilometre may be divided into tenths again, defining a point to two decimal places of a kilometre thus, SP 56532257. This is an *eight-figure* reference defining the point to the nearest 10 m. On 1:2500- and 1:1250-scale plans where the grid lines are only 100 m apart it is easy to scale to the nearest metre. Thus a point may be defined to this accuracy by a *ten-figure* reference, *e.g.* SP 5653422573.

NOTE

   (*i*) The letters defining the particular 100-km grid square are required to give a unique grid reference as the numbered reference can define a position in any 100-km square.

  (*ii*) When working in an area covered by one 100-km grid square the designatory letters are frequently omitted in the grid reference.

 (*iii*) Grid references must always consist of an *equal* number of figures. The first half denotes eastings and the second half northings.

 (*iv*) The first *two* figures of either half always denote kilometres. In any reference of less than 10 km the zero must be included thus, 04739540. This indicates an easting of

4·73 km and a northing of 95·40 km. As it is an eight-figure reference the position is defined to the nearest 10 m.

12. Bearing and distance. It is possible to calculate the bearing and distance between points on a map from their grid reference on plane co-ordinates (*see* IV, **14**).

The eight-figure references of two points on Plan TQ 19 NW are the following:

$$A: 13739517$$
$$B: 18619206$$

What is the bearing and distance of AB?

SOLUTION

Subtracting the eastings and northings of A from B, $\Delta E = +4·88$ km and $\Delta N = -3·11$ km.

$$\tan \alpha = \frac{+4·88}{-3·11}$$

$$\therefore \ \alpha \ = 57° \ 29' \ 30''$$

The whole circle bearing $= 122° \ 30' \ 30''$ because the direction lies in the second quadrant.

$$\therefore \ \text{the length of } AB = \frac{+4·88}{\sin \alpha} = \frac{-3·11}{\cos \alpha} = 5·79 \text{ km}$$

MAP INTERPRETATION

13. Maps and plans of the Ordnance Survey.

(a) *Small scale.* The Ordnance Survey have produced small-scale maps at the following scales:

1:1 000 000	
10 miles to the inch	1/633 600
1:625 000	
¼ in. to the mile	1/253 480
1:250 000	
½ in. to the mile	1/126 720
1:100 000	
1in. to the mile	1/63 360

1:50 000
1:25 000

(b) *Large scale.* The large-scale maps produced by the Ordnance Survey are as follows:

6 in. to the mile   1/10 560
1:10 000
1:2500
1:1250

14. 1:50 000-scale maps. The First Series of these maps superseded in 1976 the popular one-inch map, the first publication of the Seventh and last Series of which was completed in 1961. Smaller scales are generally less useful technically to the surveyor and are not examined here.

(a) *Grid lines.* The maps are fully coloured enlargements of the one-inch maps, but each cover a smaller area, 40×40 km, 204 sheets in all. Grid lines at 1-km interval are overprinted in blue with full grid values at sheet corners. They serve to index the larger scale Ordnance Survey map series (*see* **10**). Overlaps, which do not occur in larger scales, are indicated by a diagram in the east margin of each sheet.

(b) *Relief.* Relief is indicated by orange contour lines. As they are the same lines as the parent one-inch their value is a straight conversion to the nearest metre and the 50-ft contour interval remains the same. Spot heights are recorded to the nearest metre.

(c) *Roads.* Motorways are coloured blue. A-class roads are coloured a darker red than before, and B-class roads, previously brown, are now orange. Minor roads are yellow as before, and untarred roads are uncoloured.

(d) *Railways.* Multiple-track railway lines are indicated by solid black lines and single-track lines by black and white spaces within double black lines, the white space being about half the length of the black.

15. 1:25 000-scale maps. These are also coloured topographical maps, but some are issued as special publications (*see* **21**).

(a) *Grid lines.* Each sheet covers an area 20 km east to west and 10 km north to south, though the 10 km square format is sometimes retained for coastal sheets. Black grid lines are overprinted at 1-km intervals. Referencing of double 10-km squares is recorded thus (*see* **10**(*a*)):

SP 42/52

(*b*) *Relief*. Relief is indicated by orange contour lines at 25-ft intervals, every fourth one of which is accented. In built-up areas the contours are pecked to indicate the general shape of the ground. Spot heights to 1 ft and occasionally to 0·1 ft are also included.

(*c*) *Roads*. Motorways and A-class roads are indicated in orange, B-class roads in orange strips with small white gaps and minor roads in equal orange and white strips, and un-tarred roads are uncoloured.

(*d*) *Railways*. Multiple-track railways are indicated by black and white strips similar to single-track lines on the one-inch maps. Single-track lines are also shown in black and white strips, but the white is larger than the black.

NOTE: The scale of these plans is already in metric form and the publication of these plans with metric contours at 10-m intervals will follow in due course.

16. 1:10 000-scale maps. The publication of these maps, which form a quarter of a 10 km square, commenced in 1969. For open country areas these will become the basic scale. In other areas they are derived from the 1:1250 or 1:2500 scales or produced by conversion from the 1:10 560 Regular Series with revisions from the latest large-scale plan data available. Most features are drawn to scale, a minimum of conventional signs being used.

(*a*) *Grid lines*. There are black grid lines at 1-km intervals. Each sheet usually covers 5 km square, but extended sheets may have 1 km added to any side producing either 5×6 km or 6×6 km formats.

(*b*) *Relief*. Contour lines are printed in brown at 5 or 10-m intervals or 25 ft (expressed in metres) according to the source of survey information available. Spot heights are given to the nearest metre, and bench mark values to two decimal places are shown on basic sheets only.

(*c*) *Roads*. Roads of all types are indicated by black lines defining both edges of the road, pecked when road boun-daries are unfenced. Road widths are not always true to scale, being sometimes enlarged to allow for the clear printing of some road names, a feature not included on smaller scales.

(*d*) *Railways*. Multiple-track railways are indicated by solid black lines. Single-track lines are shown by equal black and white spaces within double black lines.

17. 1:2500- and 1:1250-scale plans. These are uncoloured topographical plans which are also used for *cadastral* purposes (*see* I, 3).

(*a*) *Grid lines*. These plans cover an area of 1 km² and 0·25 km² respectively. Grid lines are pecked at intervals of 100 m. 1:2500-scale plans are generally published in the 2 km × 1 km format, but each kilometre square is still separately referenced. The kilometre grid line dividing these sheets is always odd numbered.

(*b*) *Relief*. This is indicated by spot heights and the recorded heights of bench-marks only. There are no contour lines. Spot heights are recorded to 1 ft and bench-mark values to 0·01 ft. On metric sheets spot heights are recorded to 0·1 m and bench-mark values to 0·01 m.

(*c*) *Roads*. As in the 1:10 000-scale maps, roads of all types are indicated by their boundary lines, but owing to their larger scale no distortion exists and even kerb lines are shown as pecked lines. All road names are recorded on the plan.

(*d*) *Railways*. Individual lines of rails are shown, every track being indicated by a pair of parallel lines.

NOTE: As in **15**, these map scales are already in metric form and in due course all Imperial data at present recorded on these maps will appear in S.I. units.

18. Cadastral plans. The 1:2500- and 1:1250-scale plans are used for cadastral purposes, the larger scale, if available, being used for town properties. As a result these 1:2500-scale plans contain certain information not always available on the smaller-scale maps.

The following points should be noted about cadastral maps:

(*a*) *Mereings*. This is the term used to describe the physical indication of a boundary. Topographical features are recorded on the map, but, if an administrative or legislative boundary is not clearly defined on the map by the feature, its distance from such a feature will be recorded on the map to 0·01 m. For example, a boundary, indicated by a row of dots, may be 2·50 m from the root line of a hedge or the centre of a stream, etc. The mereing would be recorded as "2·50 m R.H." or "2·50 m C.S."

(b) *Areas.* Areas of land parcels are recorded on the 1:2500-scale maps to 0·01 acre. During the change to the metric system, areas will also be recorded to 0·001 ha and eventually the acre record will be discarded.

(c) *Parcel numbering.* Each parcel of land, the area of which is recorded on the 1:2500-scale map, is given a unique parcel number. This number is in fact the eight-figure reference of the centre of the parcel, except that the kilometre values of each half of the eight-figure reference are omitted as they are of course constant for all parcels in any one sheet. As a result a parcel reference on, say, sheet TQ 2877 may be the four-figure reference 1242, the true eight-figure reference being TQ 28127742.

To prevent single land parcels which fall across the corners of two or more sheets from having different reference numbers, each such parcel is allocated a number from 0001 to 0006 in such a way that the number allotted to a corner parcel will not be repeated on any plan surrounding that corner. Other parcels divided by the plan edge are allotted the grid reference of the midpoint of the plan edge, thus the same reference for the same parcel will appear on both adjacent plans.

Joining adjacent areas into one parcel is known as *bracing*, denoted by the brace symbol (∫) placed across the common division.

In *built-up areas* where there are too many small parcels to be numbered separately, they are banded together without braces and treated as a single parcel. The present method of defining the perimeters of such parcels is to place a symbol like a Belisha beacon (ρ) at regular intervals around the perimeter of the area.

19. Revision points. On the 1:2500- and 1:1250-scale maps the letters r.p. will frequently be seen. These refer to *revision points*, which are permanent features on the ground the co-ordinates of which have been calculated from survey data to an accuracy of 0·1 m. Such points can be used by Ordnance

Survey surveyors as a basis for revising maps where redevelopment has taken place or for tacheometric surveys.

These r.p. details are available to the public in *Minor Control Point Albums* which contain, in addition, a record of permanent traverse stations (P.T.S.) and their co-ordinates. While these stations are all of sufficient accuracy for mapping purposes, their co-ordinate values are often insufficiently precise to be used in connection with large-scale engineering or site surveys.

20. Land-use maps. These are a series of maps being prepared at King's College, University of London, under the direction of Alice Coleman, M.A., F.R.G.S. Although based on Ordnance Survey maps the Ordnance Survey have no responsibility for them.

(*a*) *Land-use survey.* The aim of the survey is to record up-to-date information regarding the use of land and sixty-four categories or classes of land use have been adopted. The survey is being carried out by groups of volunteers on site who are recording the information on six-inch maps. The surveyors' names are printed on the sheets they have mapped. The information recorded in the field is transferred to 1:25 000-scale maps which are printed in pairs, side by side, to give a convenient size of sheet.

(*b*) *Land-use categories.* It would be unsatisfactory to illustrate the sixty-four land-use categories by different colours and this is overcome by using different shade intensities. Only thirteen types of land use are represented and this is by distinctive, easily recognised colours. Lighter shading is applied to sub-groups of these thirteen main types which are illustrated by tonal variations or shaded stipples or stripes. One soon becomes accustomed to reading the subdivisions and their variations do not obscure the clarity of the thirteen main groups.

(*c*) *Main groups.* The thirteen main groups and their basic colours are as below:

(*i*) Settlement	Grey
(*ii*) Industry	Red
(*iii*) Transport	Orange
(*iv*) Derelict land	Black stipple
(*v*) Open spaces	Lime green
(*vi*) Grassland	Light green
(*vii*) Arable land	Light brown

(viii) Market gardening	Purple
(ix) Orchards	Purple stripes
(x) Woodland	Dark green
(xi) Heath and rough land	Yellow
(xii) Water and marsh	Blue
(xiii) Unvegetated land	White

(d) *Subdivisions of main groups.* As an example of the subdivision presentation, industry has four groups:

(i) A red wash represents a manufacturing industry.

(ii) Red cross-hatching shows an extractive industry such as a colliery or gravel pit.

(iii) Red dots indicate an active tip.

(iv) Horizontal red lines represent public utilities such as electricity, water supply, etc.

(e) *Details of subdivisions.* Subdivisions of groups can be further broken down by a system of letters and figures. The manufacturing industry for example is further described by fourteen numbers, No. 9 indicating precision manufacturing of instruments or jewellery, No. 10 textiles, etc. Arable land, a basic light brown, is divided into six subdivisions, legumes, cereals, root crops, green fodder, industrial crops and fallow. Individual crops are recorded by the first or first two letters of their names, *e.g.* B for barley, W for wheat, Lu for lucerne.

Apart from the particular land-use maps briefly described, such maps have been and are provided privately, generally by air survey companies, to supply information for planning departments of local authorities and for planning or redevelopment of underdeveloped areas all over the world. Land-use information is also now stored by many local authorities in computers from which land-use information is supplied not from a map representation but by means of computer read-outs.

21. Ordnance Survey services. One of the problems of providing maps printed on paper as described is keeping abreast of changes in ground topography. Revision data is no longer held back until a new edition of the map can be published, but is available in the form of *advance revision information*, issued for the 1:1250 and 1:2500 series. Also, to speed this flow of information, the conventional map is no longer the sole method of providing topographic data.

(a) *Advance revision information (ARI) maps.* These are photo-copies, either on paper or matt polyester film, of the surveyors' field sheets and contain the most up-to-date information. These are available at the 1:1250 and 1:2500 scales only, though photographic enlargements to the 1:500 scale are also available.

(b) *Supply of unpublished survey information.* This is known as the *SUSI System* whereby ARI is supplied either as:

    (i) a print-out from a microfilm,
    (ii) an at-scale transparency on stable plastic material, or
    (iii) a 35-mm mounted negative.

NOTE: All large-scale sheets are now supplied in the above forms as well as the conventional paper copies and can also be supplied to the enlarged 1:500 scale, though this scale is no more accurate than the parent 1:1250 or 1:2500.

(c) *Digital maps.* In 1973 the first digital sheet at 1:2500 was published after coding and storing data on magnetic tapes and producing print-out maps by means of a precision plotter. The map user can now buy magnetic tapes for the production of maps from his own computer. Once the data has been stored they can be recalled, programmed to predetermined detail selection, such as for roads or buildings only. Also revision details can be fed into the bank as well as specialised information not normally available on Ordnance maps, such as sewer layouts, land use details and so forth. This allows the purchaser with the right facilities to produce maps for any particular purpose without having to accept the cartographer's compromise between the many map users' requirements.

(d) *Other publications.* The following are also obtainable from the Ordnance Survey, Southampton:

    (i) Archaeological and special historical maps.
    (ii) Tourist and Route Planning Maps.
    (iii) Bench-mark lists (*see* X 6).
    (iv) Co-ordinates of and directions between Ordnance Survey Triangulation stations (*see* VII 2 (*b*)).

22. Map reading. Map reading and interpretation is a part of geography. Many excellent publications deal wholly with map study in relation to physical and human geography and this aspect of map use cannot be covered here. However, the student is advised to study in detail maps of all scales covering an area he knows, seeing how features are presented in different scales, using the conventional signs and examining the indication of relief, valleys, rivers, scarps, etc., on the map in comparison with his knowledge of the area. The conventional signs used by the Ordnance Survey cannot satisfactorily be learnt by heart but such signs are logical and many will be remembered with ease.

In describing the features represented on a map it must be remembered that a river cannot flow across a map and that a railway cannot run to a town on the map. There can be no river, railway or town *on* a map. They exist on the ground and are only *represented* by a drawing on the map itself.

PROGRESS TEST 5

1. What is a map projection? **(1)**

2. Why is Mercator's projection known as a cylindrical projection? **(2)**

3. What is meant by the term *orthomorphism*? **(3)**

4. What are the four main types of map projection and how do they differ? **(4)**

5. How is the Mercator projection adapted for use by the Ordnance Survey? **(5–6)**

6. What is the purpose of the National Grid? **(7–8)**

7. Describe how the National Grid is used for referencing Ordnance Survey maps published on grid sheet lines. **(9–10)**

8. Describe in detail how to define the position of a point in the British Isles to the nearest metre. **(11)**

*9. Calculate the grid bearing and distance between the two points A and B of which the six-figure grid references are as follows:

$$A:\text{TQ } 161607$$
$$B:\text{SU } 954414 \qquad \textbf{(12)}$$

10. Compare the following maps in respect of their grid line interval, their method of indicating relief and their roads and railways.

1:50 000-scale maps

1:25 000-scale maps

1:10 000-scale maps

1:2500-scale maps **(13–17)**

11. What is meant by the conventional symbol "r.p."? **(19)**

12. For what purposes are land-use maps required and how are uses indicated on them? **(20)**

13. What are ARI Maps and the SUSI System? How are they related? **(21)**

CHAPTER VI

THE THEODOLITE

THE VERNIER THEODOLITE

1. Elements of a vernier theodolite. The theodolite is an instrument which has evolved to enable angular measurements to be made. Although modern theodolites are refined and complex instruments, the basic components for angular measure remain the same as formerly. The theodolite is illustrated in Fig. 31 and includes the following elements:

(*a*) *A sighting device* to define the direction of a line from the instrument position to another point or survey station. This now takes the form of a telescope which provides a line of sight.

(*b*) *A horizontal circle*, a form of circular protractor, graduated to allow the direction of the line of sight of the telescope at any pointing to be read off against its edge. The difference between the readings of any two such pointings will give the angle between the directions of the two lines. Circles and verniers (*see* **7**), which allow increased accuracy of reading, are of silver-plated, polished brass with engraved graduations.

(*c*) *A vertical circle*, similar to the horizontal circle, but fixed in the vertical plane to allow angles of elevation and depression to be measured.

(*d*) *A spirit level* to enable the horizontal and vertical circles to be set in the horizontal and vertical planes. A spirit level is also used to define the horizontal plane against which angles of elevation or depression are measured. The spirit level or *bubble tube* is usually about 50 to 120 mm long and is formed by grinding the inside of a glass tube to a barrel shape before filling with a spirit of low surface tension. It can thus be used in any position, unlike the builder's spirit level, which only consists of a curved glass tube and must be set with the top of the curve uppermost.

NOTE

(*i*) By increasing the radius to which the inside of the tube is ground its sensitivity is increased as the distance the bubble is displaced by any tilt becomes greater.

(*ii*) The top of the bubble tube is graduated symmetrically from its centre, the bubble being centred against these graduations. Every bubble tube is marked with its sensitivity by reference to these graduations. If the tube were marked with one division equal to 40″, this would indicate that if the bubble were displaced by, say, two divisions from its centre then its axis would be displaced by 1′ 20″ from the horizontal.

(*iii*) In some modern instruments the traditional bubble has disappeared and definition of the horizontal plane is automatic (*see* 30).

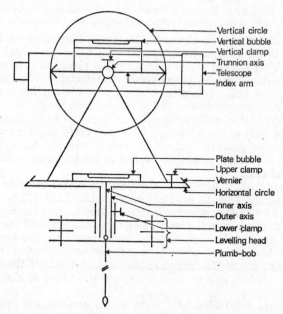

FIG. 31.—*The vernier theodolite*

The diagram shows the various necessary parts reduced to their simplest form.

(e) *Vertical and horizontal axes* to enable the telescope to be rotated in the horizontal and vertical planes so that it may be pointed in any direction. The horizontal circle should be capable of being turned to any position. In many instruments it has its own vertical axis, the *outer axis*, rotating around the *inner axis* upon which the telescope rotates. The vertical axes are of bronze and are tapered to allow the instrument to settle evenly as they wear.

(f) *Additional*, but necessary, components are the following:

(i) Reading devices for accurately defining the telescope position.

(ii) Clamps for holding the rotating parts in any required position. Every clamp has its associated *slow-motion* or *tangent* screw to enable the clamped motion to be finely set.

(iii) Levelling head for setting the vertical axis vertical.

(iv) A plummet to help in setting up over the station mark.

2. The surveying telescope. Figure 32 illustrates the functions of the internal focusing surveying telescope. Light from the object sighted penetrates the object glass and is refracted as shown to form an image inside the telescope. The concave internal focusing lens refracts the light again moving it along towards the cross hairs. The cross hairs and image are viewed through the magnifying eyepiece. The cross hairs define the line of sight of the telescope. The cross hairs, also termed the *diaphragm, graticule, reticule* or *reticle*, are crossed lines etched on an adjustable glass disc secured in the telescope across the optical axis.

Figure 32(a) illustrates the position before focusing. On looking through the eyepiece only a white haze will be seen. Figure 32(b) illustrates the position after the eyepiece has first been focused on to the cross hairs, by rotating it until the cross hairs are clearly seen in sharp focus, and after the focusing screw has been rotated, allowing the internal focusing lens to move by means of a rack and pinion connection, until the image of the object can be seen clearly in the plane of the cross hairs.

Figure 32(c) illustrates what might occur if the eyepiece were not first focused. The image has been brought to a position where it can be clearly viewed by the eyepiece, but it is not in the plane of the cross hairs which can, however, still

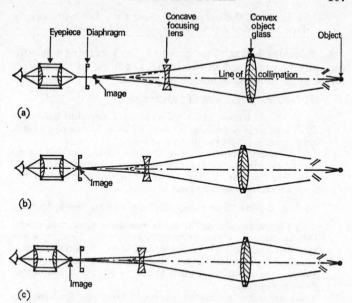

FIG. 32.—*The internal focusing surveying telescope*

(a) The course of the light rays when the telescope is wholly out of focus.

(b) The course of the light rays when the telescope is properly focused.

(c) The course of the light rays when the telescope has not been properly focused, giving rise to parallax.

be seen. It may be formed either in front of or behind the cross hairs. This will give rise to parallax (*see* **3**).

3. Parallax. Parallax is the *apparent movement* of the image of the object relative to the cross hairs caused by the image not being in the plane of the cross hairs. If a slight movement in the position of the eye while viewing results in this apparent movement it indicates that the telescope is not properly focused. If parallax exists theodolite observations will not be accurate.

NOTE

   (*i*) Parallax is *not* the gap between the image and the cross hairs, it is the apparent movement.

(*ii*) Focusing of the eyepiece to view the cross hairs clearly must be carried out to suit each individual's eye.

4. Telescope lenses. The optics of the surveying telescope can only be explained in the broadest outline as the subject forms by itself a whole branch of physics.

(*a*) *Lenses.* These are of two types:

(*i*) Convex lenses, which take various forms, but light rays always *converge* in passing through them to form a *real* image, which can be projected on to a screen.

(*ii*) Concave lenses, also in various forms, but light rays always *diverge* in passing through them, apparently emanating from a *virtual* image, which cannot be projected but from which light rays appear to come.

(*b*) *Lens defects.* The three main defects are the following:

(*i*) *Chromatic aberration* gives rise to a spectrum effect. This is caused by the different wavelengths forming white light being refracted by different amounts. This *dispersion* is remedied by cementing together a concavo–convex and a convex lens of different glass types, as shown in the object glass in Fig. 32.

(*ii*) *Spherical aberration* prevents accurate focusing because rays near the edge of the spherical lens surface are refracted more than those near the centre. The remedy is to use two lenses so that the aberration of one cancels out the other. This is adopted in the *Ramsden eyepiece* where two identical plano-convex lenses separated by a distance equal to two-thirds of the focal length of either act as a magnifier for viewing the real image.

(*iii*) *Diffusion* causes loss of light at the air glass boundaries and can be minimised by using *bloomed* lenses. This loss of light amounting to about 10 per cent for each lens can be reduced to 2 per cent by this proprietory coating of the lenses by the manufacturers.

5. Lens formula. If u is the distance of an object from a lens, v the distance of the image from the lens and f the focal length of the lens, then:

$$\frac{1}{f} = \frac{1}{u} + \frac{1}{v}$$

(*a*) *Application of the formula.* In applying the formula, f is considered positive for convex, converging lens and negative for concave, diverging lens. When images are real their distance from the lens is positive, whereas a negative v indicates a virtual image.

(b) *Images*:

(i) With a diverging lens the images are always virtual, upright and diminished in size, as in the internal focusing lens of a telescope.

(ii) With a converging lens the image is real, inverted and diminished for u greater than $2f$, as in the object glass of a telescope.

(iii) With a converging lens where u is between f and $2f$, the image is real, inverted and magnified, as in cine projectors.

(iv) With a converging lens where u is less than f the image is real, upright and magnified, as in the simple microscope and telescope eyepieces.

(c) *Power of a lens.* This is measured in diopters and is the reciprocal of the focal length of a lens in metres.

(d) *Magnification.* The magnification of a telescope is the term F/f, where F is the focal length of the object glass and f that of the eyepiece. For maximum magnification the object glass should have a long focal length and the eyepiece a short focal length. In simple terms it is the ratio of the size of the object as seen through the telescope and as seen with the naked eye.

6. Use of the lens formula. Figure 33 illustrates the convergence and divergence of light rays in a surveying telescope. An image tends to be formed at P^1 of an object P situated a distance u from O, the object glass. This image would be formed at a distance v from O under the relationship:

$$\frac{1}{f_o} = \frac{1}{u} + \frac{1}{v}$$

where f_o is the focal length of the objective.

After refraction by the object glass the rays are intercepted by the concave internal focusing lens as they converge towards P^1. P^1 can be considered to be the position of a virtual object, the image of which is formed by the lens L at P^2 under the relationship:

$$\frac{1}{f_1} = \frac{1}{u'} + \frac{1}{v'}$$

where f_1, the focal length of concave lens L, is negative and u' is also negative.

If the distance between the lenses is x and the length between the cross hairs and the object glass is l, then:

Since $u' = x - v$ and $v' = l - x$

$$\frac{1}{f_1} = \frac{1}{x - v} + \frac{1}{l - x}$$

and if either f_1 or x is unknown they may be calculated.

NOTE: The distance $x - v$ is negative as it is the distance to a virtual object and not a real object.

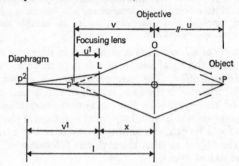

FIG. 33.—*Convergence and divergence of light rays in an internal focusing surveying telescope*

The application of the lens formula $\frac{1}{f} = \frac{1}{u} + \frac{1}{v}$ is shown.

SPECIMEN QUESTION

In a telescope the object glass of focal length 150 mm is located 200 mm from the diaphragm. The focusing lens is midway between the lens and diaphragm when an object 30 m away is in focus. What is the focal length of the focusing lens?

SOLUTION

$$\frac{1}{f_o} = \frac{1}{u} + \frac{1}{v}$$

Multiplying through by $f_o \,.\, u \,.\, v$:

$$uv = f_o v + f_o u$$
$$v(u - f_o) = f_o u,$$
$$v = \frac{f_o u}{u - f_o} \qquad \ldots (1)$$

Consider P^1 as a virtual object:

$$\frac{1}{f_1} = \frac{1}{x - v} + \frac{1}{l - x}$$

Multiplying through as before:

$$(x - v)(l - x) = f_1(l - x) + f_1(x - v)$$

$$f_1 = \frac{(x - v)(l - x)}{(l - v)} \qquad \ldots (2)$$

To evaluate v from (1):

$$v = \frac{150 \times 30 \times 1000}{30\ 000 - 150}$$
$$= \frac{4\ 500\ 000}{29\ 850}$$
$$= 150{\cdot}754 \text{ mm}$$

To evaluate f_1 from (2):

$$f_1 = \frac{(100 - 150{\cdot}754)(200 - 100)}{200 - 150{\cdot}754}$$
$$= \frac{-5075{\cdot}4}{49{\cdot}246}$$
$$= -103{\cdot}06 \text{ mm, the focal length of the concave lens.}$$

7. The vernier. To establish the direction of the telescope, readings are made against an *index*, which also has a *vernier* scale, which gives its name to this type of theodolite, to enable readings to be taken with greater accuracy.

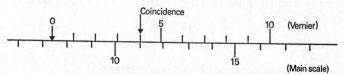

Fᵢɢ. 34.—*The simple direct vernier*

The vernier is reading to one-tenth of a unit and recording a reading of 7·4 units.

(*a*) *The simple direct vernier*. This is illustrated in Fig. 34 where n vernier spaces occupy $(n - 1)$ main scale spaces and it is read in the same direction as the main scale. In the illustration $n = 10$. As the scale moves one-tenth of the main division forward the next vernier division coincides with a main scale division providing an accurate reading of the movement.

(b) *The least count.* The least count of a vernier indicates the degree of accuracy to which readings may be taken. It is the value of the smallest division on the main scale, divided by the number of spaces on the vernier. The smallest space on the main scale in the illustration is one unit and, as $n = 10$, the least count of this vernier is one-tenth, indicating a reading accuracy of 0·1 units.

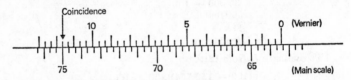

Fig. 35.—*The theodolite vernier*

The vernier is reading to 20″ and recording a reading on the main scale of 63° 20′ and on the vernier scale of 11′ 40″, thus providing a total reading of 63° 31′ 40″.

(c) *The theodolite vernier.* This is illustrated in Fig. 35, a part of the whole vernier only being shown. Here the horizontal circle degree graduations are each divided into three spaces representing 20′ each, the smallest main scale spaces. The theodolite vernier length represents 59 of these spaces and is graduated itself into 60 spaces. The *least count* is therefore:
$$\frac{20'}{60} = 20''$$

NOTE

(i) The main scale is divided into degrees and 20′.

(ii) The vernier scale is divided into minutes and 20″ covering a total range of 20′ only.

(iii) 11′ 40″ consists of 35 20″ spaces on the vernier. The point of coincidence on the main scale may be located by counting forward 35 main scale graduations from the vernier index mark.

(iv) There is never more than one vernier graduation lying between any two main scale graduations.

(v) At the point of coincidence the vernier graduations on

either side fall within the main scale graduations by a length equal to one-sixtieth of the 20′ division.

(*vi*) Vernier theodolites have two verniers, *A* and *B*, positioned diametrically opposite each other across the horizontal circle. Each thus gives readings differing by about 180°. Two verniers, *C* and *D*, at opposite ends of the index arm serve the vertical circle.

(*vii*) It is seldom necessary to read both verniers *A* and *B* on 20″ instruments except for triangulation and sights in excess of 300 m, when a vernier instrument would probably no longer be used nowadays anyway.

MODERN THEODOLITES

8. Comparison with vernier theodolites. The working parts of modern theodolites are enclosed as far as possible in dust-proof covers. Although concealed, the essential components are much the same as those of vernier instruments but greatly refined and improved. The main advances in construction are the following:

(*a*) The horizontal and vertical *circles* are now smaller and are of glass with very fine, etched graduations.

(*b*) *Axes* are no longer tapered, but are glass-hard, steel cylinders with self-centring ball-races to carry the load.

(*c*) *Verniers* are discarded in favour of optical reading devices which are simpler and more accurate to read (*see* **9**).

(*d*) Additional *refinements* are the following:

(*i*) Optical plummets allow more precise centring than is possible with only a plumb-bob.

(*ii*) Lens defects are minimised, producing telescopes with greater magnifying power and brilliancy of image.

(*iii*) The diaphragm and both circles can now be illuminated for night work.

9. Optical reading. The method of reading the glass circles of modern theodolites is based on one of the three following systems:

(*a*) *Optical scale* (*see* **10**).
(*b*) *Single-reading micrometer* (*see* **11**).
(*c*) *Double-reading micrometer* (*see* **12**).

10. Optical scale. The optical scale consists of a transparent glass scale graduated over the range of one whole glass-circle division, usually one degree. This scale may be divided into single minutes allowing readings to be taken by estimation to quarters of a division or 15″. The image of this scale is seen superimposed over the magnified image of the main scale and the position of the main scale graduation can be read off along the optical scale, as illustrated in Fig. 36.

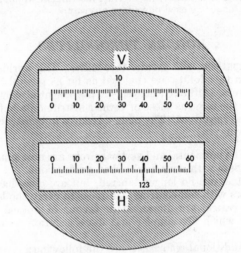

Fig. 36.—*The optical scale*

This is the reading device of the Hilger and Watts Microptic No. 1 scale model showing a horizontal angle of $H = 123° 39′ 30″$ and a vertical angle of $V = 10° 29′$.

11. Single-reading micrometer. The single-reading micrometer allows only one side of the main scale to be read. After light has passed through the circle it passes through a parallel plate of glass, which can be rotated allowing the viewed image of the circle graduation to be deflected. This deflection allows the image of the main circle graduation to be accurately set against an index mark. The amount of this deflection is then read off the micrometer scale, this reading being added to the main scale reading, as illustrated in Fig. 37. The span of the micrometer scale is usually 20′, the micrometer being graduated to 20″, allowing reading by estimation to 5″. Figure 37 illustrates the optical system of the Wild TI–A.

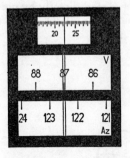

FIG. 37.—*The single-reading optical micrometer*

This is the Wild T1–A optical micrometer, in which the vertical circle reading shown is 87° 22′ 20″.

12. Double-reading micrometer. This is also called the *coincidence optical micrometer*. Light passes through diametrically opposite sides of the main circle and the deflection caused by rotating the micrometer brings these readings into coincidence. The micrometer reading is thus the mean of the two readings which would have been obtained from two fixed index marks on opposite sides of the circle and is therefore free of eccentricity error. On some instruments the circles are specially graduated to allow the coincidence setting to be made without confusion with the degree markings. In others, such as in the Wild T2 instrument, illustrated in Fig. 38, the readings of the opposite side of the circle are seen upside down and

FIG. 38.—*The coincidence optical micrometer*

This is the Wild T2 Universal theodolite, in which the reading is 94° 12′ 43″·5.

the number of whole circle graduations are counted between the corresponding degree graduations on opposite sides of the circle.

13. Classification of theodolites. Optical reading theodolites may be considered to be of three types depending on their precision:

(a) *Low-order instruments.* These read directly by optical scales or single-reading micrometers to 20″ or less. Such

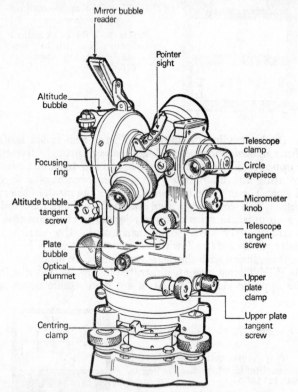

Fig. 39.—*The Watts Microptic No. 1 theodolite*

instruments are used for minor detail surveys, general engineering and building work and setting out where great accuracy is not required. Figure 39 illustrates the Watts Microptic No. 1 theodolite of this type.

(b) *Universal theodolites.* This type of instrument reads directly to a single second by means of a coincidence optical micrometer. This is the theodolite of the land surveyor, being used on all classes of work from large-scale surveys to third-order triangulation. These theodolites are single-axis theodolites as the accuracy is such that the repetition method of observing (*see* 22) is never required. The horizontal circle can, however, be rotated so that it may be set in any required position. Plate 2 illustrates the Wild T2 Universal theodolite (reproduced by courtesy of Wild Heerbrugg, Switzerland).

(c) *Geodetic theodolites.* These form the most precise type of theodolite and usually read directly to at least one-fifth of a second of arc by means of the coincidence optical micrometer. Their circles are larger and are more finely divided. Their telescopes are more powerful and the instruments are larger and heavier. They are used mainly for primary and secondary triangulation, first-order precise traversing and geodetic astronomy. Plate 5 illustrates the Kern DKM 3 theodolite of this type (reproduced by courtesy of the Survey and General Instrument Company Ltd.).

14. Theodolite developments. Theodolite manufacturers are continuously improving their instruments. Apart from the advance in the instruments' general specifications, two notable features are now being incorporated into theodolite design:

(a) *Automatic vertical collimation.* The Wild TI–A and the Kern KI–A and DKM 2–A all have devices which automatically position the vertical circle index horizontally, thus eliminating the need for the vertical bubble.

(b) *Mirror telescopes.* The effective focal length of a telescope can be extended several times its actual length by reflection from concave mirrors. This allows greater magnification in a compact telescope and a larger objective, which permits more light to enter the telescope, resulting in greater clarity of vision. The Kern DKM 3 has this type of telescope.

15. Technical data of theodolites. The following table provides a comparison of the technical data of some theodolites in general use with those of the vernier theodolite:

	Kern DKM 3 Geodetic	Wild T2 Universal	Wild TI–A	Watts Microptic No. 1 scale model	Stanley Vernier
Magnification	45×	28×	27×	25×	24×
Telescope aperture (mm)	72	40	40	38	42
Shortest focusing distance (m)	4	1·4	1·3	1·6	2·0
Stadia constant	100	100	100	100	100
Additive constant	0	0	0	0	0
Telescope length (mm)	133	148	145	146	230
Horizontal circle diameter (mm)	100	90	78	89	114
Vertical circle diameter (mm)	100	70	70	64	101
Direct reading to	0·5″	1″	20″	1′	20″
Estimation to	0·1″	0·5″	5″	15″	—
Instrument weight (kg)	11·2	5·6	4·8	5·1	7·0

MEASUREMENT OF ANGLES

16. Setting up. A theodolite is set up to prepare for observing in the following manner:

(*a*) Unstrap the tripod legs, spread them out and place the tripod securely on the ground with the top nearly level at a convenient height. If an extending tripod is being used the legs must be extended and firmly clamped.

(*b*) Remove the theodolite from its case, noting first how it has been secured so that it may be easily replaced. Loosen all clamps and, holding it firmly by the trunnion away from the verticle circle, screw the trivet firmly to the tripod-head.

(*c*) The theodolite is centred by attaching the plumb-bob to the instrument and positioning the tripod approximately over the station mark.

(*i*) Using one tripod leg only and by moving it up or down or swinging it from side to side level up the tripod head. This may be judged by eye or more accurately by using the circular bubble on the tripod head or instrument.

(*ii*) Note how far the plumb-bob hangs from the station mark.

(*iii*) Move the whole instrument bodily by this amount, disturbing the displacement of the legs as little as possible. This will more or less retain the level of the tripod head. The plumb-bob should be hanging within 10 mm or so of the station mark with the instrument roughly level.

(*iv*) Press the tripod feet down firmly into the ground.

(*v*) Loosen the clamp of the movable head and shift the instrument relative to the stable tripod until the plumb-bob hangs precisely over the station mark. By clamping the movable head the instrument is ready to be levelled.

17. Levelling. With the theodolite set up over the mark the instrument is ready to be levelled.

(*a*) Ensure that the upper clamp is loose and rotate the instrument until the plate bubble lies parallel to any two footscrews.

(*b*) Rotate these two footscrews in opposite directions to bring the bubble into the central position in its tube. Remember that the bubble will follow the direction of movement of the left thumb.

(*c*) Turn the instrument through 90° and level the bubble again using the third footscrew only.

(*d*) Return to the first position and re-level if necessary. Rotate the instrument through 180° to reverse the bubble position. If the bubble remains in its central position the theodolite is properly levelled.

NOTE: If the bubble does not remain in the centre of its run the plate bubble is out of adjustment. If it is only one division off this can be ignored except in precise work. If it is out by a greater amount the bubble requires adjustment and the action to be taken is described in **27**.

18. Centring with the optical plummet. Modern theodolites have optical plummets and extending-leg tripods, and these instruments may be set up in the following way:

(*a*) Place the instrument on its tripod approximately over the ground mark with the tribrach reasonably level. Sight through the optical plummet, focus and adjust the instrument to bring the cross hairs on to the mark without regard for levelling. This is achieved as follows:

(*i*) If the movement needed is slight use the footscrews only.

(*ii*) If the movement needed is in excess of about 40 mm choose the one tripod leg which is approximately at right angles to the movement required and move it, twisting the tribrach, to bring the cross hairs on to the mark. Complete the setting, using the footscrews if necessary. Tread the tripod feet firmly down.

NOTE

(*i*) The theodolite is not yet level nor vertically above the station, but this is centred in the plummet's line of sight. *Levelling with the footscrews now will disturb this setting.*

(*ii*) Though not absolutely necessary, it is often convenient to move two tripod legs instead of one to obtain the initial setting on to the ground mark.

(*b*) Raise or lower each extending leg in turn until the plate bubble, turned to point to the leg being adjusted, is centred and the instrument will be levelled and its centre will move to the vertical through the ground mark.

NOTE: Any resultant levelling and centring error can be taken up by the movable head and fine levelling with the footscrews.

19. Removal of parallax. With the theodolite now set up and levelled the possibility of parallax occurring (*see* **3**) must be eliminated before observing. Remove the telescope cap and rotate the eyepiece until the reticle lines appear sharp and black. Then, when viewing a signal, the image can be clearly focused on to the plane of the cross hairs, thus eliminating parallax

20. Observing on both faces. Readings should always be taken on both faces of the theodolite, *i.e.* on face left or circle left, with the vertical circle on the left side of the eyepiece, and on face right or circle right, with the vertical circle now on the right-hand side. This process is necessary to eliminate systematic errors in the adjustment of the line of sight, or *collimation*, and in the adjustment of the horizontal axis and errors due to eccentricity of the circles.

21. Measurement of a horizontal angle. To measure the horizontal angle ABC the procedure below is adopted. The theodolite has first to be set up at B, then levelled and then the eyepiece focused on the cross hairs.

(*a*) Loosen both upper and lower clamps and rotate the graduated horizontal circle until a zero setting is obtained with the micrometer pre-set to zero.

(*b*) Clamp the upper clamp and using the upper slow-motion screw set the reading accurately to zero. The telescope is then free to point in any direction and, as it is clamped to the horizontal circle, the direction reading will not alter.

(*c*) Point the telescope towards the signal at A and clamp the lower clamp when the signal is nearly bisected and focus the telescope without parallax.

(*d*) Clamp the vertical clamp and using the vertical slow-motion screw bring the view of the signal at A to the approximate centre of the field of view.

(*e*) Using the lower slow-motion screw bring over the vertical cross hair to accurately bisect the signal. In accurate work the final movement to bring the vertical hair on to the signal should always compress the slow-motion spring. The telescope is then pointing towards A with a zero circle setting.

(*f*) Release the upper clamp. This frees the telescope leaving the graduated circle stationary. Swing the telescope in a clockwise direction on to the signal at C and again bisect the signal using the upper clamp and upper slow-motion screw only. Record the reading, which will give the direction of B to C, say, 63° 31′ 40″.

(*g*) Subtracting the zero direction of B to A from this reading the angle ABC, 63° 31′ 40″, is obtained. This value may be in error because of an observer's mistake or instrumental errors so the measure must be repeated on the other face.

(*h*) Transit the telescope by swinging it through 180° in the vertical plane. Loosen the upper clamp, swing round through 180° and again bisect the signal at *C* using the upper clamp and upper slow-motion screw once more, thus changing face.

(*i*) Again take a reading which will now differ by about 180° and be, say, 243° 31′ 20″.

(*j*) Release the upper clamp and swing back, this time in an anti-clockwise direction to *A*. Clamp the upper clamp and again bisect the signal at *A*.

(*k*) This reading too will differ by about 180° and be, say, 179° 59′ 20″.

(*l*) The difference between these two readings, 243° 31′ 20″ −179° 59′ 20″, is 63° 32′ 00″, giving a second value for the measure of angle *ABC*. The close agreement indicates that there are no observing errors and the mean of the two measures, being 63° 31′ 50″, gives a result which has mini-mised the instrumental errors.

NOTE

(*i*) On circle left swing right, and on circle right swing left.

(*ii*) Once the lower clamp and lower slow-motion screw have been used to provide an initial reading setting, or *orientation*, they are not touched again. If they are the graduated circle will be displaced and the angle measurement will be in error.

(*iii*) There is no need to set a zero reading for the initial obser-vation. The horizontal circle can remain clamped in any position and by simply subtracting the readings to the first station from the readings to the second station the values of the angle will be obtained.

(*iv*) Three methods of noting down theodolite readings are shown in IX, 8–10.

22. Reiteration and repetition. To increase the accuracy of the resultant angle the whole process may be repeated several times on both faces to provide several measures of the angle which are then meaned. This is called the *reiteration method* and is the method most commonly adopted in accurate work. If the angle is measured using different parts of the circle each time, any errors in the circle graduation will tend to be elim-inated from the final result.

Repetition is the method adopted for the measure of small angles as the measuring accuracy of the instrument can be greatly increased. The instrument must have a double axis and the process in measuring an angle ABC is as follows:

(a) Sight A in the usual way and book the initial reading.

(b) Release the upper clamp, swing right and sight C.

(c) Release the lower clamp, swing right, carrying the reading forward, and sight A again.

(d) Release the upper clamp, swing right and sight C again.

(e) This gives two measures of the angle, but the process may be continued n times and only the final reading on to C is booked. This final reading on to C, plus any multiples of 360°, is divided by n to give the value of the angle. This process would also be repeated on the other face.

23. Measurement of vertical angles. Vertical angles are measured relative to the horizontal plane defined by the vertical bubble. For every reading of a vertical angle of elevation or depression the vertical bubble must first be centred by means of the *clip screw* in order to position the vertical circle index horizontally.

The vertical circle is sometimes graduated from 0° round to 360° with the 90°–270° graduations or the 0°–180° graduations defining the horizontal. Such circles are read after clamping the vertical movement of the telescope and setting the horizontal cross hair accurately on the mark with the vertical slow-motion screw.

On some vernier instruments the circle is graduated in quadrants with 0°–0° defining the horizontal and the graduations on either side increasing upwards to 90° and downwards to 90°, the vernier must be adapted to allow for the change in direction of the circle graduations for angles of elevation or depression.

On such circles verniers extend outwards on either side of a central index. Care must then be taken to use that vernier the graduations of which increase in the same direction as the portion of the vertical circle being read.

THEODOLITE ADJUSTMENTS

24. Errors in angular measurement. As in linear measurements (*see* II, 12), angular measurements are subject to the three error types. They are as follows:

(a) *Systematic errors.* These are cumulative in effect and are caused by badly made or badly adjusted instruments.

They may be reduced by following the correct observing sequence and by adjusting theodolites carefully.

(*b*) *Compensating errors.* These errors are unavoidable and are caused by human limitations in reading, handling and pointing the theodolite and by the small, non-adjustable, instrumental, residual errors. Their effect may be reduced by increasing the number of angular observations and by meaning the result.

(*c*) *Gross errors.* These are caused simply by making mistakes. They can only be avoided by careful work and as proper checks are always applied they will be shown up by other measurements or calculations (*see* I, 5 (*b*)).

25. Temporary adjustments. These adjustments are so called because every time a theodolite is used they must be carried out. These adjustments have already been described and consist of the following:

(*a*) Setting up and centring the theodolite (*see* **16, 18**).
(*b*) Levelling the instrument to position its vertical axis truly vertical (*see* **17**).
(*c*) Eliminating parallax (*see* **3**).

26. Permanent adjustments. These adjustments are so called because once carried out they do not alter unless the instrument is roughly handled or the adjustments are tampered with. There are certain basic requirements in a properly adjusted theodolite and their existence must be established every once in a while and particularly when using a theodolite for the first time. These basic requirements are as below:

(*a*) The *vertical axis* should be truly vertical (plate bubble adjustment). (*See* **27**.)
(*b*) The *line of sight* should be perpendicular to the horizontal axis (collimation adjustment). (*See* **28**.)
(*c*) The *horizontal axis* should be truly horizontal (trunnion axis adjustment). (*See* **29**.)
(*d*) The *cross hairs* should be truly vertical and horizontal (diaphragm adjustment). (*See* **30**.)
(*e*) The *vertical circle* should be at zero when the line of sight is horizontal (index error adjustment). (*See* **31**.)

27. Plate bubble adjustment.

(a) *Aim.* To set the vertical axis truly vertical when the plate bubble is central.

(b) *Test.* Level the instrument as described in **17**, which is summarised as follows:

> (*i*) Set the bubble parallel to two footscrews and bring central.
>
> (*ii*) Turn through 90° and bring central.
>
> (*iii*) Turn back to first position and bring central.
>
> (*iv*) Turn through 180°. If still central, the instrument is levelled and the bubble is in adjustment.

(c) *Adjustment:*

(*i*) If the bubble is not central bring it back half-way to its central position using the footscrews.

(*ii*) Turn through 90° and again set it half-way to the central position, the same position in the bubble tube, as in (c) (*i*) above.

(*iii*) Turn again through 90°. The bubble should remain in this position because by correcting half the error on the footscrew the perpendicular axis has been positioned vertically. The instrument has been levelled and only the bubble is wrong.

(*iv*) Using the bubble adjusting screws bring the bubble back to its central position.

NOTE: The instrument has been properly levelled once the bubble remains in one position in the tube. A central bubble is a convenience and not a necessity for the correct levelling of the instrument.

28. Collimation adjustment.

(a) *Aim.* To set the line of sight perpendicular to the trunnion axis.

(b) *Test:*

(*i*) Sight a well-defined object with the centre of the cross hairs in the middle distance at about the same level as the instrument and read the horizontal circle.

(*ii*) Transit and again read the horizontal circle on the other face.

(*iii*) The two readings should differ by exactly 180°. If not, a collimation error exists.

(c) *Adjustment:*

(*i*) Half the difference from 180° must be added to one reading and subtracted from the other to give the correct reading. For example:

Circle left reading: 27° 31′ 00″
Circle right reading: 207° 32′ 40″
Difference from 180°: 1′ 40″
Add 50″ to circle left reading: 27° 31′ 50″
Subtract 50″ from circle right reading: 207° 31′ 50″

(*ii*) Using the slow-motion screw set the circle right reading correct. This will move the telescope off the point.

(*iii*) Move the line of sight back on to the point by adjusting the diaphragm screws.

(*iv*) Transit and check that the adjusted line of sight provides a reading differing from the previous reading by just 180°.

NOTE: This is the practical field test and adjustment. It only provides a line of sight perpendicular to the horizontal axis if there is no eccentricity in the relation between the vertical axis and the centre of the horizontal circle. In modern instruments this error is almost negligible and is eliminated by observing on both faces, as is any residual collimation error.

29. Trunnion axis adjustment.

(a) *Aim.* To set the trunnion axis perpendicular to the vertical axis. It will then be truly horizontal when the instrument is levelled.

(b) *Test*, sometimes called the *spire test*, is as follows:

(*i*) Set up and level the theodolite and sight a high point with the centre of the cross hairs and clamp the horizontal movement.

(*ii*) Depress the telescope, sight and read a scale placed horizontally facing the instrument.

(*iii*) Change face, sight the high point again and clamp.

(*iv*) Depress the telescope once more and again read the scale. If the line of sight intersects the scale at the same point the trunnion axis is horizontal.

(c) *Adjustment.* If the line of sight does not intersect the scale at the same point, the true vertical below the high point lies midway between the two readings. The adjustment involves the following:

(*i*) Set the line of sight on the mean scale reading, elevate to the high point, and raise or lower one end of the horizontal axis by the adjusting screws until the cross hairs intersect the high point once more.

(*ii*) Repeat test and check adjustment.

NOTE: Most modern theodolites have no means of making this adjustment. Any slight errors which may exist after the manufacturers' adjustments have been made are eliminated by observing on both faces.

30. Diaphragm adjustment.

(*a*) *Aim.* To set the cross hairs truly horizontal and vertical.

(*b*) *Test.* Level the theodolite and sight a fine point. Move the telescope in elevation. If the mark remains on the hair the adjustment is correct.

(*c*) *Adjustment:*

(*i*) If the mark appears to move off the cross hair, loosen the diaphragm screws and twist the diaphragm until the mark remains on the vertical hair.

(*ii*) Check that the mark now remains on the horizontal hair when the telescope is moved laterally. If it does not the reticle must be changed as there is no means of adjusting the perpendicularity between the cross hairs on modern, etched, glass reticles.

NOTE: The effect of any lack of perpendicularity is minimised by always observing close to the point of intersection of the cross hairs.

31. Index error adjustment.

(*a*) *Aim.* To set the vertical circle reading at zero, or 90° on some instruments, when the line of sight is horizontal and the vertical bubble is central.

(*b*) *Test:*

(*i*) Set up and level the instrument. Sight a definite mark on circle left, centre the vertical bubble with the clip screw and read the angle of slope.

(*ii*) Repeat on circle right, again reading the vertical circle.

(*iii*) If the instrument is in adjustment the two angles read on each face will be equal.

(c) *Adjustment.* If the two angles are not equal, the mean value provides the true angle of slope. Half the difference between the readings is the *index error*, the amount by which either reading must be corrected to give the true reading.

(i) With the telescope still clamped on to the mark, set the true reading with the clip screw. This will cause the vertical bubble to run off centre, but the vertical circle reading defines the actual angle of slope so the bubble should be in the centre of its run.

(ii) By means of the bubble-adjusting screws, bring the bubble back to its central position.

(iii) Repeat the test to check the adjustment.

NOTE: Meaning readings obtained on both faces results in a true angle of elevation or depression even when an index error exists.

PROGRESS TEST 6

1. Illustrate by means of a simple outline sketch the essential parts of a theodolite. Name these parts and describe their purpose. (1)

2. Define what is meant by the term *parallax* and explain how it occurs, illustrating your answer to show its cause and how it may be eliminated. (2-3)

3. What are the main defects of lenses and how are they minimised in surveying telescopes? (4)

4. What is the difference between a concave and a convex lens? How does this affect the *images* formed by these lenses? (4-5)

*5. In a telescope the objective of focal length 100 mm is located 130 mm from the diaphragm. The internal focusing lens has a focal length of -85 mm. When sighting to a star how far is the focusing lens from the objective when it is in clear focus without parallax? (6)

6. Explain in detail how to set up a theodolite over a station mark (a) using a plumb-bob only and (b) using an optical plummet. (16-18)

7. What is meant by *observing on both faces* and why is it necessary? (20)

8. Describe in detail how to measure a horizontal angle. (21)

9. Describe in detail the five permanent theodolite adjustments that should be tested from time to time. (26-31)

10. Optical circle reading devices take three forms. What is the difference between them and how do they allow accurate circle readings to be read? (9-12)

CHAPTER VII

TRIGONOMETRICAL SURVEYING

TRIANGULATION

1. Basic principle of triangulation. If the length of one side of a triangle is known and any two angles of the triangle are measured then the lengths of the other two sides can be calculated. The relative positions of the three points forming the triangle can thus be established. This basic principle is adopted in triangulation surveys, where a series of connected triangles forming a network is laid out over the ground, all the angles of which are measured. Once the length of one side of one triangle in the network is known, all the other lengths can be calculated. From these data the relative positions of all points can be co-ordinated and plotted.

NOTE

(*i*) Not all the angles of every triangle need be observed as the third angle can be deduced.

(*ii*) In order to provide the necessary check on the work and to eliminate as far as possible the inevitable observational errors, all angles of every triangle should be measured if at all possible.

2. Primary triangulation. In order to apply the principle of working *from the whole to the part* (*see* **1, 5**), the area to be surveyed must first be covered by a network of triangles which should be as large as possible. The positions of these *primary* control points are then finally established and subsequent work is confined and adjusted to fit inside the primary triangles. This prevents the build-up of error which would otherwise occur.

(*a*) Triangulation surveys, until recently, formed the most economic and accurate method of surveying whole countries. The triangulation provides accurately positioned control points upon which subsequent surveys are based. As large

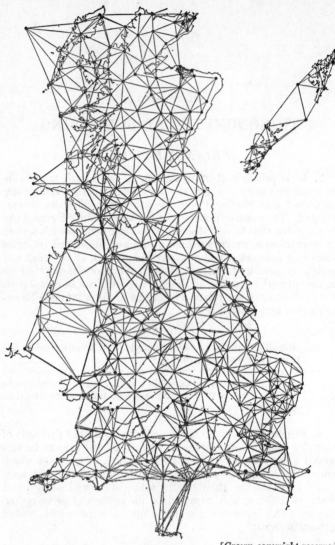

FIG. 40.—*Retriangulation of Great Britain*

The primary network of triangulation and the three bases from which the triangle sides were calculated are shown.

areas are covered account must be taken of the earth's curvature and thus this method of surveying is known as *geodetic triangulation* (*see* I, **3**).

The sides of the triangles usually range in length from 50 to 80 km, but sides of length of over 150 km are not uncommon. It is necessary for the triangles to be well conditioned (*see* II, **29**(*c*)) with angles as close to 60° as possible. Angles are measured with geodetic theodolites to one-tenth of a second of arc. Observational errors in any one triangle should not exceed 2″ and overall should average 1″ or less. The probable error of computed distance will be between 1/60 000 and 1/250 000.

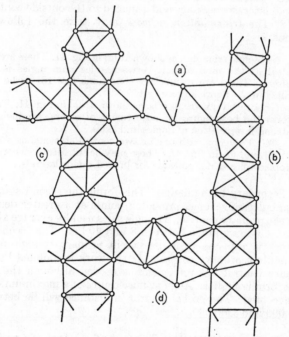

FIG. 41.—*Example of a primary grid*

(*a*) A network of triangles.
(*b*) A network of braced quadrilaterals.
(*c*) A network of centre-point polygons.
(*d*) A network formed by a double centre-point polygon.

(b) In Great Britain the Ordnance Survey maps were based on a primary network observed between 1783 and 1853 and, while this was of a comparatively high order, it proved to be inadequate for modern requirements. A new primary triangulation was started in 1935 and was virtually completed in 1962. The layout of this primary network is illustrated in Fig. 40. The average line length is 57 km. As Great Britain is comparatively small the triangulation network covers the whole country.

(c) In larger areas, as in India and Africa, *primary grids* are used instead, as illustrated in Fig. 41. This provides the initial overall control required, the inside areas being surveyed later as necessary and adjusted to the outside control.

(d) The *triangulation network* may take the following forms:

(i) Simple triangles, as shown at (a) in Fig. 41. These are not ideal as the interrelation between sides and angles is too direct. There are insufficient conditions (*see* 15) to be fulfilled in the figure adjustment.

(ii) Braced quadrilaterals, as shown at (b) in Fig. 41. These form the best figure for adjustment of errors, producing a strong interrelation of angles and sides.

(iii) Polygons with one or two central stations, as shown at (c) and (d) in Fig. 41. These may be substituted where the topography is not suitable for braced quadrilaterals.

3. Secondary triangulation. This forms the second stage of a triangulation scheme, providing points at a greater density than the primary control. Triangle sides usually average about 12 km, but may range between 8 and 40 km. The secondary network is adjusted to fit its parent primary triangle or its surrounding primary control. As the work is confined by the primary control less refinement is needed although the network form is similar. Angular misclosures of a maximum of 5″ are accepted. The probable error in distance will lie between 1/20 000 and 1/50 000.

4. Tertiary triangulation. This is the final stage of a national triangulation scheme. Sides of triangles are about 2 to 8 km long, and points are fixed by bearings from the surrounding secondary control. In undeveloped areas tertiary stations are not usually required, but in towns stations are provided at a density of one or two every 2 km². Most stations can be occupied, but many points, such as church steeples, television masts, etc., are fixed by forward intersection only. The probable error in distance will lie between 1/5000 and 1/20 000.

5. Base extension. The initial side of a primary network could not, until the advent of electro-distance measurement, be measured directly. A method of obtaining the length of the side of a primary triangle (*see* **1**) is by means of a *base extension*. A base line is chosen in a suitable area to provide as

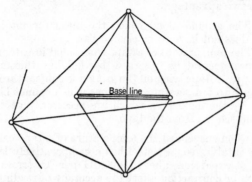

FIG. 42.—*A base extension*

The directly measured base may be extended by well-conditioned triangles to allow the long sides of the main triangles to be calculated.

long a line capable of direct measurement as possible. The base line should be about half as long as the average length of the main triangles, but this may not always be possible. The base line is extended by means of a *base net* expanding the line to meet the main triangles, as indicated in Fig. 42, which illustrates an ideal base extension.

NOTE

(*i*) In Great Britain the Ridge Way base, measured in 1951, is 11·06 km long and the Caithness base in Scotland, measured the following year, is 24·83 km long.

(*ii*) Two geodetic bases at least must be measured at the extremes of the triangulation network so that the length of one may be calculated from the other. A comparison of the *calculated* and *observed* lengths is indicative of the accuracy of the triangulation network.

6. Base measurement. The main source of error in precise length measurement is the expansion or contraction of the apparatus caused by temperature changes. Early bases were measured either with metal bars surrounded by ice or, like Colby's bars, with two rods in boxes connected in such a way that compensation for expansion was made. This apparatus was only 10 ft long and although six bars were used at once they were not as convenient nor as accurate as long tapes.

For long, very precise measurements *tapes* are useful because they can be hung clear of the ground, in *catenary* (*see* **7**). This has two advantages:

(*a*) The ground along which the measurement is being taken does not have to be cleared flat.

(*b*) The temperature of a tape suspended in catenary can be more accurately observed by holding thermometers against it. A tape lying on the ground is subject throughout its length to temperature variations which cannot be established by thermometers, which are necessarily of different size and section from the tape.

Even when suspended the temperature of a tape cannot be precisely established. As steel has a comparatively large coefficient of expansion, about 0·000 011 per °C, errors due to expansion or contraction affect the accuracy of readings. The use of *invar* helps considerably to reduce these errors as this material, an alloy of nickel and iron, has the lowest coefficient of expansion of any metal, being about 0·000 000 2 per °C. Slight errors in establishing the temperature of an invar tape make little difference to its length.

Invar tapes are more delicate than steel tapes and cannot stand up to everyday survey use. Also the degree of accuracy they can provide is unnecessary on most survey work. However, they are invaluable on precise base measurements, all the British bases being measured with 100-ft invar tapes.

7. Catenary. Figure 43 illustrates the principle of precise catenary measurement. Measuring tripods are set out along the line and measuring heads are attached which can be accurately levelled and possess fine index marks. The tape is strung between the heads, and weights, attached to wires passing over pulleys on the straining trestles, are fixed to the tape to apply an even tension. Several readings of the tape graduations at each end are made through reading glasses attached to the measuring heads. The base line is measured at least twice with different tapes, agreement between measurements of one or two parts per million being acceptable.

Fig. 43.—*A base measurement in catenary*

The tape is supported by weights over straining trestles and it hangs in contact with the measuring heads on tripods. The next measuring head is shown set up ready for the suspended tape to be moved forward for the measurement of the next bay.

8. Corrections to base measurements. Every measurement in a base line must have certain corrections applied to it. The five corrections which may have to be calculated are for the following:

(a) *Temperature (see 9).*
(b) *Slope (see 10).*
(c) *Sag (see 11).*
(d) *Tension (see 12).*
(e) *Height above sea level (see 13).*
(f) *Scale factor (see V, 6).*

9. Temperature correction. Tapes and bands as supplied by the manufacturer are only at their nominal or *standard* length under particular conditions of temperature and tension, usually 20°C and either 4·5, 5, 6·8 or 7 kg force, the standard temperature and tension being stamped on the tape. Tapes usually stretch or creep with use and soon lose their nominal length at the standard temperature and tension. A standardisation correction could be applied, but as field temperatures seldom coincide with the standard it is usual to combine the two corrections establishing the new temperature at which the tape is at its nominal length.

A tape is *standardised* by measuring a base of known length under the standard tension and noting the tape temperature during the measurement. The change in tape length due to temperature, required to bring the tape to its nominal length, may be calculated from the temperature correction formula:

$$\text{Correction} = L \times \alpha \times t$$

where L = the tape length,
　　　α = coefficient of expansion and
　　　t = change in temperature.

Take the following as an example:

A 30-m tape was standardised against a base known to be 30·000 m long. The tension applied was 7 kg force and the temperature of the tape during the measurement was found to be 16·3°C. The observed length was 29·997. The correction required is 0·003, therefore in the formula:

$$0\cdot003 = 29\cdot997 \times 0\cdot000\ 011 \times t$$
$$\therefore\ t = \frac{0\cdot003}{0\cdot000\ 33}$$
$$= 9\cdot1°C$$

Therefore the temperature at which the tape is standard at a tension of 7 kg force is:

$$16\cdot3 - 9\cdot1 = 7\cdot2°C$$

Once the tape has been standardised any subsequent measures at a different temperature will require correction in order to provide the measure that would have been obtained had the tape been at its standard temperature.

NOTE

　(i) As temperatures increase, the tape expands and readings become too small.

　(ii) Where the field temperature is higher than standard, the correction must be added to the observed reading and vice versa.

10. Slope correction. This correction is always negative as the slope distance is always longer than the horizontal distance required. Slope corrections are usually made in one of two ways in accurate work (*see* II, **9**), either by observing angles of slope between the measuring heads or by running a line of levels along them. They are as follows:

　(*a*) *Angle of slope:*

　　　Horizontal distance = $L \cos \alpha$　or
　　　　　Correction = $- L (1 - \cos \alpha)$

(b) *Difference in height between tape ends:*

$$\text{Correction} = -\left(\frac{h^2}{2L} + \frac{h^4}{8L^3} - \cdots\right)$$

$$\doteqdot \quad \frac{h^2}{2L}$$

11. Sag correction. If a tape is standardised lying along flat ground, a negative sag correction is necessary (if it is supported in catenary in use) as the chord distance across the bay required is always less than the distance along the tape.

The formula for correction is as follows:

$$\text{Correction} = \frac{w^2 L^3}{24 F^2}$$

where w = the weight of the tape per metre length in newtons or kilogrammes force,

L = length of tape between supports and

F = tension applied to the tape in the same units as w.

NOTE

(i) If the chord joining the tape ends is sloping at an angle α the sag will be deformed and the sag correction will be reduced. The reduced correction is obtained by multiplying the correction by $\cos^2 \alpha$. This is only significant on steep slopes.

(ii) If the tape is standardised in catenary no sag correction is required provided the bay length and tension remain the same.

(iii) Tape weights may be obtained by weighing the tape and case or winder together and then weighing the case or winder with the tape removed. The difference between these values divided by the tape length gives the required weight per unit length.

12. Tension correction. If the tension applied to a tape is different from standard a correction will have to be applied. It is seldom necessary to vary tension in this way and this correction is not applied in normal practice. The formula is as below:

$$\text{Correction} = (F - Fs)\,\frac{L}{AE}\,\text{m}$$

where $(F - Fs) =$ difference from standard tension in newtons,

$\qquad L =$ tape length under tension in metres,

$\qquad A =$ cross-sectional area of tape in square millimetres and

$\qquad E =$ Young's modulus of elasticity for the
material of the tape in newtons/mm².

NOTE

(i) To convert kilogrammes force to newtons multiply by 9·81.

(ii) Young's modulus of elasticity for typical steel tapes is
200 kN/mm² or 200 000 N/mm², and for invar tapes it is
150 kN/mm².

13. Correction for height above sea level. Owing to the
curvature of the earth, a length l measured at sea level between two points will increase to a length L as these points are
produced to a height H above sea level, each normal to the
curve of the earth. By simple proportion:

$$\frac{l}{R} = \frac{L}{R + H}$$

$$\therefore \; l - L = - \frac{LH}{R + H}$$

or, since H is small:

$$\text{correction} = \frac{LH}{R}$$

and must be deducted for heights above sea level.

NOTE

(i) The radius of the earth R may be taken as $6·367 \times 10^6$ m.

(ii) The above correction is not necessary in any ordinary work
unless it forms the basis of a national triangulation system
or if the height above sea level is large and the survey is to
be connected to an existing triangulation network.

SPECIMEN QUESTION

Reduce the absolute length at sea level of two bays of a base
line using the following data:

Bay	Observed length (m)	Temp. (°C)	Level difference (m)	Tension (kg)
1	29·9732	10·6	+ 0·36	9
2	30·0025	10·8	− 0·45	9

The tape weighs 0·016 kg per metre and has a cross-sectional area of 2·08 mm². It was standardised on the flat at 20°C under a pull of 5 kg force. The coefficient of expansion of the tape material is 0·000 011 per °C and Young's modulus is 200 kN/mm². The mean level of the base is 527·3 m above sea level.

SOLUTION

Tabulate data and record L^3, h^2 and $\dfrac{h^2}{2L}$ for use in the correction calculations which follow:

Bay	L	L^3	h	h^2	$\dfrac{h^2}{2L}$
1	29·9732	26 928	+ 0·36	0·130	0·0022
2	30·0025	27 007	− 0·45	0·162	0·0027
Σ	59·9757	53 935			0·0049

(a) *Temperature correction:*

$$\text{Correction} = L \times \alpha \times t$$
$$= 59 \cdot 9757 \times 0 \cdot 000\ 011 \times (20 - 10 \cdot 7)$$
$$= 0 \cdot 0061 \text{ m}$$

(b) *Slope correction:*

$$\text{Correction} = \frac{h^2}{2L}$$
$$= 0 \cdot 0049 \text{ m, tabulated above.}$$

(c) *Sag correction:*

$$\text{Correction} = \frac{w^2 \Sigma(L)^3}{24F^2}$$
$$= \frac{0 \cdot 016^2 \times 53\ 935}{24 \times 9^2}$$
$$= \frac{13 \cdot 807\ 36}{1944}$$
$$= 0 \cdot 0071 \text{ m}$$

(d) *Tension correction:*

$$\text{Correction} = (F - Fs)\ \frac{L}{AE}$$
$$(F - Fs) = 9 - 5$$
$$= 4 \text{ kg force}$$
$$= 39 \cdot 24 \text{ N}$$
$$\text{Correction} = \frac{39 \cdot 24 \times 59 \cdot 9757}{2 \cdot 08 \times 200 \times 10^3}$$
$$= 0 \cdot 0057 \text{ m}$$

(e) *Reduction to sea level:*

$$\text{Correction} = \frac{LH}{R}$$
$$= \frac{59\cdot9757 \times 527\cdot3}{6\cdot367 \times 10^6}$$
$$= 0\cdot0050 \text{ m}$$

(f) *Absolute length:*

$$\begin{aligned}
\text{Absolute length} &= \text{Observed length} + \text{Corrections in } (a)\text{--}(e) \\
&= 59\cdot9757 - 0\cdot0061 - 0\cdot0049 - 0\cdot0071 + \\
&\qquad\qquad 0\cdot0057 - 0\cdot0050 \\
&= 59\cdot9583 \text{ m}
\end{aligned}$$

14. Triangulation surveys. The principles applicable to geodetic networks may be applied to plane surveys requiring a layout of control points for engineering projects (*see* I, **3** (*iv*) and **5**).

(*a*) *Base line.* A suitable base line is chosen of length close to half the average length of triangle sides or, on smaller surveys, equal to one of the triangle sides. If refined base measuring equipment is not available sufficient accuracy can be obtained by using a steel tape and spring balance, supporting the tape in catenary and measuring the air temperature. Instead of measuring tripods, wooden stakes may be used with nails or scratch marks on zinc plates as index marks. A line of levels is run along the tops of the pegs and provides data for the slope corrections. An alternative method is to set up a theodolite on the line between the measuring pegs, measuring each distance in two halves from the instrument to each back and forward peg. Angles of slope can then be directly observed. The base is measured in each direction and the final reduced distances compared. Differences of about 1/50 000 should easily be obtained by this method.

NOTE

(*i*) The tape should be standardised at the tension at which it is to be used so that no tension correction will be needed.

(*ii*) Reduction to sea level should not be applied even if the site is high above sea level. Construction dimensions are designed to suit the site and if this correction is applied all along design measurements will also need to be reduced to sea level (*see* **13**).

(*b*) *Base extension.* The base line is next extended to the triangulation, unless it forms a triangle side, by means of an extension network, all the angles of which are observed and may be adjusted as described in **15**.

(*c*) *Triangulation.* All the angles of the network are observed and equal corrections applied to the observed angles of each triangle so that the corrected angles amount to 180° in each case. If necessary an approximate linear adjustment may be applied to the main triangles of the network (*see* **15**).

(*d*) *Calculation.* After adjustment the lengths and bearings of the sides of the triangles are calculated and from these all points are co-ordinated and used as control points for subsequent survey work.

15. Adjustment of triangulation. It is obvious that the sum of the three angles of any triangle should be 180°—plus spherical excess in geodetic triangles. Owing to observational

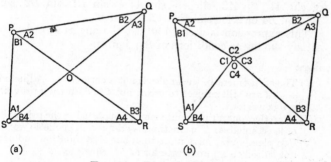

(a) (b)

FIG. 44.—*Figural adjustment*

(*a*) A braced quadrilateral.
(*b*) A centre-point polygon.

Each has the angles marked to correspond with the adjustment calculations shown in **16** and **17** respectively.

errors, however, this *condition* will seldom be satisfied. In order to provide geometrical consistency in the calculations, so that they may be checked, observations are adjusted to fit the conditions that should apply.

(*a*) *Angular conditions.* The simple condition that the angles *A*, *B* and *C* of a triangle should equal 180° is not the only angular condition required in figures formed by several triangles. Figure 44 illustrates two figures which arise most frequently and their approximate adjustment only will be considered (*see* **16** and **17**).

(*b*) *Linear conditions.* In a triangle there is no linear condition. In the braced quadrilateral and polygon with a centre point it would be possible starting from, say, *OS* to calculate the length of *OP* both clockwise—or anti-clockwise—around the figure.

In triangle *OSP*:

$$OP = \frac{OS \sin A1}{\sin B1}$$

and from triangles *ORS*, *OQR* and *OPQ*:

$$OP = \frac{OS \cdot \sin B4 \cdot \sin B3 \cdot \sin B2}{\sin A4 \cdot \sin A3 \cdot \sin A2}$$

$\therefore \sin A1 \cdot \sin A2 \cdot \sin A3 \cdot \sin A4 = \sin B1 \cdot \sin B2 \cdot \sin B3 \cdot \sin B4$ or $\Sigma \log \sin A\text{'s} = \Sigma \log \sin B\text{'s}$.

This expression is used to adjust the angles in order to satisfy the linear conditions of the figures.

NOTE

(*i*) The adjustment of the angles is not a correction. Adjusted angles are still subject to error, but the data they provide are consistent.

(*ii*) More rigorous adjustments may be made using the principle of least squares. This method is adopted in geodetic work.

(*iii*) Complex figures have more than one side equation and are not suited to approximate forms of adjustment.

16. Adjustment of braced quadrilateral.

(*a*) In the braced quadrilateral the three *angular conditions* and one *linear condition* to be fulfilled are the following:

(*i*) The sum of all angles must equal 360°.
(*ii*) Angles $A1 + B1$ must equal angles $A3 + B3$, and angles $A2 + B2$ must equal angles $A4 + B4$.
(*iii*) $\Sigma \log \sin A$'s must equal $\Sigma \log \sin B$'s.

(*b*) The *approximate, non-rigorous* or *equal shifts adjustment* is so called because the principle of least squares is not applied and the adjustments to each angle are equal in satisfying each condition. The adjustment is tabulated below:

(1) Angle	(2) Observed angles			(3) 1st adjst.	(4) Pairs	(5) 2nd adjst.	(6) Adjst. angle
	°	′	″	″		″	″
A1	50	21	23	+0·5		−3·5	20·0
B1	56	21	40	+0·5	63	−3·5	37·0
A2	43	19	44	+0·5		−1·5	43·0
B2	29	57	21	+0·5	65	−1·5	20·0
A3	47	21	13	+0·5		+3·5	17·0
B3	59	21	36	+0·5	49	+3·5	40·0
A4	34	52	13	+0·5		+1·5	15·0
B4	38	24	46	+0·5	59	+1·5	48·0
	359	59	56				

(7) Log sines	(8) Diff. for 1″	(9) 3rd adjst. ″	(10) Final angle ″	(11) Final log sines
9·886 501 2	17·5	+3·4	23·4	9·886 507 1
9·920 403 7	14·0	−3·4	33·6	9·920 398 9
9·836 439 1	22·3	+3·4	46·4	9·836 446 7
9·698 386 0	36·6	−3·4	16·6	9·698 373 6
9·866 619 3	19·4	+3·4	20·4	9·866 625 9
9·934 698 5	12·4	−3·4	36·6	9·934 694 3
9·757 189 7	30·2	+3·4	18·4	9·757 200 0
9·793 322 4	26·6	−3·4	44·6	9·793 313 4

ΣA's = 9·346 749 3   9·346 779 7
ΣB's = 9·346 810 6   9·346 780 2

613/179·0 = 3·4″   5

(*i*) The angles are designated in column 1. It is advisable to make a sketch of the figure and to label the angles in correct sequence as illustrated.

(*ii*) The observed angles are recorded in the second column. They are summed, their difference from 360° is divided by eight and this equal correction is recorded in the third column.

(*iii*) Column 4 is a record of the summation of the observed seconds only of each pair of *A*'s and *B*'s. The difference between the first and third pair, 14″, is divided by four and the equal correction applied to the angles, negative to the greater pair, positive to the lesser pair. The same adjustment is made to the second and fourth pairs where the difference is 6″.

(*iv*) The two adjustments are now applied to the observed angles, column 6 recording the seconds only of the observed angles adjusted to the angle conditions.

(*v*) In column 7 the seven-figure logarithm sines of the adjusted observed angles are recorded. The *A*'s and *B*'s are summed separately and their difference obtained.

(*vi*) At the same time the logarithm sines are extracted, the difference for one second for each angle is tabulated in column 8 and the column is summed.

(*vii*) By dividing the sum of column 8 into the difference between the logarithm sines of *A*'s and *B*'s, the number of seconds is obtained, which, when applied as an adjustment, will tend to equalise the sums of the logarithm sines of the *A*'s and *B*'s.

(*viii*) The line condition adjustment needed is $613/179 = 3 \cdot 4''$, applied positive to the *A*'s and negative to the *B*'s. These adjustments are tabulated in column 9, the seconds of the final adjusted angle being recorded in column 10.

(*ix*) In column 11 the logarithm sines of the final adjusted angles are again extracted and tabulated as a check. This time the difference between the logarithm sines of the *A*'s and *B*'s is so small as to warrant no further adjustment.

17. Adjustment of centre-point polygon.

(*a*) In a polygon with a central station the *angular conditions* and the one *linear condition* to be fulfilled are the following:

(*i*) The sum of the angles in each triangle must equal 180°.

(*ii*) The sum of the angles around the centre point must equal 360°.

(*iii*) Σ log sin *A*'s must equal Σ log sin *B*'s.

(*b*) The approximate *adjustment* of this figure is tabulated opposite and described as follows:

(*i*) The angles are designated in column 1 as before.

(*ii*) The angles of each triangle are summed and the difference from 180° recorded. One-third of this difference in each case is applied to each angle of each triangle producing the first adjusted angles, the seconds of which are tabulated in column 3.

(*iii*) The second adjustment consists of summing all the *C* angles, amounting to 359° 59′ 58·8″. The difference from

(1) Angle	(2) Observed angles ° ′ ″	(3) 1st adjst. ″	(4) 2nd adjst. ″	(5) Log sines	(6) Diff. 1″	(7) Final angle ″	(8) Final log sines
A1	75 38 44·0	44·3	44·2	9·986 225 6	5·4	43·1	9·986 225 0
B1	33 24 40·2	40·5	40·3	9·740 870 8	31·9	41·4	9·740 874 3
C1	70 56 34·8	35·2	35·5			35·5	
	59·0	0·0	0·0			0·0	
A2	43 02 35·6	34·2	34·1	9·834 131 0	22·5	33·0	9·834 128 6
B2	44 09 14·0	12·6	12·4	9·842 972 5	21·6	13·5	9·842 974 9
C2	92 48 14·7	13·2	13·5			13·5	
	4·3	0·0	0·0			0·0	
A3	34 25 13·7	14·5	14·4	9·752 251 8	30·7	13·3	9·752 248 4
B3	50 15 28·8	29·6	29·4	9·885 888 5	17·5	30·5	9·885 890 4
C3	95 19 15·2	15·9	16·2			16·2	
	57·7	0·0	0·0			0·0	
A4	33 58 40·7	40·0	39·9	9·747 311 5	31·2	38·8	9·747 308 1
B4	45 05 26·2	25·5	25·3	9·850 168 8	21·0	26·4	9·850 171 1
C4	100 55 55·3	54·5	54·8			54·8	
	2·2	0·0	0·0	ΣA's		0·0	
			ΣB's				
				9·319 919 9			9·319 910 1
				9·319 900 6			9·319 910 7
				193/181·8 = 1·1″			6

360° of 1·2″ is divided by four and applied equally to each
C angle. As this now disturbs the initial adjustment, the
adjustment applied to C is applied, half each, to the respective
A's and B's, but of the opposite sign, thus retaining their
summation to 180°.

(*iv*) Having recorded the seconds of the adjusted angles in
column 4, the angular conditions are satisfied.

(*v*) The remainder of the adjustment is concerned with the
linear condition and is carried out as shown in the same way
as described in **16**.

18. Triangulation stations. Triangulation stations are
usually permanently marked by means of a metal plug set in
concrete about 1 m below ground. Above this a second mark
is placed vertically above the original, either in a concrete slab
at ground level or on top of a concrete or stone pillar about
1·2 m high, which forms a stable platform for the theodolite.
The pillar usually has a centre pipe over which the theodolite
is centred and into which a signal, such as a ranging rod with a
flag attached, may be inserted. If the pillar is destroyed the
underground mark will generally remain undisturbed. To
prove its position and to replace it if necessary the mark is
usually unobstrusively *witnessed* by brass witness bolts set in
rock or concrete some distance away.

In *plane surveys*, where less elaborate stations are needed,
the points may be any one of the types described in II, **30**,
although for a triangulated control of an engineering construction permanent concrete markers would often be specified.

In flat land it is sometimes necessary to raise the observer
and signal above the ground. Two *towers* are always necessary.
The inner tower supports the instrument plumbed over the
station mark. The observer stands on the outer tower and can
thus move around the instrument without disturbing it. *Bilby
towers* are designed for this work and can form an elevated
station 36·5 m high. They can be dismantled and used again
elsewhere.

19. Signals. Signals on triangulation stations, to enable
them to be seen over the long distances necessary, may be of
two types—luminous and opaque.

(*a*) *Luminous signals.* For geodetic work over long distances it is usual to use an electric beacon lamp run off

batteries. Such lamps have a parabolic reflector to direct the rays giving a spread of about 5°. Acetylene lamps and even oil lamps are sometimes used when haze prevents ordinary sighting to opaque signals.

Heliotropes or *heliographs*, known as *helios*, are used where long periods of sunshine can be expected. A 13-cm mirror is used to reflect a dark spot in the centre of the beam on to a small target placed on line to the distant observer. A second mirror is necessary when the sun lies behind the helio. The helio has to be adjusted to the sun every two minutes.

(*b*) *Opaque signals.* These may take a variety of forms depending on the distances over which they are to be viewed. If great distances are involved large quadripod beacons are constructed and covered with painted boarding or brightly coloured material. It is often advisable to attach a flag on top to help in locating the beacon as its movement helps to distinguish the signal in a hazy field of view.

Signals formed by a vertically held pipe or pole with two vanes attached at right-angles allow observations to be made to it from any direction. In conditions of good visibility the vertical support can be seen and as conditions deteriorate the larger vanes can be bisected. For observations up to 5 or 6 km an ordinary ranging rod can be seen especially if red and white flags are attached to assist in locating its position.

Care must be taken when observing to distant opaque signals that if only part of the signal is in sunlight and the remainder in shadow the whole signal is bisected by the cross hairs and not just the brightly illuminated part. The error introduced by bisecting the bright part of the signal only is termed *phase*. It is most likely to occur when sighting cylindrical objects which are not against the skyline, particularly when the sun is well to one side.

20. Resection. The position of a point in a triangulation network, which has not been previously observed to, can often be established by observing from it to surrounding control. This is known as *resection* or the *three-point problem*. The problem is one of orientation; it is necessary to establish the bearings from at least one known station to the occupied point. This can most readily be obtained by observing from a known station to the point to be fixed. This is desirable for achieving accuracy and would be adopted in primary and secondary networks. Resected stations can only conveniently be established when suitably surrounded by three or more pre-marked points. If the surrounding control is not already marked with signals the opportunity can be taken when doing so to observe to the station to be fixed so that it will no longer be a true resected point. In laying out a triangulation control the reconnaissance would preclude the need for resected stations. The principle of resection is explained under plane tabling in VIII, 8–10.

TRIGONOMETRICAL LEVELLING

21. Vertical heights. The height difference between two points A and B can be obtained by observing the vertical angle α between them. If the horizontal distance s between them is known the height difference may be calculated from the formula:

$$h = s \tan \alpha$$

In Fig. 45 (a) it can be seen that it is not always possible to measure the angle exactly at A, as allowance must be made for H.I., the height of the instrument. The height difference between A and B is thus:

$$s \tan \alpha + \text{H.I.}$$

If the height of B above C is required the length h' is also required. This may be obtained by measuring down to C directly from the position of the horizontal line of sight. Alternatively if angle β is also measured then:

$$h' = s \tan \beta \text{ and}$$
$$BC = h + h' = s (\tan \alpha + \tan \beta)$$

22. Vertical height problems. Problems in height calculations often relate to obtaining the horizontal distance s, which is needed for the $s \tan \alpha$ formula. The three common forms of problem are illustrated in Fig. 45:

(a) If the length l, in Fig. 45 (a), along the slope between A and C were measured then this distance must first be reduced to the horizontal. If the angle of slope of the tape is γ, then $s = l \cos \gamma$.

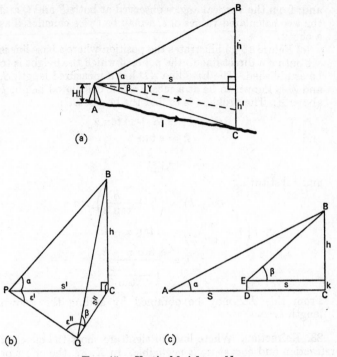

FIG. 45.—*Vertical height problems*

(a) The position where the height BC is required to be calculated from the vertical angles α and β measured at A when the slope distance l between A and C has been measured.

(b) The position where it is not possible to measure directly from the instrument to the point C. Here a base PQ is measured so that the distance s' can be calculated.

(c) The position again where it is not possible to measure directly to C. A base line AD is measured on line to C, and from the two vertical angles α and β the height of BC may be calculated.

(b) If s cannot be obtained directly because the point C, vertically below B, is not accessible, then a base line must first be set out in order that s may be calculated. Figure 45 (b) illustrates the position where a base line PQ has been measured and the horizontal angles ε' and ε'' have been observed. In triangle PQC the sides s' and s'' can be calculated and, from the vertical angles observed at both P and Q and the two calculated values of s, h may be twice calculated as a check.

(c) Figure 45 (c) illustrates the position where a base line is set out on a direct line to the point of which the height is to be established. The base line AD has a measured length S, and E is known to be at a measured or calculated height k above A. The problem is to find the height BC:

$$(h + k) = (S + s) \tan \alpha$$

and

$$h = s \tan \beta$$

$$\therefore \ s = \frac{h}{\tan \beta}$$

and substituting:

$$(h + k) = \left(S + \frac{h}{\tan \beta}\right) \tan \alpha$$

$$\therefore \ h\left(1 - \frac{\tan \alpha}{\tan \beta}\right) = S \tan \alpha - k$$

$$\therefore \ h = \frac{S \tan \alpha - k}{1 - \dfrac{\tan \alpha}{\tan \beta}}$$

From this BC may be obtained by adding the known length k.

23. Refraction. Where lines of sight are short the effect of refraction and curvature is negligible. In X, **37**, the effect of curvature and refraction on a level line of sight is explained. The effect on inclined lines of sight is similar, as illustrated in Fig. 46. A ray of light from the signal at B to the instrument at A passes through layers of air at different pressures and temperatures. Owing to this it is refracted along a curved path depending on the varying air densities through which it passes. Light rays are taken to follow a curve of radius approximately seven times that of the earth's radius, but this varies with latitude and time of day and cannot be precisely established. By observing simultaneously from both ends of the ray the mean of the angles will nearly eliminate the effects of refraction. This is not always possible, but by observing under similar conditions reasonable results can be obtained. Refraction is at its least and steadiest during the middle of the day, when vertical observations are best made.

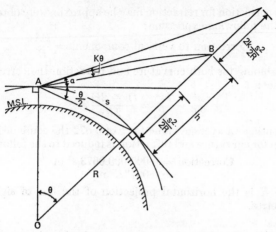

FIG. 46.—*Curvative and refraction*

The effect of curvature of the earth and refraction when establishing the height difference between points A and B by measuring the vertical angle α between them is shown.

24. Curvature and refraction correction.

The correction due to curvature is shown in Fig. 46 to be:

$$\frac{s^2}{2R}$$

The derivation of this formula arises from the proof in XVI, **18**. This amount is reduced in effect by refraction.

The *coefficient of refraction* is that factor k, which, when multiplied by the angle subtended at the centre of earth by the length of the line of sight, provides the amount of angular variation due to the effect of refraction. The value of k varies, being greater for night observations and for rays over water. In Great Britain it varies from about 0·065 to 0·081 over water. In geodetic work the value of k should be computed from reciprocal observations from:

$$k = \frac{rR \sin 1''}{s}$$

where r = the mean refraction in seconds of arc, R = the radius of the earth and s = the horizontal projection of the line of sight.

The correction for refraction may be approximately obtained from the following expression:

$$\text{Correction to vertical component} = \frac{ks^2}{R}$$

Combining for both curvature and refraction the correction becomes:

$$\frac{s^2}{2R} - \frac{ks^2}{R} = \frac{(1 - 2k)}{2R} s^2$$

Adopting an average value for k of 0·072 the combined correction for curvature and refraction is reduced to the following:

$$\text{Correction} = 0\text{·}000\ 000\ 0673\ s^2\ \text{m}$$
$$= 0\text{·}0673K^2\ \text{m}$$

where K is the horizontal projection of the line of sight in kilometres.

NOTE

(*i*) The refraction and curvature correction is positive and must always be added to the vertical component.

(*ii*) The length s is the length at the height of observation. If the co-ordinate system has been reduced to sea level the scale factor to obtain the actual distance between stations must be applied.

EXAMPLE

The following is an example of a height difference calculation:

	At Station A	At Station B	Explanation
Height of instrument:	0·26 m	1·53 m	Field measurement
Height of signal:	1·78 m	0·90 m	Field measurement
	To Station B	To Station A	
α	+0° 5′ 00″	−0° 7′ 20″	Mean of vertical angle observations
tan α	0·001 454	0·002 133	Natural tangents
s	5820·5 m	5820·5 m	Plane distance
s tan α	+8·46	−12·42	Same sign as angle
Refraction and curvature correction:	+2·28	+2·28	0·0673 (5·82)² (always positive)
Height of instrument:	+0·26	+1·53	Always positive
Height of signal:	−0·90	−1·78	Always negative
Height difference:	+10·10	−10·39	

ELECTRO-MAGNETIC DISTANCE
MEASUREMENT

25. Basic principle of electro-magnetic distance measurement. This form of measurement is usually simply termed E.D.M. In all cases the wavelengths of light (*see* **26**) or *radio waves* (*see* **29**) are used in the measurement. The method of determining the length required from the unknown number of wavelengths involved is explained as follows:

In Fig. 47 measure AB with a rod of length $u1$ without count-

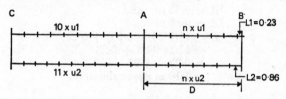

FIG. 47.—*Principle of E.D.M.*

The principle illustrates how a length BC can be obtained from an unknown quantity of known lengths by measuring only the residual distances.

ing the number of rod lengths n. Measure only the end section $L1$, which is less than one whole rod length, then;

$$D = nu1 + L1 \qquad \ldots (1)$$

Measure AB again, this time with a rod of length $u2$, again recording only the length $L2$, then:

$$D = nu2 + L2 \qquad \ldots (2)$$

Subtracting, (1) − (2):

$$L2 - L1 = n(u1 - u2)$$

If the relation between $u1$ and $u2$ is $10u1 = 11u2$, then:

$$L2 - L1 = n\left(u1 - \frac{10}{11}u1\right)$$

$$\therefore \; L2 - L1 = \frac{nu1}{11}$$

$$\therefore \; nu1 = 11(L2 - L1)$$

Substituting in (1):

$$D = 11(L2 - L1) + L1$$

Take the following as an example:

If the two rod lengths are:

$$u1 = 1 \cdot 00 \text{ m} \quad \text{and}$$
$$u2 = 0 \cdot 91 \text{ m}$$

to satisfy $10u1 = 11u2$ approximately, and in the measurement:

$$L1 = 0 \cdot 23 \text{ m} \quad \text{and}$$
$$L2 = 0 \cdot 86 \text{ m}$$

then

$$D = 11(0 \cdot 86 - 0 \cdot 23) + 0 \cdot 23$$
$$= 11 \times 0 \cdot 63 + 0 \cdot 23$$
$$= 6 \cdot 93 + 0 \cdot 23$$
$$= 7 \cdot 16 \text{ m approximately.}$$

NOTE

(i) From Fig. 47 it can be seen that the distance D is made up of 7 $u1$ measures of 1 m each plus $0 \cdot 23$. The length D is thus accurately $7 \cdot 23$ m.

(ii) The discrepancy between $7 \cdot 16$ and the correct $7 \cdot 23$ arises from multiplying $(L2 - L1)$ by 11 when the relation between $u1$ and $u2$ is not precisely $10\,u1 = 11\,u2$, an accuracy impossible to achieve.

(iii) The error of $0 \cdot 07$ between $6 \cdot 93$ and 7, which it should be, is disregarded, the nearest multiple of $u1$, $7 \cdot 0$ in the example, for $11(L2 - L1)$ being accepted. D is therefore taken as $7 \cdot 0 + 0 \cdot 23 = 7 \cdot 23$ m.

(iv) The amount by which $11(L2-L1)$ differs from an integral number of $u1$'s is an indication of the accuracy in the rod lengths—or in the adjustment and alignment of the E.D.M. equipment.

(v) With the rods used in the example only distances between 0 and 10 m can be measured by this method because $L1$ and $L2$ will be repeated again every 10 m. The $L1$ and $L2$ readings for $7 \cdot 23$ m are the same for $17 \cdot 23$ m and $27 \cdot 23$ m and so on.

(vi) By using another rod of length $u3$, where $100\,u1 = 101\,u3$, the length capable of being measured with these rods can be increased to 100 m from $L3 - L1$, but with some loss of accuracy.

(vii) To maintain accuracy the length is obtained as follows:

Length from 0 to 1 m—from $L1$.
Length from 0 to 10 m—from $L2 - L1$.
Length from 10 m to 100 m—from $L3 - L1$.

26. Principle of the geodimeter. The geodimeter uses light modulated at a known frequency by a Kerr cell to provide the means for measuring the length of a line. The light is directed from the instrument to a retro-directive prism reflector, which has the property of reflecting light back along the same line so that alignment of the reflector with respect to the geodimeter is not critical. The phase of the modulation on the beam received back at the instrument compared with the transmitted beam provides a measure of the length L in **25**. The wavelength of the modulated light beam is about 10 m. As the instrument is capable of distinguishing between each half wavelength and as the reflected light may be in or out of phase with the transmitted beam by 180°, which can also be detected, the unit length used is one quarter wavelength or 2·5 m, the equivalent of $u1$ in **25**.

27. Length calculation. The following procedure is used to measure length:

(a) The reflected light returned to the instrument is converted into electrical pulses by a photo cell. This allows the phase comparisons between the transmitted and received signals to be made. The comparison is made by adjusting a variable delay. When the desired phase relationship is obtained, a null indicator points to zero and the delay line readings are displaced digitally on the instrument panel which are proportional to L.

(b) To convert the delay line readings the speed of light must be considered. The speed of light in a vacuum is accepted as 299 792·5 km/s, but a correction must be applied for the temperature and pressure at the time of observation. This is read off a nomogram in practice and applied as a correction to the final result. The delay line readings are converted to metres from a calibration table individually prepared for each instrument.

(c) From the values of L converted to metres the overall distance is calculated using the basis of the method in **25**. The value of $u1$ in the geodimeter model 6 is 2·500 000 m and its relation with $u2$ and $u3$ is such that:

$$400 \times 2u1 = 401 \times 2u2 = 2000 \text{ m}$$
and $$\quad 20 \times 2u1 = 21 \times 2u3 = 100 \text{ m}$$

From these values only distances up to 2000 m can be calculated as the differences $L2 - L1$ are repeated every 2000 m. However, distances to be measured can be estimated or scaled from an existing map to within 2000 m and whole distances of 2000 m are added to the calculated results as necessary.

Finally a correction must be applied to allow for the path of the light through both the geodimeter and the reflector.

28. Geodimeter model data. The original geodimeter was devised by Dr Bergstrand of the Swedish Survey Office. It was

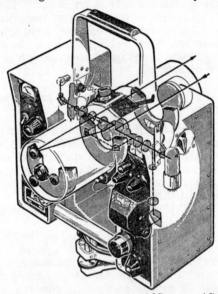

[*Courtesy AGA (U.K.) Ltd.*

FIG. 48.—*The geodimeter Model 6*

The illustration shows the optical details with the light source on the left being first modulated by the Kerr cell before being refracted and reflected through the instrument to the distant reflector. The returned rays are converted to electrical impulses by the photo-electric cell on the right and the phase comparison is made on the null indicator meter, with the original light rays shown as a pecked line across the instrument.

then constructed as a practical field instrument by the AGA Corporation, Stockholm, the first model appearing on the market in 1950. Models 2, 3 and 4 appeared in the following years, each an improvement on the last.

In 1965 the *Model 6*, illustrated in Fig. 48, was first produced. Range depends on lamp type, visibility and reflector size.

Normal range	Daylight	Darkness
Tungsten lamp	15 m to 2–5 km	15 km
Mercury lamp	15 m to 5–10 km	25 km
Accuracy ± 10 mm ± 2 ppm (parts per million)		

The *Model 6BL laser geodimeter* now supersedes the proven model 6 series. The receiving lens has a filter that shuts out all light having a wavelength differing from the modulated laser beam. Day and night ranges are now practically the same, *see* **34**. The new 1977 Model 600 with improved laser optics doubles the range up to 50 km, for the first time providing a near visible light instrument comparable with microwave in range.

29. The tellurometer. The tellurometer uses radio waves transmitted from one instrument, known as the *master*, to another identical instrument, known as the *remote instrument*, which receives the signal, monitors it and returns it to the master. A check on the measurement is obtained by reversing the roles of the *master* and *remote* instruments.

(*a*) A *carrier frequency* is frequency modulated by one of the *pattern frequencies*, say 10 Mc/s, as in models MRA 1 and MRA 2. In these instruments the phase delay on return to the master is measured by means of a break in a circular trace formed on a cathode-ray tube. The cathode-ray tube display is engraved with a circular scale divided into 100 parts corresponding to one wavelength of the signal. As the 10 Mc/s wavelength is about 30 m, one division on the tube display represents 0·30 m, but since the transmitting time for the double distance is measured this represents about 0·15 m of the line length.

(*b*) The scale readings represent millimicroseconds (10^{-9}" or 1 mμs) and are the equivalent of the L readings in **25**. The velocity of radio waves, 299 792·5 km/s *in vacuo*, has to be corrected to the temperature, pressure and humidity at which the observations are made in order to convert these readings to a linear measure.

(c) Fine A readings at one frequency are taken and by repeating the observations with B, C and D readings, at different frequencies, course readings are obtained equivalent to $L2$ and $L3$ in 26 but include an $L4$ here.

(d) To increase the accuracy of the fine reading A a "negative" A reading is introduced having a reversal effect similar to the *circle left* and *circle right* positions of a theodolite. In addition to the $+A$ and $-A$ readings, both are reversed in phase producing a mean result of the fine A readings from which the final distance is calculated. These fine readings help to minimise the effect of *ground swing* caused by reflections of the microwave signal.

30. Tellurometer models.

In 1954 the Director of the Trigonometrical Survey of the Union of South Africa suggested to Mr T. L. Wadley of the S.A. Telecommunications Research Laboratory that they should investigate the production of an electronic instrument for the measurement of distance suitable for geodetic work. Thus the early models MRA 1 and MRA 2 of the *tellurometer*, or *microdistancer*, came into being. Model MRA3 was the first transistorised unit introduced in 1962. Then followed the MRA 101 and the MRA 4, which showed further improvements and provided a direct read-out in millimetres. Production of this model ceased in 1977.

(a) *Model MRA 5* is specifically designed to military standards and provides a fully automatic seven-digit read-out. Its antenna unit may be detached from the instrument and mounted separately, *see* 34.

(b) *CA* 1000. This system consists of a non-interchangeable "Master" and "Remote" unit unlike the MRA series. The "Master" unit radiates a microwave carrier tunable between 10·10 and 10·45 GHz which is frequency modulated in the 19–25 MHz range providing a 300-mm modulated wave. The "Remote" unit receives the signal and retransmits to the "Master," which measures the phase difference between the transmitted and received signals. This phase difference is effectively a measure of the time taken for the signals to complete the forward and return path. It is converted into distance from the "fine" A readings, meaned to minimise ground swing, and "course" patterns E, D, C and B, which are entered and simply reduced on a field sheet. Finally, the corrections for meteorological conditions are made, *see* **34**.

NOTE: Range with the short-range horn is about 10 km and with the long-range one about 30 km. With a directional antenna range may be increased to about 50 km. This light, compact instrument effectively supersedes the earlier micro-wave models for all forms of civil long-range precise traversing, trilateration and primary geodetic control.

31. Short-range electro-optical instruments. Because of the effect of spurious light on tungsten light source EDM, the use of near infra-red radiation with a wavelength double that of visible light, about 0·9 microns, micrometres or millionths of a metre, is most common. The infra-red source is a gallium arsenide (GaAs) luminescent diode which may be simply modulated in intensity in proportion to the current supplied to it through a crystal oscillator. This amplitude modulation is capable of providing good distance resolution, though range is limited to about 2 km, as the diodes are not efficient radiators and have a very low power output, inevitably limited by portable power supplies.

NOTE

(*i*) The digital method of phase discrimination between the transmitted and reflected signal is usually used. The transmitted modulation triggers a counting mechanism whenever the wave changes from positive to negative. Similarly, the reflected wave stops the time count. The number of pulses allowed through are displayed, each pulse representing a small known distance, frequently 1 mm. A number of counts are taken and meaned and digitally displayed or recorded.

(*ii*) Brief details of six infra-red type instruments are listed in **34**.

32. The Mekometer. This advanced instrument, invented by Dr K. D. Froome of the National Physics Laboratory, is an electro-optical distance-measuring instrument with a range limit of 3 km, and unlike most other short-range EDM instruments, except for the MA–100, it is capable of high accuracy (*see* **34**). This is achieved by the use of an intermittent signal of high frequency near 500 MHz. The effect of atmospheric refraction is estimated within the Mekometer, and the read-out is direct without the need for calculation.

33. Reduction of EDM distances.

All distances measured with EDM equipment are curved path distances, due to refraction, on the slant between instruments or between instruments and reflectors. The following corrections must therefore be applied.

(a) Reduction of the curved signal path to the straight-line distance between stations of differing heights.

(b) Slope correction to the horizontal.

(c) Reduction to sea level, the straight line between the points perpendicularly below the stations at sea level, being the chord to the spheroid.

(d) The spheroid length, being the distance along the spheroid, the mathematically accepted curved shape of the earth.

(e) Summary of corrections:

$$l - s = \frac{h^2}{2l} - \frac{h_m\left(l - \frac{h^2}{2l}\right)}{R + h_m} + \frac{l^3}{(33 \text{ or } 43) \, R^2}$$

where l = reduced path distance,

s = spheroidal distance,

h = difference in height between stations,

$R = 6\cdot38 \times 10^6$ metres,

h_m = mean height of stations,

33 = constant used for light and

43 = constant used for microwaves.

34. Comparison of EDM instruments.

The table on the opposite page provides a brief comparison of some modern electronic equipment in general use:

35. Trilateration.

The measurement of a triangulation network by EDM results in the lengths being known instead of the angles. This may be considered as a reversion to chain surveying, although on a larger scale. It is suitable for providing control on plane surveys, though it is usually less economic than the primary or zero-order EDM traversing, which now supersedes triangulation as a means of providing geodetic control.

Comparison of modern electro-magnetic distance measurement (EDM) equipment

Instrument	Carrier Wave	Range	Resolution	Accuracy	Remarks
Aga Geotronics Geodimeter 6BL	1 mW He-Ne Laser	20/25 km	1 mm	±5 mm ± 1 ppm	Supersedes tungsten or mercury lamp of Model 6
12	Infra-red	700 m (1 prism) 1700 m (3 prisms)	1 mm	±5 mm ± 10 ppm	Mounted on theodolite telescope
710	Laser	1700 m (1 prism) 5000 m (6 prisms)	1 mm	±5 mm ± 1 ppm	Combination electronic theodolite, distance measurer and calculator
Hewlett Packard 3810A Total Station	Infra-red	1600 m (3 prisms)	1 mm	±5 mm ± 10 ppm	Incorporates a theodolite and automatic distance reduction
Kern DM 500	Infra-red	500 m (3 prisms)	1 mm	±5 mm ± 5 ppm	Compact attachment for DKM 2-A and KI-S Kern theodolites
Mekometer Tellurometer	Xenon gas lamp	3 km	0·1 mm	±0·2 mm ± 2 ppm	Most accurate instrument, *see* **32**
CD 6	Infra-red	1000 m (1 prism) 2000 m (7 prisms)	1 mm	±5 mm ± 5 ppm	Attached to tripod or theodolite standards or telescope
CA 1000	Microwave (*see* **30**(b))	10 km 30 km	3 mm	±15 mm ± 5 ppm ±15 mm ± 10 ppm	Master and Remote instruments with two-way speech contact
MA-100	Infra-red	1000 m (3 prisms)	0·1 mm	±1·5 mm ± 2 ppm	High-accuracy instrument
MRA-5	Microwave 10 to 10·5 GHz	50 km	10 mm	±10 mm ± 10 ppm	Automatic Digital Display. Two-way speech contact. Antenna unit may be mounted remote from instrument
Wild Heerbrugg Distomat D13S	Infra-red	1000 m (1 prism) 1600 m (3 prisms) 2000 m (9 prisms)	1 mm	±5 mm ± 5 ppm	Combines with T1, T16 and T2 Wild theodolites. Automatic digital readout. Reduces distance to the horizontal
Zeiss Oberkochen Reg Elta	Infra-red	500 m (1 prism) 1200 m (7 prisms)	1 mm	±5 mm ± 10 ppm	Combination electronic theodolite, distance measurer and programmable computer

(a) *Figural adjustment.* A trilateration network, even a braced quadrilateral, which again forms the strongest figure, is best adjusted by means of *variation of co-ordinates.* This method provides adjusted co-ordinates without evaluation of the angles although they would probably be needed for subsequent work. The condition equations again involve angles, but unless directly measured they are dependent on linear measures. Where both are measured the number of conditions is increased.

(b) In practice network adjustments would be carried out on a computer. It would be uneconomic to attempt the adjustment of anything but the simplest figures in any other way. For details of mixed network adjustments see pp. 202–8 of *Surveying* by J. B. Garner, D. James and R. G. Bird, published in 1976 by the Estates Gazette Ltd.

PROGRESS TEST 7

1. What is the basic principle of triangulation surveys? (1)
2. Why is it necessary to produce primary, secondary and tertiary triangulation? (2–4)
3. What is a base extension and why is it needed? (5)
4. Describe briefly the field work involved in making a base line measurement. (6–7)
5. Why is it seldom necessary to reduce a base line measurement to sea level or to apply a tension correction? (12–13)
*6. Reduce the absolute length at sea level of three bays of a base line using the following data:

Bay	Observed length (m)	Temp. (°C)	Angle of slope	Tension (kg)
1	29·8916	6·3	0° 13′ 40″	10
2	29·9077	6·5	0° 17′ 10″	10
3	10·7632	7·0	0° 22′ 00″	10

The invar tape used weighs 0·026 kg/m and has a cross-sectional area of 3·27 mm^2. It was standardised on the flat at 20°C under a pull of 5 kg force. The coefficient of expansion of the tape material is 0·000 000 2 per °C and Young's modulus is 150 kN/mm^2. The mean level of the base is 850·0 m above sea level. (13)
*7. Make an approximate adjustment of the braced quadrilateral in Fig. 44 where the observed angles have the following values:

$$A1 \qquad 41° 17′ 34″$$
$$A2 \qquad 37° 26′ 41″$$
$$A3 \qquad 46° 01′ 27″$$

$A4$	48° 09′ 02″
$B1$	34° 35′ 25″
$B2$	66° 40′ 24″
$B3$	29° 51′ 26″
$B4$	55° 58′ 02″

(16)

*8. Make an approximate adjustment of the six-sided centre-point polygon where the observed angles of each triangle in clockwise sequence have the following values:

$A1$	48° 25′ 07″	$A4$	51° 52′ 26″
$B1$	43° 54′ 56″	$B4$	50° 45′ 53″
$C1$	87° 39′ 55″	$C4$	77° 21′ 42″
$A2$	74° 35′ 41″	$A5$	75° 20′ 11″
$B2$	62° 38′ 23″	$B5$	57° 49′ 15″
$C2$	42° 46′ 00″	$C5$	46° 50′ 40″
$A3$	55° 11′ 53″	$A6$	54° 32′ 45″
$B3$	72° 44′ 13″	$B6$	72° 09′ 50″
$C3$	52° 04′ 09″	$C6$	53° 17′ 30″

(17)

9. What is a *resected point*? (20)

*10. An abney level was used to measure the height of a television mast, measurements being made from a point at a sloping distance of 100·0 m from the foot of the mast, as follows:

Elevation to the top of the mast = 17°
Depression to the base of the mast = 35°

The angle of slope of the ground was also measured and found to be 33°. Calculate the height of the mast. (22)

*11. In Fig. 45(c) the height of a tower BC is required. The angle of elevation to the top of the tower from A is 24° and at E, 1·5 m above A, the angle of elevation to the same point is 44°. The horizontal distance between A and E was set out at 50·00 m. Find the height of the tower. (22)

*12. In Fig. 45(b) the vertical height BC = 80·0 m. If the horizontal angle PCQ = 48° and the angles of elevation α and β at P and Q respectively are 32° and 40°, what is the length PQ? (22)

*13. Calculate the height difference between two points X and Y, allowing for refraction and curvature, from the following observations from X:

Height of instrument   = 0·26 m
Height of signal at Y = 1·26 m
Angle of elevation   = −0° 12′ 40″
Distance X–Y = 2927·5 m   (24)

*14. The wavelengths used in a fictitious EDM instrument produced unit lengths u for a one-way measure of the line, where $10\ u1 = 11\ u3$ and $100\ u1 = 101\ u2$. Calculate the length of a line known to be between 350 and 450 m long if the phase comparisons produced the following values for L where the distance $D = nu + L$:

$$L1 = 0\cdot85\ \text{m}$$
$$L2 = 2\cdot43\ \text{m}$$
$$L3 = 1\cdot54\ \text{m}$$

The values of u are $u1 = 2\cdot500$ m, $u2 = 2\cdot475$ m, $u3 = 2\cdot273$ m. (26)

15. What corrections are required to be made to a long distance directly measured by EDM between two points on the surface of the earth? (33)

16. What is the difference between triangulation and trilateration? Discuss the application of trilateration. How may a trilateration network be adjusted? (35)

CHAPTER VIII

PLANE TABLE SURVEYING

1. Plane tabling. Plane tabling is a method of surveying in which the plotting of the survey is carried out directly in the field. The *plane table* consists of a drawing board mounted on a tripod which can be set up in any convenient position on the site to be surveyed.

In the past plane tabling was the method used for supplying topographical detail for maps at scales of 1 : 10 000 to 1 : 250 000, but its use in this respect has largely, although not entirely, been superseded by air survey.

Plane tabling is still a valuable survey technique, conditions under which it is still used, although more frequently in North America, the Continent and the East than in Great Britain, being the following:

(a) Supplying topographical detail in the *dead ground* of an air survey, *e.g.* the position of streams and roads in jungles hidden by the upper foliage of trees.

(b) Carrying out the reconnaissance for a triangulation survey, the network drawing immediately indicating the suitability and strength of the layout.

(c) Establishing additional points economically, yet with sufficient accuracy, from a triangulation network as additional ground control for air survey.

(d) Revising maps, useful for planners requiring a quick revision of a minor area depicted on out-of-date maps.

(e) Surveying small sites where graphic accuracy only is required.

(f) Helping the student to understand the principles of surveying, as contouring, traversing, polars and triangulation techniques may be directly illustrated.

2. Equipment. Plane tabling equipment consists of the following items, as illustrated in Plate 3 (reproduced by courtesy of Rank Precision Industries Ltd.):

(a) *The plane table*, essentially a drawing board, usually about 600 × 800 mm, which carries the plotting sheet and is mounted in a tripod such that it can be levelled, and rotated and clamped in any position.

(b) *The sight rule* or *alidade*, which incorporates sighting vanes and a straight-edge so that a line may be drawn on the sheet in the direction of the point sighted to. The *telescopic alidade* shown consists of a small tacheometer mounted on a straight-edge. It provides greater accuracy in sighting and allows distances and elevations to be obtained by tacheometric means (*see* XII).

(c) *A spirit level*, which checks the level of the board, although a circular bubble would suffice. The spirit level is sometimes incorporated in the alidade or the compass.

(d) *A plumbing fork*, used only in large-scale work, which allows the table to be set up so that the point on the sheet representing the occupied station can be positioned vertically above the ground mark.

(e) *A trough compass*, or the plane table compass illustrated, which are not essential, but are useful for orienting the table to the magnetic meridian or for obtaining an approximate orientation for *resection* (*see* 8).

(f) *A waterproof cover*, which is generally necessary to protect the table from rain.

3. Drawing materials. Ideally the drawing sheet should be stable and remain unaffected by humidity changes. Varieties of mounted paper are used, including mounting on aluminium sheets. Plastic drawing sheets are now generally used, being stable and waterproof. Drawing sheets are glued or taped down, sometimes with edges turned under the board. Drawing pins should not be used as they damage the board and there must be no projections to snag the alidade.

Butt-joined plates are used by the Ordnance Survey as sheets for filling in detail from control provided by air survey. These plates are coated aluminium and data are scribed on to them. Each plate is 200 mm square and any four may be clipped together. This has the advantage that when working near the edge of the board the plates can be brought in and another pair inserted.

Pencils, erasers, scales, etc., as for normal, clean draughting, are required. Pencils are usually 3H or harder for sharp, fine lines. Inking up the drawing is usually done after each day's work.

4. Plane tabling methods. The four basic methods of using the plane table for surveying are the following:

    (*a*) *Radiation* (*see* 5).
    (*b*) *Triangulation or intersection* (*see* 6).
    (*c*) *Traversing* (*see* 7).
    (*d*) *Resection* (*see* 8).

5. Radiation. This is the most direct method of use, but is more suitable for smaller sites. The process is illustrated in Fig. 49. The plane table is set up at a convenient station *P*,

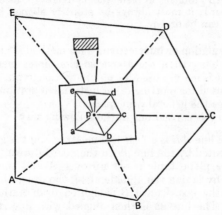

FIG. 49.—*Radiation*

This shows the method of surveying details by lines of sight radiating from a station point, the lengths to each feature being measured to locate its position.

from which all points of the site to be surveyed can be seen. The board is set up and levelled over this point, rotated to such a position that all data will fall within the limits of the sheet, and clamped. Point *p* is marked on the drawing sheet to represent *P* on the ground, its position being vertically above the ground mark. The survey is then performed in the following way:

(*a*) The alidade is placed against *p*, *A* is sighted and the line *pa* is ruled on the board. Similarly the other rays are drawn as shown, all radiating from *p*.

(*b*) The length *PA* is measured on the ground either by direct taping or by tacheometric means and is scaled off along the drawn ray and *a* is plotted. This process is repeated for all the other radiating lines.

(*c*) *The survey* is completed by drawing in the features such as the boundary lines *ab*, *bc*, etc. As a check these distances should also be measured and compared with their scaled lengths.

NOTE: The plane table is *oriented* in that every line on the board is parallel or aligned with every equivalent line on the ground. All problems in plane tabling relate to the orientation of the board; it must always be properly aligned before any final rays can be drawn.

6. Triangulation or intersection. This method is more suited to plane tabling than the above as less direct measuring is required. It is mainly used for mapping topographical details, but is also used for plotting other instrument stations. Figure 50 illustrates the general principles.

The survey is carried out in the following way:

(*a*) The line *AB* is a base line measured on the ground. It is represented by the line *ab* on the board drawn to scale.

(*b*) The plane table is set up over *A* and the board is oriented by laying the alidade along the drawn line *ab* and rotating the board until *B* is sighted from *A* through the alidade. The line *ab* is then aligned with line *AB* on the ground.

(*c*) The alidade is then placed against *a* and sighted towards the points to be fixed, such as *P*, *Q*, *R* and *C*. Lines or rays are drawn on the board to represent the lines of sight to these features.

(*d*) When all points required to be fixed have been sighted to and the rays have been drawn the board is moved to *B*. Point *b* on the board is plumbed over *B* on the ground. The board is again rotated for orientation by laying the alidade along *ba*, sighting this time to *A*. When it is clamped in position rays are again drawn to the points previously observed to. The rays from *B* will intersect those drawn from

A, thus establishing the positions of *p, q, r* and *c* on the board.

(*e*) The relative positions of these points and any others required have now been plotted, but not *checked*. By setting up at *C*, orienting the board off *ca* and checking that the ray to *B* passes through the plotted position of *b*, the board

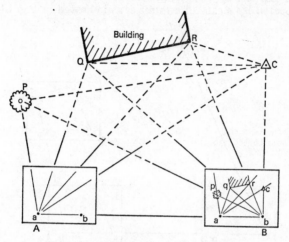

Fig. 50.—*Triangulation or intersection*

Lines of sight to features are plotted so that their intersections locate the positions of the features being observed to.

is again oriented as before. By observing and drawing the rays from *C* again to *P, Q* and *R*, a check is obtained if the rays pass through the previously fixed points *p, q* and *r*. If all is in order further points may be sighted to for additional fixing and checking from other stations until the complete network of triangulated points is built up by intersection.

NOTE

(*i*) The base line is only required for a minor isolated survey. Where plane tabling is used for filling in topographical detail in an area with a triangulated control, these control points are pre-plotted by co-ordinates on the drawing sheets and are used instead as the basis of the plane tabling survey.

(*ii*) Points to be fixed by intersection must form the apex of well-conditioned triangles. Rays intersecting at less than 30° or more than 150° are unacceptable in the fixing of any point.

7. Traversing. Where it is inconvenient to establish plane table stations by forward intersection, station positions may be located by means of a *traverse*, as indicated in Fig. 51. If

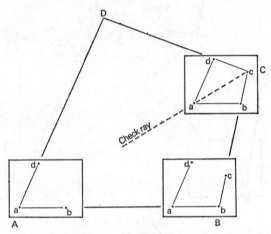

Fig. 51.—*Traversing*

The figure of the survey lines is built up on the plane table.

it is desired to plot the relative positions of points A, B, C and D, as illustrated, the procedure is as follows:

(*a*) After the traverse stations have been set out in the required positions the plane table is set up over the first point A. Its position is represented by a on the board and through this point rays are drawn to the two adjacent traverse stations such as D and B. These lengths are measured on the ground, or tacheometrically if a telescopic alidade is being used, and the points d and b are plotted on the sheet as shown.

(*b*) The plane table is next set up at B and oriented as before along the line BA and a forward ray bc is drawn towards station C. This length is also measured and c is plotted.

(c) The process continues, the board being oriented at each station until the final point, D in the figure, initially plotted from A, is again plotted from C, the preceding station.

(d) The two plotted positions of D are indicative of the accuracy of the plane table traverse. If the two positions coincide reasonable accuracy on a small-scale survey will have been obtained. On larger-scale work a *closing* error is likely to occur, its magnitude represented by the distance between the two positions of d. This will be due to observational and plotting errors and provided no *gross* errors are suspected this misclosure would be graphically adjusted in the same way as a compass traverse (*see* III, 22). Gross errors are likely if the closing error is comparatively large. As a check on their existence *check rays* should be observed across the traverse where possible, as indicated.

8. Resection or the "three-point problem." This is a process whereby the position of an occupied station may be plotted if its position has not previously been fixed. The need for this arises when a position suitable for plane table detailing has not previously been observed to and delay would arise in occupying a previously fixed point in order to establish the required position by forward intersection.

In order to fix the position of any point by the forward intersection of rays, two rays provide the fix and the third ray the check. However, as the direction of the rays is unknown, three rays at least are needed to resect a point, hence the name, the *three-point problem*.

If the plane table is properly oriented at the station to be fixed, as it has been in all previous cases considered, then rays drawn through the plotted positions of known fixed stations must intersect at the point required. This is simply the reverse of ordinary intersection. However, the table cannot be oriented in the same way as before as there is now no ray drawn on the sheet towards the occupied station. The problem then is one of *orientation*.

9. Solution of the three-point problem. There are several solutions of the three-point problem, but *Collins' point solution* only will be considered. This can be used easily for calculation purposes from observed angles as well as graphically on the plane table. Figure 52 illustrates the position where P, the point to be fixed, may lie either inside or outside the triangle formed by the three fixing stations. In either case the following procedure applies:

(*a*) Join AC and set off angle α = angle BPA at C as shown. If α is greater than 90°, then 180° − α must be set off at C instead, as shown in the alternative case.

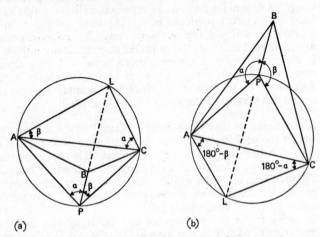

(*a*)   (*b*)

FIG. 52.—*The Collins point solution*

(*a*) The geometry of the situation where the point P to be located lies *outside* the triangle formed by the three known stations.

(*b*) The geometry of the situation where P lies *inside* the triangle formed by the three known points.

(*b*) Repeat the process at A, setting off either angle β or 180° − β as necessary. The two rays formed will intersect at a point L.

(*c*) Join LB and produce this line as necessary to intersect the circumscribing circle through A, C and L.

(*d*) The intersection of LB with the circle is the point P required because, by construction, the circumferential angles of chord LC, angle LAC and angle LPC = β and similarly, in relation to chord LA, angle LCA = angle LPA = α.

EXAMPLE

The following illustrates Collins' point solution—which may be undertaken graphically on the plane table as in (a) or may be calculated as in (b). With the plane table set up at P it is required to plot its position p from the plotted positions a, b and c of stations A, B and C.

(a) By rotating the table angle BPC can be constructed at a and angle BPA can be constructed at c as shown in Fig. 52. The line joining Lb will then pass through the occupied point. By laying the alidade along this drawn line and sighting B the table will be oriented. Then, by drawing the rays Aa and Cc on the board they will meet at point p, the required position.

(b) If the angles α and β were measured by theodolite observations instead of being drawn and the co-ordinates of A, B and C were known, then the co-ordinates of P could be calculated from first principles as follows:

(i) Triangle ACL is first solved from the base AC and the two angles. The co-ordinates of L can then be computed and thus the bearing of the straight line LBP can be established.

(ii) From the bearing of LP the bearings PC and PA can be obtained from the observed angles, thus all the angles of triangle PAC can be evaluated.

(iii) From AC and the known angles triangle APC can be solved, and the co-ordinates of P calculated by bearing and distance from both A and C as a check.

NOTE: If the point P lies on or near the circle through A, B and C, then it is impossible to establish its position from these points. The reason for this is that the observed angles α and β will subtend at any point along the circumference of this circle and the actual position of P cannot be defined from their values alone. (This circle is known as the danger circle because of the danger of attempting to resect a station near its circumference.)

10. Plane table resection. Although Collins' point solution is used in plane tabling it is not always convenient, particularly when the point L falls off the drawing board. Three *practical* plane table resection methods are the following:

(a) *Tracing paper method* (see **11**).
(b) *Trial and error method* (see **12**).
(c) *Intersection of loci method* (see **13**).

11. Tracing paper method. This method involves the following procedure:

(*a*) Fasten a sheet of tracing paper to the board. Choose a point p' to represent P on the ground. Draw rays on the tracing paper against the alidade from p' towards A, B and C, the points on the ground. These rays will not pass through their plotted positions, a, b and c, unless p' has been chosen in the correct place.

(*b*) Release the tracing paper and adjust its position until the three drawn rays accurately pass through a, b and c, when p' will be correctly positioned.

(*c*) Prick through the position of p' on the tracing paper, marking the position of p on the plotting sheet.

(*d*) As a check, draw one sight line, say, pb, lay the alidade against it and rotate the table until B is sighted. The table should then be *oriented*. Rays Aa and Cc are then drawn and should pass through p, thus proving its position.

12. Trial and error method. This is the method used by experienced plane tablers. It is more satisfactory than the previous method because unless great care is taken in positioning the tracing paper the position of p will not be precisely established. The three drawn rays will not then meet at a point, but will form a *triangle of error*. The trial and error method is illustrated as follows:

(*a*) The plane table is approximately oriented by eye or with the aid of the box compass. Laying the alidade against a, A is sighted and a ray Aa is drawn. Similarly, Bb and Cc are drawn. Unless the table is perfectly oriented these three rays will not meet at a point which defines the position of p, but will form a triangle of error.

(*b*) By examining the triangle of error it is possible to estimate the position of p from the following rules, first formulated by Lehmann and called *Lehmann's rules*:

(*i*) The point p will lie either to the right of *all* three lines, when looking towards the ground stations, or to the left of them.

(*ii*) If P lies within the triangle formed by A, B and C, then p will fall within the triangle of error, or otherwise it will lie outside it.

(*iii*) The distance of *p* from each line is proportional to the length of that line.

(*d*) Re-orient the board, once *p* has been chosen, by laying the alidade against its assumed position and against one of the stations and by rotating the board until the station is sighted.

(*e*) If *p* has been correctly chosen the rays *Aa*, *Bb* and *Cc* will meet at a point. If not, another smaller error figure will be formed in relation to which a more reliable position of *p* is chosen. The process is continued until *p* is established on the intersection of the three rays. This should, with experience, be possible to achieve with two or three triangles of error only.

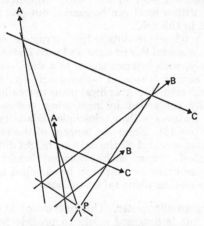

FIG. 53.—*Intersection of loci*

The method of resection using loci of the intersection of rays from two triangles of error is shown.

13. Intersection of loci method.

This method is illustrated in Fig. 53 and may be described as follows:

(*a*) The plane table is approximately oriented and the rays *Aa*, *Bb* and *Cc* are drawn producing a triangle of error.

(*b*) Without attempting to choose a position for *p*, rotate the board about 10° or so and repeat the process of drawing in rays *Aa*, *Bb* and *Cc*. Another figure in error will result.

(c) Draw the loci of the intersection points of the rays as shown. As the two triangles are similar the lines joining the equivalent corners of the two triangles will meet at the point where all rays will converge when the board is properly oriented. The point p is thus located and the board is finally oriented as before and the position of p is checked when all three rays Aa, Bb and Cc pass through the one point.

14. Vertical control. Plane table survey plans may be *contoured* (*see* XIII) in a number of ways:

(a) On small sites spot heights may be established with a level, the positions of the heighted points being located on the plane table like any other feature. The contour lines are then interpolated later in the office. Alternatively, direct contouring with a level can be carried out and the contour lines drawn in the field.

(b) With a telescopic alidade the instrument can be set to provide a horizontal line of sight and used instead as a level. Alternatively, with inclined sights to a staff, vertical height differences can be evaluated tacheometrically (*see* XII).

(c) In large areas topographical plans to smaller scales can be vertically controlled by measuring vertical angles to prominent features with a telescopic alidade or an Indian clinometer (*see* **15**). From the tangent of the vertical angle and the distance scaled off the drawing height differences can be established. From such evaluated height differences reasonably accurate contours can be sketched in from vantage points used as plane table stations.

15. The Indian clinometer. This instrument is used with a plane table, but is designed solely to provide height differences. It consists of a hinged base plate about 200 mm long with a spirit bubble attached. The upper part of the base can be set level with the bubble by a tilting screw.

At each end of the adjustable upper part of the base a vane is attached which is raised at right-angles to the base when in use. There is a sight hole in one vane and one face of the other vane is graduated on one side in degrees and on the other in natural tangents upwards and downwards from a central zero mark. A horizontal marker can be moved up and down the graduated vane. When it is set at zero it is on the horizontal line through the sight hole.

When in use the instrument is placed on the plane table and levelled. The station of which the height is required is sighted through the sight hole. The horizontal index is moved along the graduated vane until it is on the line of sight to the station. Either the angle of elevation or its natural tangent to three decimal places can then be read off. The tangent value, multiplied by the scaled distance, provides the height difference above or below the level of the plane table. The accuracy of sighting with the Indian clinometer is such that corrections for refraction and curvature (*see* VII, 24) are not warranted.

PROGRESS TEST 8

1. What type of survey can conveniently be carried out by a plane table? (1)

2. List the essential equipment for plane tabling. What additional equipment is also useful under certain circumstances? (2, 3, 15)

3. What forms do the drawing sheets take and why is ordinary cartridge paper not used? (3)

4. What are the four basic methods of plane tabling? (4)

5. Describe the principles of the three plane table methods where orientation is simply achieved by direct sighting. (5–7)

6. What is the "three-point problem"? (8)

7. Evaluate the Collins point solution of the three-point problem. (9)

8. Describe three practical methods of plane table resection. (10–13)

9. Describe two methods of producing contours on a large-scale plane table drawing. (14)

10. How are contours produced on small-scale topographical maps by plane tabling? (14)

11. Describe the construction of the Indian clinometer and explain for what purpose, and how, it is used. (14, 15)

CHAPTER IX

TRAVERSE SURVEYING

PRINCIPLES OF TRAVERSING

1. Definition of a traverse. The position of a point on the ground may be established if its bearing and distance from another known point are measured (*see* IV, 6). This process may be extended to successive points and the resulting series of connected lines, of which the bearing and distance are known, is called a *traverse* (*see* Fig. 54).

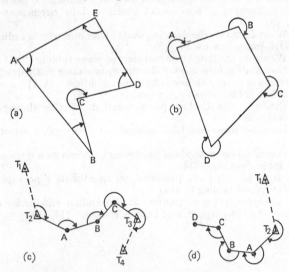

FIG. 54.—*Examples of traverse layouts*

(a) A traverse closing back on to its starting point with the internal angles measured.
(b) A traverse closing back on to its starting point with the external angles measured.
(c) A closed traverse between two fixed co-ordinated points.
(d) An open traverse.

2. Open and closed traverses.

(a) *The closed traverse.* If a traverse proceeds from one co-ordinated point to another it is known as a closed traverse. A closed traverse may therefore close back on to its starting point or any other co-ordinated point (*see* Fig. 54 (a) to (c)). It is thus capable of being checked and adjusted to fit accurately between these known points.

(b) *The open traverse.* An open traverse on the other hand does *not* close on to a known point. It cannot be easily checked nor can it be properly adjusted and it is a form of traverse which should only be used in exceptional circumstances (*see* Fig. 54 (d)).

3. The purpose of traversing. Traverses are used for two main purposes:

(a) *For surveying detail.* A traverse network of survey lines and ground marks provides a system of control points which can be accurately plotted on a map or plan. The positions of natural and artificial features are located on the ground relative to this network and these details can then be plotted in their proper position by reference to the plotted traverse lines and stations.

(b) *For setting out.* The position of roads, buildings and other new constructions can be established by the surveyor relative to the traverse control points from information supplied by the designer, architect or engineer. Pegs can then be set out on the ground from the traverse to define the position of such new works.

4. Comparison with chain surveying. Chain surveying provides a network of survey lines which enables the position of features to be located by offsetting and tie-lines. The position of the main lines is governed by the need to provide well-conditioned triangles.

In traverse surveying the positioning of lines is not limited in this way. The main advantages of traverse surveying are the following:

(a) *Convenience.* Survey lines can be more conveniently positioned on the ground. Also, the co-ordinates of the station points can be easily calculated.

(b) *Accuracy*. The positions of the survey stations can be more accurately established and plotted. Distances not directly measured can be calculated from co-ordinates to the same degree of accuracy as the field measurements. In chain surveying unmeasured lengths can usually only be scaled from the plot with a resultant loss of precision.

(c) *Checking*. Traverse surveys can be more easily checked against observational and plotting errors.

(d) *Less measuring*. Less lines have to be laid out and measured directly to enable the network to be plotted and checked.

5. Measurements required in traversing. The length and bearing of each line of the traverse must be measured:

(a) *Length measurement*. The length of each line may be measured by a variety of methods depending on the accuracy required and the purpose of the survey. Methods of measurement may be any of the following:

    (i) Direct linear measurement (*see* II, 1).
    (ii) Catenary measurement (*see* VII, 7).
    (iii) Electro-magnetic distance measurement (*see* VII, 25).
    (iv) Tacheometric measurement (*see* XII, 1).

(b) *Bearing measurement*. The bearings of the traverse lines may be roughly obtained from compass observations (*see* III). In most cases this is too inaccurate and the bearings are usually obtained from the angles between the lines, which are measured with a theodolite at each station.

6. Measurement of angles. The field work involved in the measurement of an angle has already been discussed in VI. However, in traversing two procedures are adopted for the measurement of the angles between the lines to facilitate the calculation of the required bearings and to reduce the possibility of observational and calculation errors arising.

These two procedures are the following:

(a) The first theodolite observation is always made to the *back station* and the next observation to the *fore station*, i.e. the station at which the theodolite is to be set up at next. This helps to prevent errors arising when deciding which angle has actually been measured.

NOTE

(i) In a closed traverse which closes back on to its starting point this observational procedure will provide, after reduction, the *internal angles* of the figure if the stations are observed in sequence in an anti-clockwise direction (*see* Fig. 54(a)). Conversely the *external angles* of the figure will be produced if the traverse is observed in a clockwise direction (*see* Fig. 54(b)).

(ii) In traverses which do not form a closed figure the question of internal or external angles does not arise (*see* Fig. 54(c) and (d)). Because of this the observational procedure described in (a) should always be maintained.

(iii) It is inadvisable to deliberately measure internal angles in a closed figure by reversing the accepted procedure because calculation time is likely to be increased and errors are more likely to arise.

(b) Angles are measured on *both faces* of the theodolite and the results are meaned. This eliminates instrumental errors and provides *two* measures of the angle, thus checking against a gross error in either measurement.

7. Booking and reducing angular observations.

There are several accepted methods of booking the angular observations, all of which tend to eliminate instrumental errors and prevent possible observational errors. Many of these methods were designed to suit early forms of the double-axis vernier theodolite and their continued use with modern theodolites is unnecessary. The following paragraphs (**8–10**) illustrate three methods of booking and reduction which are in common use today.

8. Method 1.

This method can be used where observations are taken with either a vernier or an optical-reading theodolite to an accuracy of about 20″.

At Station A

Nail in wooden peg

	°	′	″	°	′	″	°	′	″
(1) E	0	00	00						
(2) B	76	28	20	76	28	20			
							76	28	10
(4) E	180	00	20						
(3) B	256	28	20	76	28	00			

NOTE

(*i*) The station over which the instrument is set up and its description are clearly recorded above the observations.

(*ii*) The first column contains the station names or letters to which observations are being made.

(*iii*) Theodolite readings are booked in the second column, the first pair being face left readings, the second pair face right.

(*iv*) The instrument has been oriented to read zero on to Station E. This is to facilitate reduction of the angle and is not absolutely necessary.

(*v*) The order of booking is shown by the bracketed numbers before the station designation. After the face left reading pointing to B, face is changed and B is again observed before returning to sight to E once more, this time on face right.

(*vi*) The third column contains firstly the angle reduced from the face left readings, which is obtained by subtracting the first or back station reading from the second or fore station reading, and secondly the angle which has been reduced in the same way from the face right readings.

(*vii*) A comparison of the angles in the third column indicates that no gross observational error has occurred.

(*viii*) The fourth column contains the mean of the two reduced angles in the third column and is the required measure of the angle.

9. Method 2. This method should be used when making observations with a single-second theodolite. It should also be used with less accurate instruments in the following circumstances:

(*a*) Where more than two pointings are being made from a station, *i.e.* more than one angle is being measured.

(*b*) Where it is advisable to check that the instrument has not been disturbed between any observations.

(1)	(2)	(3)			(4)			(5)			(6)		
Instrument at	To station	C.L.			C.R.			Mean			Angle		
		°	′	″	°	′	″	°	′	″	°	′	″
A	E	0	00	00	180	00	20	0	00	10			
	B	76	28	20	256	28	20	76	28	20	76	28	10
	R.O.	0	00	00	180	00	00	0	00	00			
B	A	26	27	40	206	28	20	26	28	00			
	C	57	21	00	237	21	20	57	21	10	30	53	10
	R.O.	26	27	40	206	28	20	26	28	00			

NOTE

(*i*) The first column indicates the station from which observations are being made.

(*ii*) The second column indicates the station to which observations are being made.

(*iii*) The third column contains the face left or circle left booked observations.

(*iv*) The fourth column contains the circle right booked observations.

(*v*) The fifth column contains the mean of the circle left and circle right observations.

(*vi*) The sixth column records the final observed angle reduced from the mean of the circle left and circle right observations.

(*vii*) A check against gross error is made by confirming that the degrees noted in the circle left column differ by precisely 180° from those listed in the circle right column.

(*viii*) The degrees are not meaned in the fifth column as those listed first in the third column have already been checked as correct. Frequently the degrees are omitted from this column (*see* **10**).

(*ix*) In the observations from A the theodolite was oriented to give a zero bearing on to E, as in **8**. At B, however, no orientation was made, the initial bearing being simply that read from the clamped horizontal circle.

(*x*) *R.O.* stands for *referring object*, which, with the theodolite at A, is Station E. By observing back to this station on each face it can be shown that the instrument has not been disturbed during the round of observations.

10. Method 3. This method is used when it is desired to carry the bearings through the series of observations at each traverse station. In the two previous booking methods angles only were reduced. In order to obtain the bearings needed, a separate calculation has to be made, as demonstrated in **32**.

This method is useful in that angles need not be reduced at all, although corrections may have to be made to the observed

At B

Nail in wooden peg

	C.L.			C.R.			Mean	
	°	′	″	°	′	″	′	″
A	316	28	00	136	28	00	28	00
C	347	21	20	167	21	00	21	10
R.O.	316	28	00	136	28	00	28	00

bearings, particularly if precise orientation is not possible as in most single-second theodolites.

At C

Nail in wooden peg

							+10	
B	167	21	00	347	21	00	21	00
D	76	34	00	256	34	00	34	00
R.O.	167	21	00	347	21	00	21	00

NOTE

(*i*) The four columns are identical to the columns numbered (2) to (5) of the second method (*see* **9**), except that an initial orientation on to the back station in each case is made, which is equal to the forward bearing from the previous station $\pm 180°$, *i.e.* the actual bearing of the line being observed.

(*ii*) After meaning the circle left and circle right readings there is likely to be a slight loss in the exact carry-through of the orientation. For example: the mean bearing obtained for *BC* is 347° 21′ 10″, but at C the mean bearing for *CB* is 167° 21′ 00″, therefore *all* the mean readings from C must be increased by +10″ as indicated.

(*iii*) In a closed traverse the final bearing observed is compared with the final known bearing, the difference between the two indicating the accuracy of the angular observations (*see* **44**).

11. Types of traverse. Traverses may be graded into different classes or orders, depending on their accuracy. Opinions differ on standards of accuracy required for different classes, but generally traverses may be divided into two types:

(*a*) *Precise* traverses (*see* **12**).

(*b*) *Ordinary* traverses (*see* **13**).

12. Precise traverses. These are traverses where the angular and linear measurements are made with greater refinement and, if distances are taped, bands are standardised and temperature and other corrections are applied similar to those required for base measurement (*see* VII, **8**).

Angular measurements are made with a theodolite reading direct to 1″ or even one-tenth of a second and the mean of several *arcs* or *rounds* of observations is taken. Accuracies may vary depending on requirements from 1/10 000 to over

1/100 000. Precise traverses are used for the following purposes:

(a) To supply *precise control points* for mapping in flat country unsuitable for triangulation.

(b) To provide *accurately positioned reference points* for cadastral and engineering surveys.

(c) To provide *data for engineering works* where great precision is required, *e.g.* in tunnelling.

13. Ordinary traverses. These are traverses where accuracy is less than 1/10 000 and temperature corrections are not normally applied when steel bands are used. The lengths of the traverse legs may also be obtained by chained measurements, by linen or plastic tapes, or by tacheometric methods, depending on the purpose of the survey and the accuracy required. Angular measurements would be made with a theodolite reading usually to 20″, sometimes to 1′ only or even less. At the lower end of the scale distances may be estimated by counting the revolutions of a wheel, usually with a revolution counter known as an *odometer*, or even by pacing.

Ordinary traverses are used for the following surveys:

(a) For *site surveys* for architectural and engineering development. This forms the most common type of traverse survey. The accuracy is between 1/5000 and 1/10 000.

(b) For surveying *topographical details* for mapping or cadastral purposes, traverses being run between control points fixed with greater precision by traversing or triangulation. The accuracy is between 1/100 and 1/5000.

(c) For *exploratory* or *preliminary surveys* in unmapped country. They are less frequent today, but are sometimes necessary for calculating quotations for large engineering works in poorly mapped regions. The accuracy is between 1/50 and 1/500.

FIELD WORK

14. Field party. A traverse field party may consist of a surveyor and one chainman only or a chief surveyor with assistants and labourers, which may amount to twenty or thirty men. A large party would be needed on precise traversing work where lines have to be cleared of bush and other obstacles and where substantial and permanent traverse stations have to be built. On large projects a chief surveyor may control several parties engaged on the same overall survey.

The majority of site and engineering surveys are undertaken by a surveyor with either one or two assistants. The surveyor will observe the angular observations and may also read and book the linear measurements unless two assistants are available, one at least with experience who can take reliable readings which are then booked by the surveyor.

15. Equipment.

(a) Equipment for a *site survey*, where the accuracy to be achieved lies between 1/5000 and 1/10 000, is as below:

    (i) Theodolite, plumb-bob or plumbing rod and tripod.

    (ii) Steel band, 30 m or 100 m long.

    (iii) Linen or plastic tape, 20 m long, for offsetting detail.

    (iv) Measuring rod, 2 m long, for short offsets.

    (v) Hammer, wooden pegs, nails, drill and paint or chalk for marking stations.

    (vi) Ranging rods for marking station positions and ranging in long lines.

    (vii) Chain pins for marking off measured tape lengths.

    (viii) Extra plumb-bob for plumbing ranging rods, step chaining and for plumbing over obscured station marks for accurate sighting with the theodolite.

    (ix) Field book and pencil.

(b) For more *accurate work*, where the tape has been standardised, the equipment includes a spring balance, tape clip, or "littlejohn," for attaching the balance to the tape, and a tape thermometer.

(c) *Zero-order, precise traversing* requires the use of catenary equipment (*see* VII, 7), as for base measurements, or electronic distance measuring instruments, and is too specialised to be considered here.

16. Reconnaissance. On arrival on site a reconnaissance is made during which an overall picture of the area is obtained. The method of survey is considered and the most suitable positions for the traverse stations are decided on. The purpose of the survey and the accuracy required will be known as these will affect the choice of station positions.

In precise traversing of a high order, accuracy takes

precedence over all other considerations. In ordinary traversing, convenience, low cost and time of work are of primary importance, so long as the required accuracy can be maintained.

17. Selection of station positions. In deciding the most suitable positions for stations the following ten points must be borne in mind:

(a) Apply the principle of working from the whole to the part. A simple, main traverse should be set out to a high degree of accuracy to provide control points dispersed around the site. Subsidiary, intermediate traverses, which need not be so accurate, can then be run between these points for picking up additional detail.

(b) The stations should be positioned in such a way that as few as possible are needed, but this must not result in any loss of accuracy or omission of detail.

(c) Sights should be as long as possible with all traverse legs of about the same length to prevent inaccuracies of angular measurement.

(d) Sight lines should not pass too close to the ground as inaccuracies in the angular measurements can arise owing to shimmer and lateral refraction, particularly in hot weather.

(e) The ground around stations must be stable to prevent movement of the theodolite. Thick, matted grass must be removed or avoided, and marshy ground is also unsuitable.

(f) The stations should be positioned so that the lines run close to the features to be surveyed by offsetting.

(g) As far as possible lines should be free of natural obstructions and pedestrian and vehicular traffic. Stations should be clearly intervisible, preferably with the actual marks on the ground (see **21** (b)).

(h) Stations should not be placed where the theodolite is liable to be damaged or where observations could be delayed by traffic or disturbed by the vibration of heavy vehicles and trains.

(i) Stations should be positioned so that they can easily survey important detail by means of bearings and distances, i.e. polars, from individual traverse stations.

(j) Always consider the possibility of surveying a remote feature or station by observing its bearing from at least three of the traverse stations as this can save the time and labour of direct measurement. Also cross bearings to other traverse stations will help to localise any angular errors which may arise (*see* **23** (*c*)).

18. Marking stations. The station positions are decided on, after consideration of the ten points listed above, allowing such weight to each factor as the particular problems of the site demand. Stations are then marked and witnessed as described in II, **30**, although, in practice, on smaller surveys where a single surveyor only is involved the witnessing is often omitted. For practical examination tasks, however, witnessing of stations ought to be included.

19. The survey. Traverse angles are then observed in sequence and booked as illustrated in **8, 9** or **10**. Angles of slope are measured to reduce the taped distances to the horizontal or, if levelling is to take place, then the $h^2/2l$ formula can be used instead (*see* II, **9**). Lines may be measured before proceeding to observe the angles at the next station or they may be left until all the angular observations of the traverse have been made. Linear measurements are made as described in II, **33**, and the offsetting procedure, if any, is the same as for chain surveying.

20. Sources of error. When traversing, errors may arise in the two following kinds of measurement:

(*a*) *Linear measurements.* Errors in linear measurements have already been dealt with in detail in II, **11**. They apply equally of course to the measurement of the traverse lines.

(*b*) *Angular measurements.* There are two main sources of error in the measurement of the traverse angles:

    (*i*) *Observational* errors.
    (*ii*) *Instrumental* errors.

21. Precautions against observational errors.

(*a*) Owing to lateral refraction, haze and wind, the line of sight may not be truly straight, even though the signal has been properly bisected in the field of view. It is therefore important *to keep the line of sight 1 m above ground on hot, sunny days. In wind and haze suspend any attempt at accurate readings.*

(b) If the signal is too large it is not possible to bisect accurately, and if the signal is not plumbed vertically above the station mark the wrong direction will be observed. For these reasons *try and always observe directly on to the station mark. If this is not possible sight to a plumb-bob or accurately plumbed target or signal; never sight to a hand-held ranging rod.*

(c) Errors can arise in misreading and misbooking observations of the vernier or micrometer, so always *check that the reading booked appears on the instrument.*

22. Precautions against instrumental errors.

(a) Errors in the adjustment of the theodolite have been considered in VI, 26. For the reasons given there, *always observe on both faces of the theodolite when measuring horizontal and vertical angles.*

(b) The theodolite must be properly levelled before observations are made and so *ensure that the plate bubble remains in the same position in its tube when the theodolite is rotated through* 360°.

(c) *Ensure that the theodolite tripod is stable* with the legs firmly planted in solid ground and that the tripod adjusting screws are properly tightened.

(d) *The theodolite must be properly centred over the station mark with an optical plummet or plumbing rod,* or otherwise angles will not be measured at the point to which the sighting was taken from the previous station. If a plumb-bob is being used, it must be shielded from the wind. An error in centring of only 5 mm can produce an error in the angle of 1' 9" where the sights are 30 m long.

(e) If the horizontal circle is moved between observations the reduced angles will be in error. This can occur for any of the following reasons:

(i) Screwing the theodolite too loosely to the tripod head.
(ii) Omitting to secure the movable head.
(iii) Omitting to clamp the lower plate.
(iv) Using the lower tangent screw instead of the upper tangent screw.
(v) Moving the orientation screw on single-axis theodolites.

It is therefore important to *complete each round of observations on each face by closing back to the initial point sighted and compare the first and last readings* (see 9).

23. Field checks on closed traverses. In order that any errors may be located before leaving the site it is advisable for the following checks to be made in the field:

(*a*) *Summation of angles.* In a traverse forming a closed figure the angles should be reduced and summed. If internal angles are reduced their sum should equal $(2n - 4)$ right-angles, where $n =$ the number of traverse stations, and if external angles are reduced their sum should equal $(2n + 4)$ right-angles. A small difference due to minor observational errors is to be expected. A large difference will indicate a gross error which must be located and the incorrect angle must be re-observed before leaving the site.

(*b*) *Comparison of bearings.* In closed traverses where bearings have been carried through, a comparison with the final observed bearing and the true bearing should be made to detect any gross error which may have occurred.

(*c*) *Cross bearings.* In order to localise any gross angular error, which may be shown up by the above checks, it is always advisable to observe cross bearings to other visible traverse stations (*see* **17** (*j*)).

(*d*) *Linear errors.* Any errors in the measurement of the traverse legs will show up later in the calculations. Traverse legs are sometimes taped twice in the field to locate any gross errors prior to calculation.

24. Field checks on open traverses. In an unclosed traverse field checks may be obtained by observing to other stations on the traverse or by observing to prominent points to the side of the traverse line.

With reference to Fig. 55, the following points should be noted:

(*a*) If the direction of AD is observed from A as well as its reverse direction, or *backsight DA*, from D, a check will be provided on the angular work between A, B, C and D.

(*b*) If X is observed from both A and D, its position can be calculated from the triangle ADX. Then bearings FX, GX, etc., can be calculated and checked against the observed bearings.

(*c*) Graphically, once X is plotted, then all bearings from any point on the traverse should intersect at this point.

These intersections can also be computed to show the extent of any error.

(*d*) Gross irregularities in the measured distances will also be shown up in the graphical or calculated plot of *X*, but as the traverse is unclosed there are no absolute terms against which adjustments can be made as in a closed traverse.

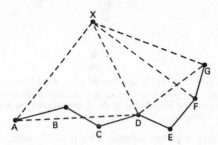

Fig. 55.—*Method of checking an open traverse*

This is achieved by observing to a common point *X* from several stations along the traverse.

25. Field problems. Problems sometimes arise in the application of the basic field-work methods, and suitable methods of overcoming difficulties and obstructions must be devised, depending on the peculiarities of individual sites. However, problems often arise in the following situations:

    (*a*) *When a short traverse leg* is necessary (*see* **26**).
    (*b*) *When checking isolated points* (*see* **27**).
    (*c*) *When centring errors accumulate* in precise work (*see* **28**).

26. Short traverse legs. The insertion of a short leg in a traverse should be avoided (*see* **17** (*c*)), but if this is not possible the short leg should form part of the sight to a more distant point and the forward angle should be measured in each case.

In Fig. 56 the angle at *B* is obtained by observing to *A* and "Far," a distant point. Station C is placed on the straight line *B*–Far, and is accurately aligned with the theodolite. At *C* the angle Far–*CD* is measured and angle *BCD* deduced and used in carrying forward the bearings with the same degree of accuracy as before. Angle *BCD* should also be measured and compared with the deduced value of the angle to ensure that no gross errors exist, but, owing to the short length of the sight *BC*, it is too inaccurate to be used in the calculations.

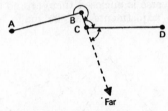

FIG. 56.—*Bearing measurement of a short traverse line*

The method of overcoming the inaccuracies of measuring the angles at *B* and *C* when the length *BC* is short in comparison with the other traverse lines is shown.

27. Checking isolated points. The co-ordinates of a feature may be calculated from its observed bearing and distance from a co-ordinated traverse station. To confirm the correctness of

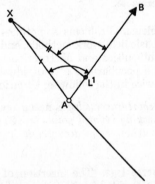

FIG. 57.—*Checking a point from a line station*

The method of ensuring a complete check on the calculated co-ordinates of point *X* is shown.

the calculated co-ordinates of the point, they should be calculated again from the observed bearing and distance from another co-ordinated traverse station. The two co-ordinates may differ slightly owing to minor observational errors, but the two results are meaned to give final checked co-ordinates of the point.

Where no other traverse station is sufficiently close, a *line point* may be established, as indicated in Fig. 57, and the second bearing and distance are observed from there. It should be noted that the triangle of lines thus formed does *not* have to be well conditioned, because at A angle XAB is measured and at $L1$, the line point, angle $XL1B$ is measured, a similar construction to that illustrated in 26 above. The co-ordinates of X are thus again obtained twice from two independently measured bearings and distances.

28. Centring errors. A series of very short traverse legs is often unavoidable, particularly in mines and tunnels. In these cases it is necessary for centring errors of the theodolite over or under the station mark to be kept to a minimum. Also, in precise traversing centring errors can have an appreciable effect on bearings. They can be almost entirely eliminated by the use of special traversing equipment consisting of three or more tripods with targets interchangeable with the theodolite. Once the rounds or arcs of angular observations at a station have been completed, the theodolite is removed without disturbing the levelling head attached to the tripod. A special target then takes the precise position of the theodolite while the theodolite is moved forward and placed on the undisturbed tripod head of the forward station which previously held a target. A new forward station, consisting of a tripod and target with an optical plummet, is again set up ahead. In this way the theodolite is set up precisely over the mark to which observations were made and the centring error is almost entirely eliminated from the readings.

CALCULATIONS AND PLOTTING

29. The traverse calculation. Traverses may be plotted directly from the observed bearings and distances in the way that compass traverses are usually plotted (*see* III). However, to maintain a required degree of accuracy and to enable other calculations to be made, the co-ordinates of the traverse stations are usually computed and adjusted.

There is only one basic method of computation, but the layout of the calculations may differ according to personal preferences. The traverse calculation opposite shows a simple

Line	Length (m)	Observed angle (° ′ ″)	Whole circle bearing (° ′ ″)	Reduced bearing (° ′ ″)	Log ΔE / Log.sin / Log.l / Log.cos / Log ΔN	ΔE (depts.) +E / −W	ΔN (lats.) +N / −S	Station	Co-ordinates (m) E / N
								A	500·00 / 500·00
A B	76·28	76 28 10 / −10 / 76 28 00	136 28 00	S 43 32 00 E	1·720 49 / 9·838 08 / 1·882 41 / 9·860 32 / 1·742 73	+E 52·54 (0·02)	−S 55·30 (0·01)		+52·56 / −55·31
								B	552·56 / 444·69
B C	38·07	30 53 10 / −10 / 30 53 00	347 21 00	N 12 39 00 W	0·921 01 / 9·340 43 / 1·580 58 / 9·989 33 / 1·569 91	−W 8·34	+N 37·15		−8·33 / +37·15
								C	544·23 / 481·84
C D	42·53	269 12 50 / −10 / 269 12 40	76 33 40	N 76 33 40 E	1·616 64 / 9·987 94 / 1·628 70 / 9·366 25 / 0·994 95	+E 41·37 (0·01)	+N 9·88		+41·38 / +9·88
								D	585·61 / 491·72
D E	51·36	60 16 50 / −10 / 60 16 40	316 50 20	N 43 09 40 W	1·545 71 / 9·835 09 / 1·710 62 / 9·862 99 / 1·573 61	−W 35·13 (0·01)	+N 37·46		−35·12 / +37·45
								E	550·49 / 529·17
E A	58·32	103 09 50 / −10 / 103 09 40	240 00 00	S 60 00 00 W	1·703 35 / 9·937 53 / 1·765 82 / 9·698 97 / 1·464 79	−W 50·51	−S 29·16 (0·01)		−50·49 / −29·17
								A	500·00 / 500·00
Sum =	266·56	540 00 50 / −50 / 540 00 00 (sh/be)				+E 93·91 / −W 93·98	+N 84·49 / −S 84·46		

Sum = 93·98 / 93·91   84·49 / 84·46
sh/be =
Corrns = −0·07 / +0·03
0·00 / 0·00
+0·07 / −0·03

layout using logarithms. Details of this calculation are explained in the following paragraphs (30–44). Reference should also be made to Fig. 54 (*a*), which illustrates the layout of the traverse.

30. Measured lines. The length of each traverse line named in the first column is corrected for slope, etc., in the field book or on a separate sheet, if more convenient, which is then filed for reference. The final horizontal distances are then recorded in the second column. Their sum, being the total distance traversed (266·56 m), is recorded at the bottom of the column as shown.

31. Observed angles. The observed angles are first reduced (*see* **8** (*vi*) and (*viii*)) and then extracted from the field book and recorded in column 3. They are then summed and an equal correction is applied to each angle so that the sum of the corrected angles = $(2n - 4) \times 90°$, or $(2n + 4) \times 90°$ if exterior angles are reduced.

NOTE: This observed angle column will be omitted if bearings are carried through the traverse (*see* **10**) instead of the angles being measured. It is sometimes omitted anyway, these calculations being part of the rough calculations, but this is undesirable as it is then more difficult to locate any errors that may occur.

32. Whole circle bearings. The whole circle bearings are next computed as below, using a known or adopted initial bearing (a bearing of 136° 28′ 00″ has arbitrarily been adopted for the line *AB*):

AB	136° 28′ 00″	*DC*	256° 33′ 40″
BA	316° 28′ 00″	∠*D*	60° 16′ 40″
∠*B*	30° 53′ 00″	*DE*	316° 50′ 20″ —
BC	347° 21′ 00″ —	*ED*	136° 50′ 20″
CB	167° 21′ 00″	∠*E*	103° 09′ 40″
∠*C*	269° 12′ 40″	*EA*	240° 00′ 00″ —
CD	436° 33′ 40″	*AE*	60° 00′ 00″
	−360° 00′ 00″	∠*A*	76° 28′ 00″
CD	76° 33′ 40″ —	*AB*	136° 28′ 00″ (*check*)

NOTE

(*i*) These bearings which have now been carried forward through the traverse are recorded in the fourth column of the tabulation.

   (*ii*) After using the four angles *B*, *C*, *D* and *E* all bearings are
       computed, but the fifth angle *A* must be used as well in
       order to provide a check by calculating again the bearing
       of *AB*, as shown.
  (*iii*) The above reduction works on the same principle as the
       plotting of compass bearings explained in III, **21**.

33. Reduced bearings. The reduced bearings column is
introduced simply to make it easier to look up the logarithms
of the sines and cosines of the whole circle bearings, as described
in IV, **10**. It also makes it simpler to apply the signs correctly
to the calculated differences in eastings and northings. In
more advanced work this column is omitted.

34. Logarithm calculations. The layout of the logarithms
in the table should be noted. The logarithm distance is only
written down once (*see* IV, **12**). These calculations may be
included as part of the rough work if numerous, untidy amend-
ments are likely to arise. The logarithms must, however, be
recorded as shown to indicate that the calculations have been
carried out correctly and to help locate errors in examination
of the work.

    NOTE: Five-figure logarithms are only adequate for calcula-
tions in ordinary traversing where bearings are known to the
nearest 10″ and distances are known to 10 mm. In precise
traversing and for work to a single second of arc and three
decimal places of a metre, seven-figure logarithms are used.

35. Differences in eastings and northings. The columns of
△E's and △N's are divided into two to facilitate the application of sign and the algebraic summation, which appears
at the bottom of each column.

    NOTE: ∆E is the equivalent of the term *departure* and ∆N is
the equivalent of the term *latitude*. If these terms had been
used the columns would have been interchanged because latitudes are recorded before departures. Common practice today
seems to favour the use of eastings and northings, as shown in
this computation.

36. Adjustment of error. The *closing error* in the △E's is
shown to be −0·07. The difference between the two columns
should have been zero as the traverse started and finished on
the same point; *i.e.* the total movement in an easterly direction

should be nil because the traverse ends where it started. A *correction* of +0·07 must therefore be applied so that the sum of the △E's is in fact zero. Similarly the closing error in the △N's is +0·03 and the necessary correction to obtain the zero sum in the same way as for the △E's must be −0·03.

Each of these corrections must be applied proportionally to each △E and △N. There are several ways of achieving this, but the two main ways are by using either one of the following methods:

    (*a*) *The Bowditch adjustment* (*see* **37**).
    (*b*) *The transit rule* (*see* **38**).

37. The Bowditch adjustment. This is the method which has been used in the table, where the correction is distributed proportionally to the lengths of the traverse legs.

    (*a*) *Adjustment of differences in eastings.* It can be argued that the error of 0·07 occurred over the total distance of 266·56 traversed. Therefore the proportion of 0·07 attributed to the first leg *AB* must be:

$$\frac{76\cdot28}{266\cdot56} \text{ of } 0\cdot07 = 0\cdot02$$

and so on for each leg. Where the error to be distributed is small this calculation may be simplified thus:

$$\frac{8}{27} \text{ of } 0\cdot07 = 0\cdot02$$

and can be quickly carried out by slide-rule.

As the total error of 0·07 is being distributed, the sum of the individual corrections must equal 0·07 too. Since it is necessary to round off to two places of decimals it may be found that the sum does not precisely add up to the total. The rounding off must then be taken either up or down so that the *sum* of the final individual corrections is the same as the *total correction*, but of the opposite sign as the *total error*.

    (*b*) *Adjustment of differences in northings.* The △N corrections are obtained in exactly the same way as for the △E's. For example, the correction for the line *DE* is:

$$\frac{51\cdot36}{266\cdot56} \text{ of } (-0\cdot03) = -0\cdot006$$

or, simplified and rounded off:

$$\frac{5}{27} \text{ of } (-0.03) = -0.01$$

38. The transit rule. In this method the error is distributed in proportion to the length of the co-ordinate differences instead of in proportion to the length of the traverse lines.

$$\text{Correction to } \triangle E \text{ of a line} = \frac{\triangle E \text{ of the line}}{\text{Sum of } \triangle E\text{'s}} \times \text{Total error in } \triangle E\text{'s.}$$

$$\text{Correction to } \triangle N \text{ of a line} = \frac{\triangle N \text{ of the line}}{\text{Sum of } \triangle N\text{'s}} \times \text{Total error in } \triangle N\text{'s.}$$

NOTE: This method has the advantage that the bearings are altered to a lesser degree than in the Bowditch method, but there is no theoretical foundation for this rule. Its use is mainly confined to those traverses in which the accuracy of the angular measurements is very much greater than the accuracy of the linear measurements.

39. Accuracy. The accuracy of the traverse is based upon the angular and linear misclosure.

Closing error of the $\triangle E$'s = -0.07.
Closing error of the $\triangle N$'s = $+0.03$.
Therefore, by Pythagoras, the closing error of the traverse itself = $\sqrt{(-0.07)^2 + (0.03)^2}$
    = $\sqrt{0.0058}$
    = 0.076

This closing error has occurred over a distance of 266·56 m: therefore:

$$\text{linear misclosure} = \frac{0.076}{266.56}$$
$$= 1/3507$$

NOTE: This is not an absolute indication of accuracy and where a traverse closes back on to itself it is merely an indication of the consistency of measurement.

40. Co-ordinates. The co-ordinates of the traverse stations are obtained by adding the corrected $\triangle E$'s and $\triangle N$'s of each line to the eastings and northings of the previous station. Using the same figures again, arbitrary co-ordinates of

500·00 E and 500·00 N were used for Station A. In adopting a starting co-ordinate for a survey, figures are usually chosen in such a way that all co-ordinates will be positive as this is more convenient, although not absolutely necessary.

The corrections may be applied to the $\triangle$ E's and $\triangle$ N's, the corrected values being recorded in the last two columns in the table. Alternatively they may be applied to the actual co-ordinates obtained first from the unadjusted $\triangle$ E's and $\triangle$ N's. The former method is preferable for three reasons:

(a) Unadjusted co-ordinates are seldom required.

(b) Errors can occur in correcting the co-ordinates, whereas errors in correcting the $\triangle$ E's and $\triangle$ N's would be shown by the non-closure of the final co-ordinates, which must agree exactly with the initial co-ordinates to prove that the corrections have been properly applied.

(c) A single list of corrected co-ordinates prevents confusion when extracting final co-ordinates from the calculations at a later date.

41. Station designation.

The column showing the designation of the survey stations is sometimes placed first as this position helps in indicating the observed angle. This duty is also performed by the first letter of the line designation, here shown in the first column, the angle observed being at the station at the beginning of each line referred to in each case. It is therefore preferable to place the station designation beside the co-ordinates to which they refer as this helps to prevent errors in extracting station co-ordinates from the traverse computation sheet.

42. Final data.

Owing to the adjustments made in the traverse calculations the final co-ordinates do not reflect the actual bearings and distances used to obtain them. If corrected bearings and distances are required they must be calculated from the final adjusted co-ordinates.

43. Adjustment between two co-ordinated stations.

The traverse taken as an example closes back on to its starting point at A; because of this the sum of its $\triangle$ E's and $\triangle$ N's should each be zero as has been shown. Had the traverse instead closed on to another co-ordinated point then the sum of its calculated

$\triangle E$'s and $\triangle N$'s should respectively equal the known $\triangle E$ and $\triangle N$ between the two co-ordinated stations. If they do not they must be adjusted proportionally as before so that they do finally equal these known differences in eastings and northings.

44. Adjustment of bearings. If bearings are carried forward before the angular corrections are made, then the final bearing obtained from the observations is not likely to agree precisely with the final known bearing. If the difference is large a gross

(1) ° ′ ″	(2)	(3)	(4)	(5) E	(6) N
					(metres)
				A 500·00	500·00
136 28 00					
00					
136 28 00	688 776	+52·54	−55·30	+52·56	−55·31
76·28	724 974	+ *0·02*	− *0·01*		
				B 552·56	444·69
347 21 10					
−10					
347 21 00	218 995	− 8·34	+37·15	−8·33	+37·15
38·07	975 726	+*0·01*			
				C 544·23	481·84
76 34 00					
−20					
76 33 40	972 618	+41·37	+9·88	+41·38	+9·88
42·53	232 408	+*0·01*			
				D 585·61	491·72
316 50 50					
−30					
316 50 20	684 052	−35·13	+37·46	−35·12	+37·45
51·36	729 433	+*0·01*	−*0·01*		
				E 550·49	529·17
240 00 40					
−40					
240 00 00	866 025	−50·51	−29·16	−50·49	−29·17
58·32	500 000	+*0·02*	−*0·01*		
				A 500·00	500·00
136 28 50				*sh/be 500·00*	*500·00*
−50					
136 28 00	*sh/be*				
266·56	*Sum*	−0·07	+0·03		
	sh/be	*0·00*	*0·00*		
	Error	*−0·07*	*+0·03*		

error exists and must be located. If the difference is small the error will be due to minor observational errors and an equal correction should be applied to each observed angle to eliminate the error from the calculations (*see* **31**). The correction of every angle by an equal amount has the effect of a progressive correction through the bearings. This occurs because the angular correction affects the following and all subsequent bearings by the same amount.

This method of using adjusted bearings instead of adjusted angles can be used in closed figures, as illustrated in the traverse calculation above. Compare this adjustment with the correction method shown in the calculation of the same traverse in the table above. This method of adjusting the bearings must be used in the calculation of a closed traverse which finishes not on its starting point but on a second co-ordinated point.

45. Traverse computation by calculator. The traverse calculation is frequently carried out by means of an electronic calculator using natural sines and cosines instead of logarithms. The computation shows the same traverse as before, but this time it is calculated electronically.

In the first column there are the whole circle bearings as observed by the third method in **10** above and their reduction as explained in **44** above. The horizontal distance is shown recorded below each corrected bearing. The second column contains the natural sine of the whole circle bearing written above its natural cosine. The six-figure naturals shown are adequate for work to single seconds of arc and to one millimetre. The natural sine of 136° 28′ 00″, the bearing of the first line AB, is of course $+0·688\ 766$, but in practice the sign, zero and decimal point are often omitted in this type of calculation as shown, their existence being understood in every case.

The third and fourth columns contain the calculated $\triangle E$'s and $\triangle N$'s respectively, calculated by multiplying the distances in column 1 by the sines and cosines in column 2 on the calculator. The signs of these $\triangle E$'s and $\triangle N$'s, *i.e.* whether they are positive or negative, are obtained by deciding in which quadrant their respective whole circle bearings lie. These positive and negative co-ordinate differences are not separated here into two columns as before because the summation can be made directly on the calculator, negative differences being

applied simply by pressing the appropriate button. The corrections to the calculated $\triangle E$'s and $\triangle N$'s are made exactly as
before (*see* 36).

The last two columns contain the co-ordinates of the traverse
stations obtained from the corrected co-ordinate differences as
before. This part of the calculation should be done arithmeti-
cally and *not* on the calculator as an error could arise in copy-
ing the co-ordinates from the instrument display to the
calculation sheet.

46. Detection of gross errors. Despite taking all the required
precautions it is possible that a gross error will arise in the
traverse observations. Such an erroneous observation must be
re-measured in the field to provide a satisfactory check on the
work. An error can sometimes be found by an examination of
the calculations.

47. Location of a gross angular error. If a gross angular
error occurs in a closed traverse it can sometimes be found in
one of two ways:

(*a*) By plotting or calculating the traverse from each end.
The station which has the same co-ordinate in each case will
be the one at which the angular error occurred.

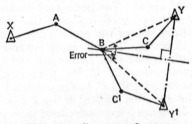

Fig. 58.—*Gross angular error*

Under certain circumstances this may be located by the graphical
procedure shown where such an error has been located at B by the perpendicular bisector of the gross closing error YY'.

(*b*) By plotting the incorrect traverse containing the gross
error as illustrated in Fig. 58. The correct position of the
station on to which the traverse should have closed should
also be plotted. Join these two points, Y and Y', and bisect

this line at right-angles. This line will then intersect the point at which the angular error occurred. This intersection takes place because the figure BYY' is an isosceles triangle formed by the gross error in angular measurement at B, the amount of the error being indicated by the angle formed by YBY'.

48. Location of a gross taping error.

A gross error in the length of any line can sometimes be found by comparing the bearing of the closing error with bearings of the individual traverse legs. If there is only one gross error in taping it will have roughly the same bearing as the line in which the error

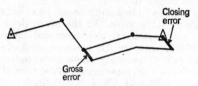

FIG. 59.—*Gross linear error*

Under certain circumstances this may be located by comparing the direction of the gross closing error with the direction of the survey lines. The closing error shown has the same bearing as the second traverse line.

lies (*see* Fig. 59). If two lines have nearly the same bearing then the error may be in either.

NOTE: If more than one gross error exists, in either length or bearing, it will not be possible to find their exact position by the methods outlined above. They may, however, be localised by the field checks described in **23**.

SPECIMEN QUESTION

The following are the calculated co-ordinate differences of a closed traverse in which the bearings have been checked. Establish where the mistake in measurement is likely to have occurred.

Line	ΔE	ΔN
	(*metres*)	
AB	$+120\cdot59$	$-201\cdot62$
BC	$-98\cdot76$	$-220\cdot13$
CD	$+332\cdot67$	$+189\cdot92$
DA	$-371\cdot89$	$+221\cdot93$
	$-17\cdot39$	$-9\cdot90$

SOLUTION

The summation of the ΔE's $= -17\cdot39$ and the summation of the ΔN's $= -9\cdot90$, indicating a gross error of closure because the sums of these co-ordinate differences should in each case be zero as the traverse forms a closed figure.

Dividing $-9\cdot90$ into $-17\cdot39$ results in approximately $+1\cdot7$, which reflects the bearing of the gross closing error. Now look for a ΔN which divides into the corresponding ΔE by about the same amount, *i.e.* a line of similar bearing.

The only pair which provides this result are the ΔE and ΔN of the line CD ($332\cdot67 \div 189\cdot92 = +1\cdot7$), indicating a similar bearing, so the error has probably occurred here.

As the error is substantial it probably arose by omitting to book one chain length of 20 m.

The length of CD will be known or can be calculated from the given co-ordinate differences. In the given data it is $383\cdot07$. This length is now assumed to be in error and if it were increased by 20 m to $403\cdot07$ then its ΔE becomes $+350\cdot04$ and its ΔN becomes $+199\cdot84$. Now using these corrected values for the line CD the sums of the co-ordinated differences of the traverse become $\Delta E = -0\cdot02$ and $\Delta N = +0\cdot02$, indicating an acceptable minor closing error.

NOTE: The error has probably been found by this examination of the calculations, but in practice the line CD must be re-measured on the ground to confirm that it is in fact $403\cdot07$ m long.

49. Omitted dimensions. If any one or two dimensions are omitted from a closed traverse then they can be calculated because the sum of the $\triangle E$'s and the sum of the $\triangle N$'s is known. For example, in a traverse which closes back on to its starting point, if l_1, l_2, ..., etc., are the lengths of each line and a_1, a_2, ..., etc., are the bearings of those lines, then:

$$l_1 \sin a_1 + l_2 \sin a_2 + l_3 \sin a_3 + \ldots = 0$$
$$l_1 \cos a_1 + l_2 \cos a_2 + l_3 \cos a_3 + \ldots = 0$$

Therefore, as there are two equations, it is possible to solve one or two of the unknowns as follows:

(a) Bearing of one line.
(b) Bearings of any two lines.
(c) Length of one line.
(d) Lengths of any two lines.

(e) Length and bearing of one line.

(f) Length of one line and bearing of another.

NOTE: The calculation of these unknowns has little practical value as the assumption must be made that no error exists in the known dimensions. A closed traverse with omitted dimensions cannot be adjusted and is really a form of unclosed traverse, which is normally avoided in practice. The calculation of omitted dimensions is therefore generally of academic interest only and more advanced textbooks should be referred to if explicit calculation details are required.

50. Plotting the survey. The traverse survey may be plotted as follows:

(a) *Grid*. A rectangular co-ordinate grid is drawn up as described in IV, **17**, and all co-ordinated points are plotted and checked by scaling for any plotting errors.

(b) *Traverse network*. The traverse lines are then drawn between the plotted stations. Their lengths are scaled and checked against their known dimensions.

(c) *Detail*. Detail is then plotted in pencil by means of offsets from the network of traverse lines exactly as in chain surveying (*see* II). In addition, points may be located by means of scaled bearings and distances from survey stations, their plotted positions being checked by scaled dimensions to other points and being compared with the actual measurements taken in the field between these points.

51. Fair drawing. Once all the features have been plotted and checked the final fair drawing can be prepared in one of the following ways:

(a) *For presentation purposes or practical examinations.* The plotted survey is completed in coloured waterproof inks on medium, hand-made paper and the title, scale, north point and all relevant notes are added. The traverse lines are ruled in red and the stations are marked with red circles or triangles. Finally the drawing is finished off with a colour washed border of green, 4 mm wide, around the inside of the site boundary.

(b) *For commercial or professional purposes.* The fair drawing is usually traced in black ink only on a transparent sheet of drawing plastic which is only subject to a very slight degree of distortion caused by humidity and temperature changes. From this transparency copy prints may be obtained easily and cheaply, although, because of the distortion, they cannot be used for accurate scaling.

An example of a traverse site plan is shown in Appendix V. The traverse lines are not usually ruled in on such a drawing as they may be confused with other detail. Occasionally a small-scale inset is included on the plan to illustrate the traverse layout and data.

PROGRESS TEST 9

1. What is the difference between "open" and "closed" traverses?   (1–2)

2. What are the two main purposes for which traverses are used?   (3)

3. State four advantages which traverse surveying has over chain surveying.   (4)

4. In what ways may the length and bearing of traverse lines be measured?   (5)

5. What are the two observational procedures usually used in traverse angular measurement and why are they adopted?   (6)

6. Illustrate with sets of assumed readings three ways of booking traverse theodolite observations.   (7–10)

7. State the difference between an "ordinary" traverse and a "precise" traverse and give three cases where each is likely to be used.   (11–13)

8. What personnel and equipment would be needed in order to undertake the traverse survey of a site about 1 ha in extent? (14–15)

9. What are the main considerations to be borne in mind while undertaking the reconnaissance for a traverse survey?   (16–17)

10. State the eight precautions to be observed against making errors in traversing.   (21–22)

11. What are the field checks it is usual to make while conducting a closed traverse survey?   (23)

12. How would you proceed to check an open traverse?   (24)

13. Describe a method of obtaining the bearing of a short traverse leg without loss of accuracy.   (26)

14. How are the co-ordinates of isolated points verified?   (27)

15. In what way and under what conditions are centring errors eliminated as far as possible?   (28)

*16. The following data were obtained in surveying the traverse illustrated in Fig. 54(c):

	Observed angles	*Distances in metres reduced to horizontal*
$T2$	131° 25′ 20″	$T2 . A$ 147·65
A	138° 37′ 00″	$A . B$ 139·10
B	147° 43′ 20″	$B . C$ 111·57
C	261° 21′ 40″	$C . T3$ 121·33
$T3$	259° 33′ 00″	

The co-ordinates of $T2$ and $T3$ in metres are:

$$T2: 405·15 \text{ E}; 351·00 \text{ N}$$
$$T3: 847·86 \text{ E}; 335·00 \text{ N}$$

and the known bearings are:

$$T2 - T1 = 345° 00′ 00″$$
$$T3 - T4 = 203° 42′ 00″$$

Calculate the final adjusted co-ordinates of stations A, B and C using the Bowditch adjustment. **(29–44)**

*17. What is the linear misclosure of the traverse observations as shown by the calculation of question 16? **(39)**

*18. The following are the reduced measurements of a closed traverse $ABCDA$. It is suspected that a gross error was made in the angular observations. Locate the station at which this error probably occurred.

Line	Length (m)	Whole circle bearing
AB	156·20	199° 21′ 00″
BC	140·50	142° 48′ 00″
CD	150·00	28° 34′ 30″
DA	116·50	330° 22′ 40″

(46–47)

*19. The following is an extract from the traverse calculations between two fixed points P and Q:

Line	Length	ΔE	ΔN
PA	86·19	−1·84 m	+86·17 m
AB	69·08	−61·52 m	−31·41 m
BC	145·40	−47·50 m	+137·42 m
CQ	82·24	−79·85 m	−19·68 m

The known correct differences in eastings and northings between stations P and Q are respectively −164·02 and +186·15. A gross error in taping is suspected. Locate the line in which it has probably occurred. What is its amount likely to be? **(48)**

20. Describe how you would plot and prepare the plan of a traverse survey. **(50–51)**

CHAPTER X

LEVELLING

PRINCIPLES AND DEFINITIONS

1. Definition of levelling. Levelling is the process of measuring the difference in height between points on the surface of the earth.

2. A level surface or a level line. This is a surface or line, all points of which are normal or at right-angles to the pull of gravity as shown by a plumb-line. The surface of a still lake is an example of a level surface, which tends to follow the curve of the earth's surface.

3. A horizontal surface or a horizontal line. This is a plane, flat surface or straight line which passes through a point at right-angles to the pull of gravity *at that point*. It is therefore a tangent to the curve of a level surface.

4. A datum surface. This is any level surface to which the elevations of points may be referred. The surface most commonly adopted as a datum is the mean level of the sea. As the mean or average level of the sea varies at different places, because of the effect of winds, currents and tides, the mean level at one place is adopted as a datum surface and is called the *mean sea level* (M.S.L.).

(*a*) *Liverpool datum.* This is the obsolete datum of levelling in Great Britain based on a fortnight's observation of the sea level in 1844. This datum was later discarded as the point of measurement on a tidal river was inaccurate, but plans still exist with levels referring to this datum.

(*b*) *Newlyn datum.* This is the present datum of the Ordnance Survey levelling of Great Britain, sometimes called the *Ordnance datum* (O.D.). It is the mean level of the open sea at Newlyn in Cornwall as computed from hourly observations taken over a period of six years, 1915–21.

5. A reduced level. The reduced level of a point is its height or elevation above the surface adopted as a datum.

6. Bench-marks. Bench-marks are stable reference points, the reduced levels of which are accurately determined by spirit levelling. There are two main types of bench-mark:

(a) *Temporary bench-marks* (*T.B.M.s*). These are stable points, but of a less permanent nature, established close to the site of a survey to save continual reference to a bench-mark (B.M.), which may be some distance away.

(b) *Ordnance bench-marks* (*O.B.M.s*). In Great Britain bench-marks are established by the Ordnance Survey, the most common form being a horizontal line cut in brickwork or masonry with the government's broad arrow cut below it. The reduced level always refers to the *middle* of the horizontal line. There are three other kinds of Ordnance bench-mark:

(i) *Fundamental bench-marks*. These form part of the main levelling network and consist of 225-mm square granite or concrete pillars built into rock or chalk with a metal bolt set on top.

(ii) *Flush brackets*. These are metal plates cemented into the face of buildings. The reduced level refers to the small platform at the *point* of the broad arrow mark.

(iii) *Bench-marks on horizontal surfaces*. These occur less frequently and consist of *bolt* bench-marks, *rivet* bench-marks and *pivot* bench-marks. The pivot bench-mark consists of a hollow cut to contain a 15-mm diameter ball-bearing as a pivot support for the staff.

The reduced levels of Ordnance Survey bench-marks are expressed in feet *above the ordnance datum* (A.O.D.). On Ordnance Survey plans and in the bench-mark lists published by the Ordnance Survey reference is made to the datum used, being either Newlyn or Liverpool.

These reduced levels will eventually be expressed in metres to two decimal places, but for the time being the recorded values in feet will need to be converted to metres by multiplying by 0·3048.

7. Difference of level between two points. In order to find this it is necessary to establish a level surface above or below the two points and to measure the vertical distance from it to the points. The difference between these measurements will give the difference in level between the points (*see* Fig. 60).

It is impossible to establish this curved level surface so a horizontal surface is used instead. This horizontal surface is obtained from the line of sight of a telescope adjusted into the horizontal position. This is done by using an instrument known as a *level*. The difference between the level surface and the horizontal surface is negligible over normal sighting distances, which are usually less than 100 m.

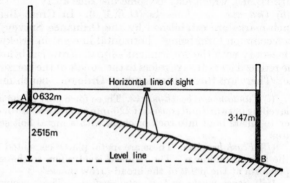

FIG. 60.—*The difference in level between two points*

This is shown to be 2·515 m, the difference between the two staff readings of 3·147 m and 0·632 m.

In Fig. 60 it can be seen that the length down from the horizontal surface to *A* is 0·632 m and from the same surface down to *B* it is 3·147 m. The difference in level between the two points is therefore 3·147 − 0·632 = 2·515 m.

8. Levelling staffs. The vertical distance above or below the horizontal surface is read off a *levelling staff*. These may be either *telescopic* or *folding*, extending to a length usually of 4 m, and graduated to be easily read in the field of view of the level telescope.

The Sopwith staff is a levelling staff with a form of graduation into feet, and tenths and hundredths of feet, which was very common before metrication. Levelling staffs are now gradu- ated in metres, and tenths and hundredths of metres, as illustrated in Fig. 61, although several other forms of metric graduation exist, all designed to increase the ease and accuracy of reading.

Staffs must be held *vertical* as any leaning of the staff will result in a level reading which is too great. By holding the staff lightly between the palms of both hands on either side, it can be made to hang plumb before being placed gently

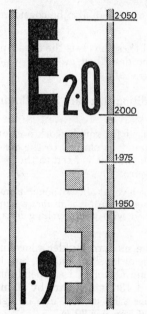

FIG. 61.—*The British Standards metric staff*

This is graduated in 10-mm divisions. Odd-numbered graduations are in red and evens in black. The staff face is either white or yellow.

on the ground or mark. Some staffs have fitted circular bubbles to ensure verticality. Another type of staff level consists of a circular bubble fitted on top of a metal angle plate, which is held against the edge of the staff while in use.

9. Changeplates. Changeplates, sometimes called *brads* or *baseplates*, are triangular metal plates with the corners turned down and a domed stud in the centre and are generally attached to a length of carrying chain. When placed on soft ground and stamped firm the central dome provides a stable point on which to hold the staff.

LEVELS

10. Main types of surveyor's level. There are three basic types of level in common use:

(a) *Dumpy levels* (*see* **13**).

(b) *Tilting levels*, of which the *quickset* and *precise level* are particular kinds (*see* **14–16**).

(c) *Automatic levels*, some of which can also be considered as precise levels (*see* **17**).

The common factor between all these levels is the telescope, similar to the theodolite telescope described in VI, **2**, which when levelled defines a horizontal line of sight.

11. Other types of level. In addition there are the following levels:

(a) *Hand levels*. These are used for rough work and exploratory surveys. This instrument is similar to the *abney level* (*see* II, **10**), except that the bubble is fixed to the level tube and there is no graduated arc.

NOTE: The abney level is *not* a level at all. Although it may be used as a hand level when set to zero, it is in fact a *clinometer* and must not be confused with true levelling instruments.

(b) *The Cowley level*. This is a modern builder's levelling instrument. It has no telescope or levelling bubble, but, by means of reflecting mirrors, one attached to a pendulum contained in a metal case about 130 mm square by 50 mm thick, the instrument furnishes a horizontal line of sight claimed to be accurate within 6 mm per 30 m.

12. The bubble tube. On most levels a spirit level is attached to the telescope and adjusted so that when the bubble is central in the tube the line of sight of the telescope is horizontal. This gives rise to the term *spirit levelling*. Level bubbles are the same as those on theodolites described in VI, **1** (*d*).

(a) *The coincidence bubble reader*. Increased accuracy in setting the bubble is obtained with a coincidence bubble reader or *split bubble*, illustrated in Fig. 62. The arrangement of prisms reflects an image of both ends of the bubble and in the bubble eyepiece one half of each end of the bubble is seen next to the other half. As the telescope is tilted the two halves seem to move in opposite directions. Centring is achieved by bringing the two ends together into coincidence. This doubles the actual bubble movement, doubling the sensitivity. By magnification of the images sensitivity is increased even more, yet the real bubble sensitivity may be quite low. This increases the speed of setting and stability

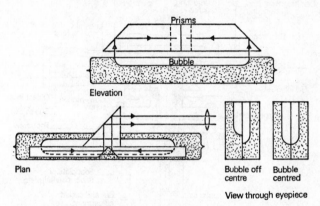

FIG. 62.—*The coincidence bubble reader*

The two ends of the same bubble are brought into one field of view by reflective prisms.

of the bubble without loss of accuracy. In some instruments, such as the Watts precise level and the Kern GK 3, the image of the split bubble can be seen in the field of view of the telescope itself.

(*b*) *Circular bubbles*. These are fitted on many levels for approximate levelling only as their accuracy of setting is not normally so great.

13. The dumpy level. Figure 63 is a diagrammatic sketch of a dumpy level. The bubble tube is mounted on the left-hand side of the telescope. The instrument is levelled by means of three footscrews separating two plates. The telescope is mounted on a vertical spindle in the upper plate and the lower plate screws directly on to the tripod head. The two plates and their connecting levelling screws or footscrews are known as the *levelling head*.

The *essential* difference between the dumpy level and other types is that the telescope is rigidly attached to the vertical spindle.

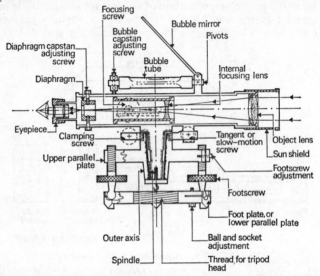

FIG. 63.—*Diagrammatic sketch of a dumpy level*

14. The tilting level. In this level (*see* Fig. 64) the telescope is not fixed rigidly to the vertical spindle but is capable of a slight tilt in the vertical plane about a point just below the telescope. The vertical movement of the telescope is made by rotating a *tilting screw* below the eyepiece. If the tilting screw is graduated this level is then termed a *gradienter* as the line of sight can be set to a known gradient and not just horizontally. *Two bubbles* are fitted to tilting levels; one, a *circular* bubble on the upper plate, is designed for approximate levelling by means of the three-footscrew levelling head, and the other, a *telescope* bubble, usually a split bubble in the more accurate instruments, is levelled for every sighting by the tilting screw only.

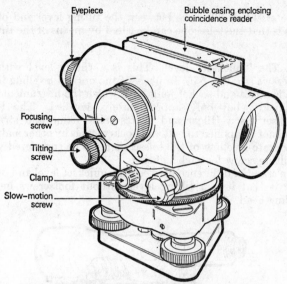

Eyepiece

Bubble casing enclosing
coincidence reader

Focusing
screw

Tilting
screw

Clamp

Slow-motion
screw

Fig. 64.—*Watts Microptic tilting level SL 80*

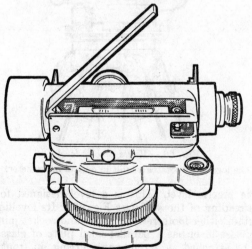

Fig. 65.—*Watts Microptic Quickset level SL 10*

The *essential* difference between the tilting level and other types is that the telescope can be tilted by means of the tilting screw.

15. The "quickset" level. This is a tilting level without footscrews (*see* Fig. 65). In place of the normal levelling head there is a ball-and-socket joint with which the instrument can be quickly, but only approximately, levelled. The term "quickset" is a Hilger and Watts trade name and strictly should not be applied to ball-and-socket levels by other makers.

Accurate levelling of the telescope must be completed with the tilting screw for each sighting.

The *essential* difference between the quickset level and other types is that it is a tilting level without footscrews in the levelling head.

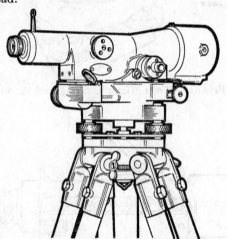

Fig. 66.—*Watts precise level*

The level incorporates a built-in optical micrometer.

16. The precise level. This is a level designed for more accurate reading of the staff (*see* Fig. 66). Its levelling head may contain either footscrews or a ball-and-socket joint.

The precise level has a parallel-sided plate of glass, either built in or attached as a removable fitting, in front of the object lens. A slight rotation of this glass plate moves the line of sight in a vertical plane because of refraction through the glass. The line of sight can therefore be shifted on to a precise staff graduation and the amount of shift required to do this is read off the micrometer drum which rotates the glass plate. The staff reading is therefore obtained, not by estimation between staff graduations only but by a measure on the micrometer drum of the distance from the whole graduation to the point of intersection on the staff that would have occurred had the horizontal line of sight not been shifted. The optical micrometer may also be fitted on automatic levels to increase the accuracy of reading the staff.

The *geodetic level* is a very accurate, precise, tilting level with a very sensitive split bubble and a high-powered telescope. Automatic levels cannot achieve the precision of these instruments. They are used with precisely graduated invar staffs.

The *essential* difference between a precise level and other types is that it is fitted with an optical micrometer for precise reading of the staff.

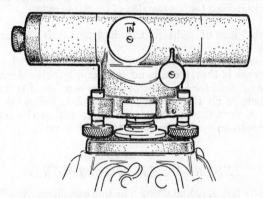

Fig. 67.—*Watts Autoset level 2*

This requires no bubble to establish a horizontal line of sight.

17. The automatic level. This is a level, the levelling head of which may again contain either footscrews or a ball-and-socket joint (*see* Fig. 67 and Plate 6). (Plate 6 is reproduced by courtesy of Survey and General Instrument Company Ltd.) However, the level also automatically gives a horizontal line of sight without a bubble having to be accurately set.

The line of sight is always horizontal once the instrument has been approximately levelled, allowing either suspended mirrors or prisms attached to a pendulum to control the light rays through the telescope.

The automatic level made by Hilger and Watts is called the *Autoset*, a name frequently applied to all levels of similar type. The system of prisms which automatically stabilises the

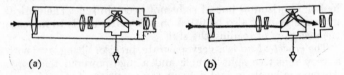

(a)   (b)

FIG. 68.—*The principle of the automatic stabiliser*

(a) The path of the horizontal line of sight passing through the instrument with the telescope horizontal.

(b) The path of the same light ray passing through the instrument with the telescope slightly tilted, the pendulum effect of the two lower prisms maintaining the horizontality of the line of sight.

horizontal line of sight in this instrument is illustrated in Fig. 68.

The *essential* difference between the automatic level and other types is that there is no telescope bubble. As a result there is no need for the telescope to be capable of tilting, and thus there is no tilting screw either. Another point of difference is that the automatic stabiliser within the telescope gives rise to an *upright image* in the field of view.

INSTRUMENT ADJUSTMENTS

18. The line of collimation. The line of collimation of a level telescope is the *line of sight* defined by the optical centre of the object glass and the centre of the cross hairs. The line of collimation must not be confused with a horizontal line. The line of sight or collimation is only horizontal when a level in perfect adjustment is set up and levelled.

After a level has been set up it is frequently necessary to know the height of the resulting horizontal line of collimation, shortened to the phrase *height of collimation* (H.C.). This means the same as *height of instrument* (H.I.). If the level is set up close to a point of known level, then the height of the line of collimation can be found by measuring the height of the centre of the eyepiece lens above the point. This can be done by direct measurement or by viewing a staff held vertically on the point close to the eyepiece lens. By looking at the staff through the object glass of the telescope the height of instrument can be obtained.

19. The basic requirement. The basic requirement for any level is that when it is set up and levelled the line of sight will be horizontal. Owing to their differences in basic construction, the dumpy, the tilting and the automatic level are adjusted differently to give this basic requirement. Adjustments are of two types:

(*a*) *Temporary adjustments*, which are concerned with the levelling up of the instrument and the focusing of the telescope.

(*b*) *Permanent adjustments*, which are necessary to provide the basic requirement of a level.

20. Collimation error. When any level is set up and levelled and the line of sight or collimation is not truly horizontal it

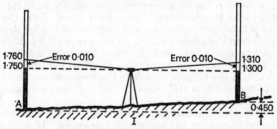

Fig. 69.—*Collimation error*

The illustration shows that a level with collimation error, in this case an elevated line of sight, still provides the true level difference between points when it is set up midway between them.

will sweep out a cone as it is rotated. This cone will be either above or below the horizontal plane that it would have swept out had it been in the correct adjustment.

The line of collimation illustrated in Fig. 69 is raised above the true horizontal line. Were the instrument in adjustment the horizontal line would intersect staff A at 1·750 m and staff B at 1·300 m. This gives a *true* difference of level of 0·450 m. However, as the line of collimation is out of adjustment and raised, it intersects staff A at 1·760 m. If the instrument is set up such that the distance $AI = IB$, then the two triangles on either side of the instrument are equal and the error on staff A of 0·010 will equal the error on staff B. Therefore the staff reading at B will be 1·310 m. The difference between these two observed, erroneous readings is $1·760 - 1·310 = 0·450$, the true level difference between A and B.

This shows that even when a level is out of adjustment, by setting up midway between any two staff positions the *true level difference* will still be obtained.

21. Temporary adjustment of the dumpy level. The procedure involved will be as follows:

(*a*) *Setting up and levelling:*

(*i*) Attach the level to the tripod and, by moving one leg of the tripod only, adjust the tripod head so that it is approximately level, judging roughly by eye.

(*ii*) Tread the tripod shoes firmly into the ground.

(*iii*) Place the bubble tube parallel to two footscrews and bring the bubble to the central position by rotating these screws in a direction opposite to each other. Note that the bubble follows the direction of movement of the *left thumb*.

(*iv*) Turn the telescope through 90°, placing the bubble tube at right-angles to the first position. Bring the bubble to the central position again by rotating the third footscrew only.

(*v*) Turn the telescope back to the first position and check that the bubble is still central. Adjust the two footscrews again if necessary.

(*vi*) Rotate the telescope through 180°, reversing the bubble-tube position over the same two footscrews. If the bubble remains central the instrument is properly levelled and the telescope bubble is in adjustment. If it does not remain central *see* 22.

(*b*) *Adjusting for parallax:*

(*i*) Turn the focusing screw until no object can be seen in the field of view to distract from the view of the cross hairs.

(*ii*) Rotate the eyepiece until the cross hairs appear sharp and clear.

(*iii*) Focus the telescope on to a distant object (or the staff) with the focusing screw and check that when the eye is moved slightly there is no relative movement between the cross hairs and the image of the object or staff.

22. Permanent adjustment of the dumpy level.

(a) The bubble tube axis must be at right-angles to the vertical axis of the level; *i.e.* when the bubble is central the vertical spindle axis should be truly vertical and the bubble should remain central in all directions. To adjust the *bubble tube* permanently, the level is set up and levelled through stages **21**(a) (i) to (vi) above. If the bubble does not remain central in the reverse position the following procedure is required:

(i) Count the number of divisions by which the bubble is off-centre and repeat the levelling process bringing the bubble to *half* the number of divisions off-centre each time.

(ii) Check that the bubble remains in this same place in the tube in all three levelling-up positions. This will indicate that the vertical axis is truly vertical and only the bubble is in error, *i.e.* not at right-angles to the vertical axis.

(iii) Using the bubble capstan adjusting screws bring the bubble back to the central position, where it should remain in all directions.

NOTE: This position is seldom obtained perfectly as the adjustment is always subject to slight errors. Also, because of instability of the tripod support and thermal movement of the instrument, the bubble will move off the central position. It is therefore generally necessary to adjust the footscrews slightly in order to bring the bubble exactly central each time a reading is taken to a staff.

(b) The line of collimation should be parallel to the axis of the bubble tube; *i.e.* the line of sight should be at right-angles to the vertical axis and should sweep out a horizontal plane. The adjustment procedure is as follows:

(i) Set up two stable staff stations about 100 m apart on fairly level ground. In soft earth wooden pegs hammered firmly into the ground are generally used, hence the term *the two-peg test*.

(ii) Set up the level exactly midway between the two staff stations A and B.

(iii) Take readings on to a staff held first at *A* and then at *B*. Assume that the following results were obtained:

Reading on to staff at A = 1·400 m
Reading on to staff at B = 1·250 m

The *true* difference in height between A and B is $1·400 - 1·250 = +0·150$ m, which is the amount by which Station B is higher than Station A.

(*iv*) Set up the level close to the staff position A and obtain the height of instrument by viewing the staff through the object glass while it is held about 10 mm from the eyepiece. Assume that this reading is 1·600 m.

(*v*) Calculate the reading that should be obtained on the staff at B. The staff reading at the instrument at A minus the true difference in level should equal the staff reading at B; *e.g.* $1·600 - 0·150 = 1·450$ m.

(*vi*) Observe the reading on the staff at B. If the reading is as calculated (1·450 m), the line of collimation is horizontal and the instrument is in adjustment. If not, adjust the *cross hairs* using the diaphragm adjusting screws until the reading is as calculated. If the observed reading is greater than calculated, move the cross hairs upwards, or vice versa.

23. Temporary adjustment of the tilting level.

(*a*) *Setting up and levelling:*

(*i*) Set up the tilting level in the same way as for the dumpy level, as described in **21**(*a*) (*i*) and (*ii*).

(*ii*) Using the footscrews or the ball-and-socket joint bring the circular plate bubble into the centre of its ring.

(*iii*) Using the tilting screw bring the telescope bubble to the centre of its run or into coincidence for each sighting to a staff position.

(*b*) *Adjusting for parallax.* The telescope eyepiece must be adjusted to eliminate parallax as described before in **21**(*b*).

24. Permanent adjustment of the tilting level.
The bubble tube adjustment of the dumpy level does not apply to tilting levels because in the latter the bubble is never fixed permanently at right-angles to the vertical axis.

The line of collimation should be parallel to the axis of the bubble tube so that with the bubble centred the line of sight is truly horizontal. Perform the *two-peg test* exactly as described for the dumpy level in **22** (*b*) to test the horizontality of the line of sight, bringing the telescope bubble exactly central with the tilting screw for each staff reading. If the reading on to the staff at B is not as calculated, adjust the tilting screw to move the line of sight on to the reading required. This movement will cause the bubble to move from its central position, but the line of sight will then be horizontal and the bubble should be central. Therefore adjust the bubble by its adjusting screws to bring it back to the central position.

NOTE

(*i*) In the *d*umpy adjust the *d*iaphragm.
(*ii*) In the *t*ilting level adjust the bubble *t*ube.

25. Temporary adjustment of the automatic level. The automatic level is set up and approximately levelled with the circular bubble only in the same way as for a tilting level (*see* **23**).

The adjustment for parallax must be carried out in the same way as above (*see* **21** (*b*)).

26. Permanent adjustment of the automatic level. The line of sight should be horizontal once the instrument has been approximately levelled using the circular bubble only. To check this requirement the two-peg test is carried out as before. If the calculated reading is not obtained the adjustment is made by moving the diaphragm in most instruments, as is done for the dumpy level. In some levels, such as the Kern GK 1AC and the Wild NA 2, the stabilising unit can be adjusted by means of a special screw and the cross hairs are not altered. Unless this special adjusting screw is provided on an automatic level the stabilising unit should not be touched as its setting is too precise to be corrected except under laboratory conditions.

27. Adjustment of the precise level. The temporary and permanent adjustments of precise levels are the same as for the parent tilting or automatic level. In addition the micrometer drum tilting the glass plate should be rotated and the vertical shift in the line of sight checked to ascertain that it moves precisely one staff graduation. If it does not it may indicate that the thickness of the glass does not suit the drum graduations, although this is normally checked by the makers to whom it would then be returned. The micrometer range varies, but frequent graduations are of 0·02 ft or 5 mm (*i.e.* one staff graduation), which are then graduated to 0·001 ft or 0·1 mm (*see* Fig. 70).

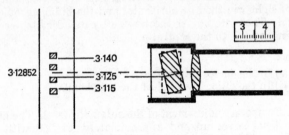

FIG. 70.—*The parallel-plate optical micrometer*

This is shown set on a staff reading of 3·125 m. The staff is graduated in 5-mm divisions and the micrometer drum reading, shown inset, is 3·52 mm. The micrometer range is 5 mm and is graduated to 0·1 mm. The total reading (in metres) is thus:

Staff graduation	3·1250
Micrometer reading	0·00352
Total reading	3·12852

The final decimal place is obtained by estimation; it refers to a very small quantity, is not reliable and may be ignored in practice.

28. Reversion levels. Some levels, such as the Wild NK 2 surveyor's level, are constructed so that the telescope may be rotated in its mountings, moving the bubble tube from the left-hand to the right-hand side of the telescope. With the bubble centred with the tilting screw for a reading in each position of the bubble, the mean of the two staff readings thus obtained will give the true level reading. The bubble tube should be adjusted until the same reading on the staff is obtained with the bubble in both positions. This dispenses with the need for the usual two-peg test (*see* Plate 7, reproduced by courtesy of Wild Heerbrugg, Switzerland).

29. Extent of error. Most problems in levelling are related to correcting readings which have been taken with a level with an unadjusted line of sight. The method of dealing with these problems depends on the relative position of staff and level. Only three cases arise (*see* Fig. 71). Assume, in considering the three cases below, that the *true level difference* between A and

B has already been established from observations made from the mid-position and that these observations show *A* to be precisely 0·200 m below *B*.

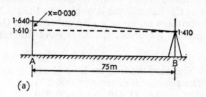

(a)

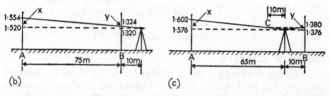

(b)   (c)

FIG. 71.—*Extent of error*

The percentage error of a level may be established in three ways relative to two pegs A and B, the height differences of which have already been established.

(a) The observations made with the level set up beside one staff position.

(b) The observations made with the level set up beyond one staff position.

(c) The observations made with the level set up between the staff positions.

SPECIMEN QUESTION

Find the percentage error of the level from the readings shown in Fig. 71(a) where the level has been set up beside one staff.

SOLUTION

(a) *By inspection of figure.* The height of the instrument at *B* is 1·410 and, as the *true level difference* is known to be 0·200, the true reading on the staff at *A* should be 1·410 + 0·200 = 1·610. In fact the *observed reading* is 1·640 and the observed difference in level is 1·640 − 1·410 = 0·230 instead of 0·200, which it should be. There is therefore an error of 0·030 m, which has occurred in a distance of 75 m.

The line of sight rises at a gradient of 0·030 m in 75 m, which by simple proportion equals 0·040/100 m. That is to say that the line of sight rises 0·040 m vertically for every 100 m horizontally. This is called the *percentage error of the level* and this particular instrument will be said to have a 0·040 per cent error.

(b) *By calculation.* The reading at staff B is assumed to be without error as the instrument is so close to the staff. At A the staff reading contains an error x. By subtracting the observed readings, corrected for error, the true level difference will be obtained.

$$\text{The true reading on A} = (1·640 - x)$$
$$\text{The true reading on B} = (1·410 \pm 0)$$
$$\text{The true level difference} = 0·200$$
$$\text{Therefore } (1·640 - x) - (1·410 \pm 0) = 0·200$$
$$0·230 - x = 0·200$$
$$x = 0·230 - 0·200$$
$$\text{Therefore } x = +0·030 \text{ m error in}$$
$$75 \text{ m}$$
$$\text{Percentage error} = 0·040$$

SPECIMEN QUESTION

Find the percentage error of the level and from it the true readings on both staffs from the observed readings shown in Fig. 71(b) where the level has been set up beyond one staff.

SOLUTION

(a) *By inspection of figure.* In this case the *true readings* are unknown as only the observed readings can be taken. The known difference in level of 0·200 is as before.

Assume that the reading on staff A is 1·554 and that on staff B it is 1·324. The *observed difference* in level is 1·554 − 1·324 = 0·230, but as the true difference in level is known to be 0·200 the error is 0·030, which gives the gradient of the line of sight between staff positions 75 m apart. Therefore the percentage error is again 0·040.

The readings that would have been obtained, had the line of sight been horizontal, are found by dropping the line of sight to the horizontal in the proportion of 0·040/100 m.

To find the true reading on staff A:

A is 85 m from the level. In 100 m the error is 0·040 m. In 85 m the error is 0·040/100 × 85 = 0·034. Therefore the reading on staff A should be 1·554 − 0·034 = 1·520.

To find the true reading on staff B:

Dropping the line of sight from 1·554 to 1·520 on staff A will also lower it on staff B in the same proportion. B is 10 m from

Plate 1. A surveying liquid prismatic compass by Hilger and Watts

Plate 2. The Wild T2 Universal theodolite

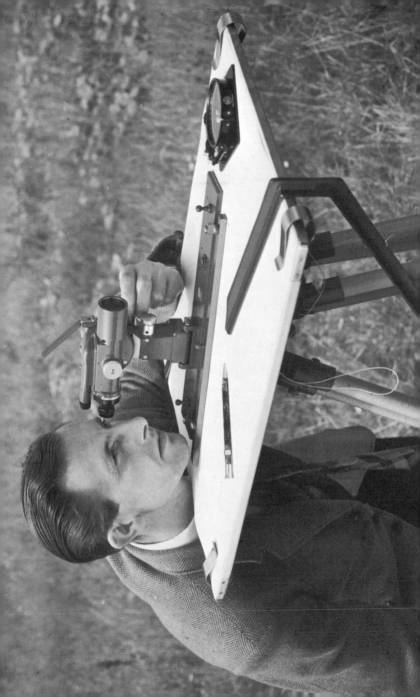

Plate 4. Tellurometer MRA 4

Plate 3 (*opposite*). Plane tabling equipment

Plate 5. The Kern DKM 3
geodetic theodolite

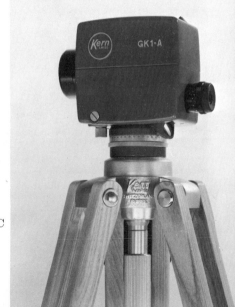

Plate 6. The Kern GKI AC
automatic level

Plate 7. The Wild reversion level NK 2

Plate 8 (*below*). A slotted template assembly

Plate 9. The Wild A7 Autograph

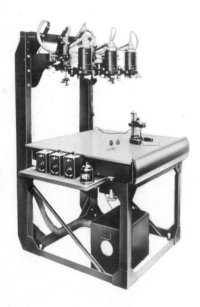

Plate 10. The Multiplex

Plate 11 (*opposite*). Vertical
air photograph

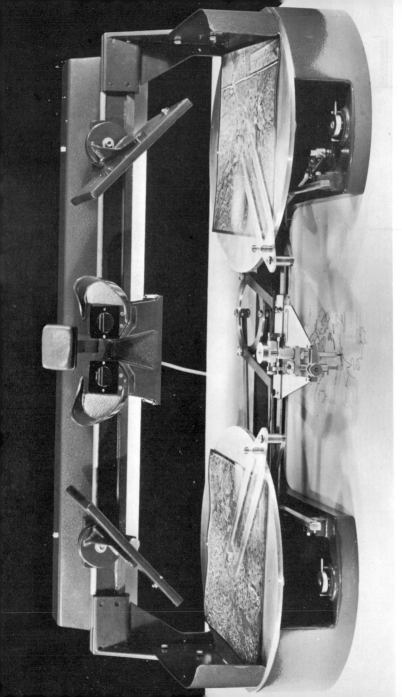

Plate 12. The radial line plotter

the level. In 100 m the error is 0·040 m. In 10 m the error is 0·004. Therefore reading on staff B should be 1·324 − 0·004 = 1·320.

To prove the corrected readings their difference should equal the known true difference of level. For example, taking the above figures, 1·520 − 1·320 = 0·200.

(b) *By calculation.* The readings on both staffs have unknown errors this time, say, x and y, but there are two equations to solve for x and y as follows:

(i) $(1·554 − x) − (1·324 − y) = 0·200$, and,
(ii) from similar triangles:

$$\frac{x}{y} = \frac{85}{10}$$

Therefore $\qquad x = 8·5y$

Therefore, solving the first equation for y:

$$(1·554 − 8·5y) − (1·324 − y) = 0·200$$
$$0·230 − 7·5y = 0·200$$
$$7·5y = 0·030$$

Therefore $\qquad y = +0·004$
and $\qquad x = +0·034$

Therefore the reading on staff A should be 1·554 − 0·034 = 1·520, and the reading on staff B should be 1·324 − 0·004 = 1·320.

SPECIMEN QUESTION

Find the percentage error of the level and from it the true readings on both staffs from the observed readings shown in Fig. 71(c) where the level has been set up between the staffs.

SOLUTION

(a) *By inspection of figure.* Again, the *true readings* are unknown, and the illustrated *observed difference* is 1·602 − 1·380 = 0·222 m. The known difference in level is still 0·200, therefore the error is 0·022, which is the gradient of the line of sight, not between A and B, because the gradient changes at the instrument, but the gradient between A and C, a point 10 m from the instrument on the line of sight towards A which has the same height as the 1·380 reading on staff B. Therefore the 0·022 error refers to a distance of 55 m, or for 100 m to obtain the percentage 0·022/55 × 100 = 0·040 per cent error as before. The readings which would have been obtained, had the line of

sight been horizontal, are found as before by dropping the line
to the horizontal in the proportion of 0·040/100 m.

To find the true reading on staff A:

A is 65 m from the level. In 65 m the error is 0·040/100 × 65
= 0·026. Therefore the reading on staff A should be 1·602 —
0·026 = 1·576.

To find the true reading on staff B:

B is 10 m from the level. In 10 m the error is 0·004. Therefore
the reading on staff B should be 1·380 — 0·004 = 1·376.

To prove the corrected readings 1·576 — 1·376 = 0·200, the
known true difference in level.

(*b*) *By calculation.* Let *x* and *y* be the errors in the observed
readings then:

$$(1·602 - x) - (1·380 - y) = 0·200$$

and

$$\frac{x}{y} = \frac{65}{10}$$

Therefore

$$x = 6·5y$$

Therefore, solving for *y*:

$$(1·602 - 6·5y) - (1·380 - y) = 0·200$$
$$0·222 - 5·5y = 0·200$$
$$5·5y = 0·022$$

Therefore

$$y = +0·004$$

and

$$x = +0·026$$

Therefore the reading on staff A should be 1·602 — 0·026
= 1·576 and the reading on staff B should be 1·380 — 0·004
= 1·376.

SPECIMEN QUESTION

A level was set up midway between two stations A and B,
100 m apart, and the following readings were recorded:

On staff held at *A*:   2·497
On staff held at *B*:   4·215

The level was next set up beside the staff at *A* and the height
of instrument was found to be 1·350. The reading on to the
staff at *B* taken from this position was 3·128. Without any
instrumental adjustments being made the level was next set up
50 m from a bench-mark with a reduced level of 21·633 m. A

backsight reading to a staff held on this bench-mark was found to be 3·012.

The following intermediate sights were then observed. What is the reduced level of each station?

Station	Staff reading (m)	Distance of staff from instrument (m)
1	1·732	20
2	2·196	40
3	1·508	60
4	0·030	80
5	0·286	100

SOLUTION

The true level difference between A and B is $4·215 - 2·497 = 1·718$, because the level was set up midway.

The percentage error is as follows:

The staff reading at A	$= 1·350$
Plus the true fall to B	$= +1·718$
Therefore reading on staff at B	$= 3·068$
However, the observed reading	$= 3·128$
Therefore the error in level	$= +0·060$ in 100 m
Therefore percentage error	$= +0·060$

The line of sight is elevated by $0·060/100$ m, therefore observed readings must be reduced by this amount.

The reading on the staff held at the bench-mark $= 3·012$. Had the level been correct the reading would have been $3·012 - 0·030 = 2·982$. Therefore the correct *height of instrument* is $21·633 + 2·982 = 24·615$.

Reduced levels of stations are obtained by subtracting the staff reading, corrected in proportion to its distance from the level, from the corrected height of instrument:

Station 1:	$24·615 - (1·732 - 0·012)$	$= 22·895$
Station 2:	$24·615 - (2·196 - 0·024)$	$= 22·443$
Station 3:	$24·615 - (1·508 - 0·036)$	$= 23·143$
Station 4:	$24·615 - (0·030 - 0·048)$	$= 24·633$
Station 5:	$24·615 - (0·286 - 0·060)$	$= 24·389$

NOTE: Had the level not been out of adjustment with an elevated line of sight, the reading on to the staff at Station 4 could not have been obtained because the base of the staff was above the horizontal line through the instrument.

FIELD AND OFFICE WORK

30. Series levelling. When the difference in level between two points cannot be obtained by one set-up, as described in **7**, it is necessary to repeat the process, which is best illustrated

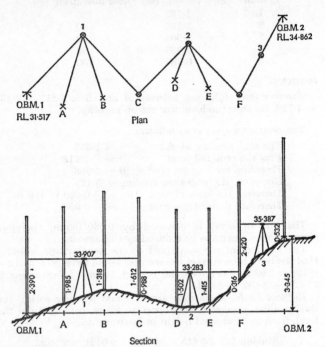

Fig. 72.—*Plan and sectional view of series levelling*

Backsights and foresights to change points should always be about equal as shown. The level does not have to be on the straight line between change points, although this is often the most convenient position, as shown at instrument position 3.

by a sketch (*see* Fig. 72). At the same time the reduced levels of other points can also be established.

The field observations are noted or booked in a levelling field book as follows and later reduced in the office:

B.S.	I.S.	F.S.	H.I.	R.L.	Remarks
2·390			33·907	31·517	O.B.M. No. 1
	1·985			31·922	A
	1·318			32·589	B
0·988		1·612	33·283	32·295	C
	1·502			31·781	D
	1·415			31·868	E
2·420		0·316	35·387	32·967	F
		0·532		34·855	O.B.M. No. 2
5·798	6·220	2·460		31·517	
2·460				+3·338	
+3·338					

NOTE

(*i*) The figures in italics are *field observations* and are usually booked in pencil.

(*ii*) The first observation made after an instrument has been set up is called a *backsight* (B.S.) and is the reading of 2·390 on the staff held on O.B.M. No. 1. It is thus booked in the first backsight column in the field book.

(*iii*) The next observation of 1·985 is to an intermediate staff position A and is known as an *intermediate sight* (I.S.), and is booked in the second column on the next line down.

(*iv*) The next observation of 1·318 is also an intermediate sight and is booked in the same column, but is written on the next line down as it refers to another staff position B.

(*v*) The next observation of 1·612 is the last observation from the instrument set up at No. 1 and is known as a *foresight* (F.S.). It is booked in the third, foresight column as shown.

(*vi*) The instrument is now moved to position No. 2 and an observation of 0·988 is made to the staff still held at C. It is the first observation of the second set-up and is therefore a backsight and is booked in the backsight column. It also refers to the same staff position as the previous reading and is therefore booked on the same line as reading 1·612, already in the foresight column.

(*vii*) The staff position C is known as a *change point* because the level is changed from one position to another. Whenever readings are booked on one line in both the backsight and foresight columns these readings indicate observations on to a change point.

(*viii*) The process of booking continues as before until a final foresight is taken on to the staff held at O.B.M. No. 2 (reading 0·532 in the foresight column).

31. Checking the levels. Errors are likely to arise both in observing and in the arithmetic of reduction. The check on the levelling observations is made by always closing a run of levels on to another bench-mark or back on to the same starting point. Then the difference between the sum of the B.S.s and F.S.s should equal the known difference in height between the starting and finishing points.

The field work is thus completed by checking the observations, which is done by summing the observations in the backsight and foresight columns as shown. The difference between these sums indicates the overall rise or fall in level between the end points. The sum of B.S.s minus the sum of F.S.s when positive indicates a rise and when negative indicates a fall.

Taking the figures in **30** above, $5 \cdot 798 - 2 \cdot 460 = +3 \cdot 338$ rise. However, the known difference in level between O.B.M. No. 1 and O.B.M. No. 2 is $34 \cdot 862 - 31 \cdot 517 = 3 \cdot 345$ and the difference between the known and observed rise of $0 \cdot 007$ indicates a small acceptable error due to minor compensating errors of observation.

The *permissible error* in levelling on ordinary site surveys may be taken as $\pm 20 \sqrt{K}$ mm, where K is the total distance levelled over in kilometres. Errors in excess of this probably indicate a mistake which must be found by re-levelling the section. In *precise work* the permissible error is generally reduced to $\pm 5 \sqrt{K}$ mm or even less.

32. Reduction of observations. The field book is reduced later in the office, generally in ink, in either one of two ways:

(a) By the *height of instrument* (*or height of collimation*) *method* (*see* **33**).

(b) By the *rise and fall method* (*see* **34**).

33. Height of instrument method. Referring to Fig. 72 it can be seen that if the reading on the staff on O.B.M. No. 1 is added to the reduced level of the bench-mark, the reduced level of the instrument line of sight will be obtained, *i.e.* $31 \cdot 517 + 2 \cdot 390 = 33 \cdot 907$. This calculation is done in the field book and the height of instrument is recorded in the appropriate column as shown in **30**.

The reduction continues as follows:

(a) By dropping down from this height, 1·985 to the ground at A, i.e. 33·907 − 1·985 = 31·922, the R.L. of A is obtained and recorded as shown.

(b) By continuing again along the height of collimation of 33·907 m to B and dropping again to the ground by 1·318 m, the R.L. of B is obtained and recorded as shown (33·907 − 1·318 = 32·589).

(c) Once more for the staff at C, the staff reading of 1·612 is subtracted from the height of the line of collimation (33·907), giving an R.L. for C of 32·295.

(d) The instrument is now moved to the second set-up position and the previous height of its line of collimation is lost. To obtain the height of the new instrument position the same process is repeated. The reading on to the change point C of 0·988, added to the R.L. of C of 32·295, gives the new height of instrument of 33·283.

(e) From this height of 33·283 subtract 1·502 to obtain the R.L. of intermediate point D.

(f) From the same instrument height of 33·283 subtract 1·415 to give the R.L. of intermediate point E, and so on.

(g) The whole reduction process is repeated until from the last instrument height of 35·387 the staff reading of 0·532 is subtracted to give the value 34·855, the *observed* value of the reduced level of O.B.M. No. 2.

34. The rise and fall method. This method is illustrated below and shows the same set of field observations with the levels reduced by this method:

B.S.	I.S.	F.S.	Rise	Fall	R.L.	Remarks
2·390					31·517	O.B.M. No. 1
	1·985		0·405		31·922	A
	1·318		0·667		32·589	B
0·988		1·612		0·294	32·295	C
	1·502			0·514	31·781	D
	1·415		0·087		31·868	E
2·420		0·316	1·099		32·967	F
		0·532	1·888		34·855	O.B.M. No. 2
5·798		2·460	4·146	0·808	31·517	
2·460			0·808		+3·338	
+3·338			+3·338			

(*a*) Referring to Fig. 72 again, it will be seen that there is a rise of 0·405 from O.B.M. No. 1 to *A*, obtained from 2·390 − 1·985 = +0·405.

(*b*) This method of reduction continues in the same way, always considering the *rise* or *fall* from one staff position to the next by subtracting the second reading from the first as though each were a simple backsight and foresight, thus:

$$B.S. \qquad F.S.$$
$$1\cdot985 - 1\cdot318 = +0\cdot667 \text{ (rise)}.$$
$$1\cdot318 - 1\cdot612 = -0\cdot294 \text{ (fall)}.$$

These readings are booked in their respective columns as shown.

(*c*) After observing to change point *C*, the instrument is moved to establish the rise or fall between *C* and *D* and the reduction is 0·988 − 1·502 = −0·514 (fall).

(*d*) To obtain the rises and falls always subtract from the figures in the B.S. or I.S. columns the figures immediately below or one line down to the right. Once a foresight has been subtracted, start again with the backsight on the same line, subtracting the I.S. or the F.S., whichever may be on the next line down. *Never* subtract from any reading one which is below it and in the next column to the left.

(*e*) After the rises and falls have been reduced, the difference between the sum of each column will give the *total* rise or fall. This must agree exactly with the difference between the sum of B.S.s and F.S.s if the reduction is correct. Taking the figures above the checked total rise is 3·338 m.

(*f*) After checking the rises and falls, the reduced level of each point is obtained by adding the rise or fall to the next station to the R.L. of the one preceding it until the final observed reduced level is obtained.

35. Comparison of methods. The *rise and fall method* contains more calculations, but all the arithmetic is checked, including the reduced levels of the intermediate sights. It should be used for most small surveys for this reason.

The *height of instrument method* is a quicker form of reduction, but the reduced levels of the intermediate sights are not checked as in the previous method. A check can be applied as follows, but it is rather tedious and is seldom used:

The sum of all reduced levels except the first should equal (Each instrument height) × (Number of I.S. and F.S. observations made from it) − (Total sum of the I.S. and F.S. readings).

Taking the figures above:

$$228 \cdot 277 = (33 \cdot 907 \times 3 + 33 \cdot 283 \times 3 + 35 \cdot 387 \times 1)$$
$$- (2 \cdot 460 + 6 \cdot 220)$$

In both methods the permissible *closing error is distributed* proportionally over the reduced levels of the change points, the reduced levels of the intermediate sights being corrected by the same amount as the change point immediately preceding it.

In the figures above the closing error of $0 \cdot 007$ has been built up over three foresights. The observed level of O.B.M. No. 2 is corrected by adding $0 \cdot 007$ to give it its true known value of $34 \cdot 862$. The value of F is therefore increased by $+0 \cdot 005$ and the value of C by $+0 \cdot 002$. The values of D and E are also increased by $+0 \cdot 002$, but there are no intermediate sights in this case following change point F which need to be increased by $+0 \cdot 005$.

In many cases the closing error will be so small that its distribution will be neglected if it is considered that this will not seriously affect the accuracy of the reduced levels.

36. The inverted staff. When the level of a point which is above the line of collimation has to be found, such as the *soffit* or *underside* level of a bridge, the staff may be held upside down with the base on the high point. Then, instead of obtaining the reduced level of the point by subtracting the staff reading from the height of instrument, it is found by adding. The process adopted here is to record a *minus sign* in front of the recorded staff reading and to apply this sign algebraically in the ordinary reduction of the field book.

The inverted staff may also be usefully employed in carrying a line of levels over a high wall, where the level of the top of the wall is used as a change point.

The following is an example of reduction using the height of collimation method:

EXAMPLE

B.S.	I.S.	F.S.	H.C.	R.L.	Remarks
2·790			19·942	17·152	O.B.M. "A" (17·152 A.O.D.)
	1·632			18·310	On centre line of road
	−2·417			22·359	Underside of bridge
−1·963		−3·162	21·141	23·104	Top of brick wall
3·082		2·396	21·827	18·745	Middle of yard
		4·680		17·147	O.B.M. "A" again
3·909		3·914		17·152	
		3·909		−0·005	Closing error
		−0·005			

The following is the same reduction using the rise and fall method:

B.S.	I.S.	F.S.	Rise	Fall	R.L.	Remarks
2·790					17·152	O.B.M. "A"
	1·632		1·158		18·310	On centre line of road
	−2·417		4·049		22·359	Underside of bridge
−1·963		−3·162	0·745		23·104	Top of brick wall
3·082		2·396		4·359	18·745	Middle of yard
		4·680		1·598	17·147	O.B.M. "A"
3·909		3·914	5·952	5·957	17·152	
		3·909		5·952	−0·005	Closing error
		−0·005		−0·005		

37. Curvature and refraction. Because of the curvature of the earth the point read on the staff is not at the same level as the instrument, since the line of sight is horizontal and not level (*see* Fig. 73). In observing from X to the staff BC a difference CD is developed, being the distance above height of instrument, so that the R.L. of B is made to be lower than it should be by this length.

(*a*) *To calculate the effect of curvature.* The following procedure is involved:

If the length of sight $= K$, and the distance from the centre of the earth to the top of the instrument $= R$, then:

$$(CD + R)^2 = K^2 + R^2$$
$$\therefore\ CD^2 + 2R.CD + R^2 = K^2 + R^2$$
$$\therefore\ CD^2 + 2R.CD = K^2$$

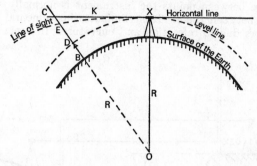

FIG. 73.—*Correction for curvature and refraction*

The effect of curvature of the earth and refraction of the line of sight on a horizontal line of sight is illustrated.

However, by comparison with R the length CD is so small that its square may be neglected:

$$\therefore\ 2R.CD = K^2$$

$$\therefore\ CD = \frac{K^2}{2R}$$

$$= \frac{K^2}{\text{Diameter of the earth}}$$

$$= \frac{K^2}{12\ 730\ \text{km}}$$

Correction for curvature $= 0 \cdot 0786\ K^2$ m (where K is in kilometres).

(b) *To include the effect of refraction.* The line of sight is not in fact straight and horizontal, but, owing to refraction, curves towards the earth as shown by the line XE. The line XE may be considered as a circular curve of radius seven times that of the earth. The effect of refraction is therefore one-seventh that of curvature, but of opposite sign so that the combined error $ED = 0.0673 \, K^2$ m (where K is the length of sight in kilometres). For example, for a sight of 1 km, the correction $= -0.067$ m and in 100 m the correction $= -0.001$ m.

38. Reciprocal levelling. In order to obtain the true level difference between points the instrument is normally set up midway between them. This eliminates instrumental errors and errors due to refraction and curvature. In some cases,

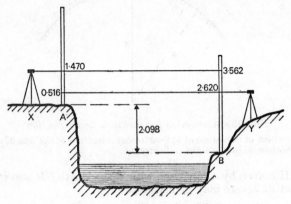

FIG. 74.—*Reciprocal levelling*

This is the process adopted when accurate observations between points such as A and B are required but it is found impossible to set up midway between the points.

such as when levelling across a wide river, it may not be possible to set up midway between the points. In these circumstances the system of reciprocal levelling is adopted as illustrated in Fig. 74.

The *difference of level* between A and B is obtained by the following procedure:

    (*a*) The level is set up at X, say 5 m from A, and both staffs are observed, the difference in readings giving an *observed* difference in level.

    (*b*) The level is next set up at Y, the same distance from B as it was from A. Again both staffs are observed, the difference in readings giving a second observed difference in level.

(c) The errors of observation from each set-up are approximately the same, although of opposite sign. Therefore the mean of the observed differences in level found from each set-up will give the *true* difference in level.

Take the following as an example:

> *Observations from Station X:*
>
> On to staff held at A = 1·470
> On to staff held at B = 3·562
> Observed difference in level = 2·092
>
> *Observations from Station Y:*
>
> On to staff held at A = 0·516
> On to staff held at B = 2·620
> Observed difference in level = 2·104

$$\therefore \text{True difference in level} = \frac{2\cdot092 + 2\cdot104}{2}$$

$$= 2\cdot098 \text{ m}$$

Reciprocal levelling is a second method of finding the true level difference between points with a level suspected of being out of adjustment. The method of *reciprocal levelling* is often used instead of the midway set-up to find the true difference in level when testing a level.

SOURCES OF ERROR

39. Sources of error. There are five sources of error in ordinary levelling and their importance must be appreciated and precautions taken to reduce their effect. These sources are the following:

    (a) *Instrumental errors (see* **40**).
    (b) *Errors in handling the equipment (see* **41**).
    (c) *Errors due to displacement of the equipment (see* **42**).
    (d) *Errors in reading and booking (see* **43**).
    (e) *Errors due to natural causes (see* **44**).

40. Instrumental errors.

    (a) The line of sight should be parallel to the bubble tube axis (horizontal in automatic levels); if it is not, the error is proportional to the length of the line of sight. Therefore, always *maintain equal lengths of backsights and foresights*.

(*b*) The bubble tube may be unsuitable. It should come to rest quickly, but the slightest movement or tilting of the footscrew must alter its position. So always *check that the sensitivity of the bubble tube is adequate for the job*.

(*c*) The level must be stable. Examine the tripod for any looseness in the joints or damage to the screw threads caused by overtightening and *tighten the tripod joints firmly*.

(*d*) Staff graduations may be in error or the staff may not be properly extended. It is advisable to *test the graduations of the staff when extended, particularly on either side of the joints*.

41. Errors in handling the equipment.

(*a*) In tilting levels the telescope bubble must be central or in coincidence *each time* a reading is taken. *Ensure that the bubble is centred both before and after reading the staff*.

(*b*) The staff should be held vertically or readings will be too great. Always *check lateral verticality against cross hairs*. *For particular accuracy the staffman should use a staff bubble or swing the staff slowly towards and away from the instrument, the lowest reading being noted*.

42. Errors due to displacement of the equipment.

(*a*) If the instrument is set up on soft or marshy ground or on thick matted grass it may settle and alter the height of collimation. Also, if the instrument is knocked the H.I. will be altered and errors will arise. Always *set up on stable ground, forcing the tripod shoes down firmly*. *Never hold, lean on or trip over the tripod*.

(*b*) Change points must be chosen so that when turning the staff round or when replacing it after removal no alteration of height takes place. Always *choose stable change points*. *On hard ground mark the staff position with chalk, and on soft ground use a change plate*.

(*c*) Sometimes inexperienced operators inadvertently move the level forward while the staffman is also changing position. *Never move the staff until a backsight has been taken; never move the level until a foresight has been taken*.

43. Errors in reading and booking. The most common mistakes made in reading and booking are the following:

(*a*) Reading the staff upwards instead of downwards.

(*b*) Reading an inverted staff downwards instead of upwards.

(*c*) Reading the staff downwards instead of upwards when using an automatic level.

(*d*) Concentrating on the decimal reading and noting the metres wrongly.

(*e*) Omitting a zero, *e.g.* recording 3·09 instead of 3·009.

(*f*) Entering a reading in the wrong column.

(*g*) Forgetting to book an entry.

(*h*) Noting a reading with the numbers interchanged, *e.g.* 1·501 instead of 1·105.

(*i*) Reading against a stadia hair instead of the horizontal cross hair.

(*j*) Noting a wrong distance or point description in the remarks column.

For these reasons, always *read the staff, book the observation and then check that the recorded entry agrees with a second reading through the telescope.*

44. Errors due to natural causes.

(*a*) The wind causes vibration of the level and tripod and of the staff, particularly when the staff is fully extended, which can make accurate sighting impossible. Therefore *in windy weather shelter the instrument and keep sights and the staff short.*

(*b*) The sun can cause an apparent vibration of the staff owing to irregular refraction. It also affects the bubble by causing unequal expansion of the level and tripod and can alter the curve of the bubble tube itself. Sighting is difficult when the sun shines into the object glass. Therefore, *in hot sun reduce lengths of the sights, keeping them at least 0·5 m above the ground throughout their length. Extend the ray-shade in front of the object glass and shade the instrument with an umbrella.*

(*c*) Rain makes accurate work difficult and unpleasant; raindrops on the objective glass and condensation on the eyepiece make sighting impossible. For precise work it is advisable to wait for better weather. However, *in rainy weather uses the ray-shade and protect the instrument with an umbrella.*

(*d*) Errors arising from refraction and curvature of the earth's surface are small and generally negligible in ordinary levelling and are eliminated by adopting the precaution in **40** (*a*) above. (*See also* **37**.) *For long sights and in precise work where equality of backsights and foresights cannot be maintained adopt the method of reciprocal levelling.*

45. Orthometric and dynamic levelling. The principles of levelling covered are not adequate for geodetic purposes. Level surfaces at different elevations are not parallel, for, due to the increase in the force of gravity, level surfaces tend to converge as they proceed from the equator to the poles. Two points on the same level surface, one near the equator and one near the pole, will thus be at different heights above datum.

(*a*) *Dynamic heights.* Two points on the same level surface have the same *dynamic height* as both lie on the same *equipotential surface.*

(*b*) *Orthometric heights.* Two points both being the same distance above datum have the same *orthometric height*, but their dynamic heights will be different, *i.e.* there will be a tendency for water to flow from the northern point to the southern point because it has a lower gravitational potential than the northern one. The relation between orthometric and dynamic heights is thus a function of latitude.

NOTE

    (*i*) In the process of levelling staff readings are orthometric, but the bubble sets itself tangential to the equipotential surface so that actual readings give rise to neither orthometric nor dynamic heights.

    (*ii*) In geodetic levelling a small correction is made to give true orthometric heights, from which dynamic heights may be obtained.

    (*iii*) The Ordnance Survey maps record orthometric levels.

(*c*) *Geopotential Numbers.* Since the acceleration due to gravity varies not only with latitude, but with height and the earth's density, allowance is now made for local gravity variations to provide the most accurate form of dynamic heighting.

$$\text{Height}_A = \int_0^A g\,dh \text{ geopotential units}$$

where g, the acceleration due to gravity, is measured in *kilogals* and h represents height in *metres* above the geoid or mean sea-level surface.

NOTE

    (*i*) 1 gal = an acceleration of 1 cm per second^2.
    (*ii*) 1 kgal = 1000 gal.
    (*iii*) A geopotential unit, gpu = 1 kgal metre.
    (*iv*) An orthometric height of say 100 metres has a geopotential number of about 98 kgal metres, depending upon the local value of g.

PROGRESS TEST 10

1. What is meant by the term "levelling"? (1)
2. What is the difference between a level line and a horizontal line? (2–3)
3. Why do the reduced levels of some bench-marks refer to the Newlyn datum and others to the Liverpool datum? (4)
4. How is the difference in level between two points obtained? (7)
5. What equipment is used by staffmen in levelling? (8–9)
6. What is the essential difference between the three basic types of level? (10, 13, 14, 17)
7. Why is the "quickset" level so called? (15)
8. When is a level termed a "precise" level? (16)
9. Define the term, "line of collimation." (18)
10. What is the basic requirement for any level? (19)
11. What is meant by "collimation error"? (20)
12. Describe how you would carry out the temporary adjustments of a dumpy level. (21)
13. Why are two permanent adjustments made to a dumpy level and only one to a tilting level? (22, 24)
14. What is the essential difference in the adjustment for collimation error between the dumpy and tilting level? (24)
15. How are automatic levels and precise levels adjusted? (26–27)
16. What is the special advantage of a reversion level? (28)
*17. The following is a series of levelling observations taken in sequence, starting and finishing on the same bench-mark with a reduced level of 22·300;

4·907; 2·136; *4·632;* 0·517; −1·789; 2·671; *1·745;* 1·956; 3·998; 4·098; 7·136; *1·000.*

Foresight readings are printed in italics. Enter these readings in level book form and reduce the observations by *both methods*, applying all checks. (30–36)

18. Show that the correction for curvature and refraction equals $0.0673 K^2$ m. (37)

*19. A level is set up beside staff A so that there is no error in establishing the height of instrument, and the following readings were obtained:

> Reading on a staff held at A: 1·448.
> Reading on a staff held at B: 1·488.

The level was next moved to a similar position beside staff B and the following readings were obtained:

> Reading on a staff held at A: 1·566.
> Reading on a staff held at B: 1·526.

(a) Is the instrument in adjustment?
(b) If the R.L. of $A = 50.000$ m, what is the R.L. of B? (38)

20. What are the five sources of error in levelling? (39)

CHAPTER XI

SECTIONING

PRINCIPLES

1. Basic principle of sectioning. Survey lines relating to any proposed construction are set out on the ground, the positions of the straight and curved lengths, if any, being marked by pegs placed by the surveyor. *Sectioning* consists of surveying the variations in height of the ground along any such line so that they may be represented to scale on a drawing.

2. Survey information required. In order to plot the variations in ground height along the line of section two types of measurement must be made:

(*a*) Levels must be taken along the line so that the changes in height can be recorded.

(*b*) Horizontal measurements must be obtained along the line to define the relative positions of the points at which the levels were observed.

3. Longitudinal sections or profiles. These are sections which follow some particular line defining a part of a new construction and are usually run along the centre lines of the proposed work such as new roads, pipe-lines, etc.

4. Cross-sections. Since a longitudinal section only provides information along a line, ground details on either side of that line are not available. For works of narrow width such as pipe-lines, sewers, etc., the absence of this information is not important as there will usually be little change in ground character close to the centre line. On the other hand, where roads, bridges, etc., are to be built, the slope of the ground at right-angles to their centre lines must also be determined. This is necessary because any variation in ground slope could have a considerable effect on the amount and type of construction work involved. This information is obtained from *cross-*

sections (*see* **15**), which are short section lines set out, usually at right-angles, to the main profile line. They must extend beyond the limits of the proposed construction so that the full character of the whole area of land to be worked is known.

5. The need for sections. Sections are provided by the surveyor so that the engineer or designer can compare existing ground levels with his proposed *formation levels*, *i.e.* the levels to which the ground is to be worked in the new construction.

(*a*) *Longitudinal sections* provide data for the following:

(*i*) Deciding the most suitable and economic levels and gradients to which the ground should be worked in its longitudinal section.

(*ii*) Supplying details at any point along the section of the amount of *cut*, *i.e.* the depth of excavation, or the amount of *fill*, *i.e.* the height to which the ground must be raised, to suit the new formation level.

(*iii*) Recording the places where neither cut nor fill occurs. These are the points at which the formation level intersects the existing ground level (for the method of calculating these points *see* **14**).

(*b*) *Cross-sections* provide data for the following:

(*i*) Deciding the most suitable and economic levels to which the ground is to be worked in the transverse direction, *e.g.* at right-angles to its length.

(*ii*) Supplying details for calculating the position, height and slope of any necessary embankments.

(*iii*) Calculating earthwork quantities for costing purposes and the suitable provision of earth-moving plant.

6. Positioning and accuracy of levels. Levels should be taken along all section lines at changes in the general slope which are sufficiently large to affect design or volume calculations. In practice, if earthworks are to be computed, the levels are taken at regular intervals as this simplifies the volume calculations. The actual spacing will depend on the nature of the ground and the type of construction, but regular spacings of 20 and 30 m are usual. Additional level observations are also made between the regular intervals at important features such as on existing roads, beds of streams, etc., and at marked changes of slope.

As levelling observations for sections are usually taken of

rough ground it is impractical to observe the staff to three decimal places. Staff readings to the nearest centimetre are therefore taken, although in more accurate work readings on change points and hard, flat surfaces, such as manhole covers, may be observed to millimetres.

LONGITUDINAL SECTIONS

7. Running a longitudinal section. This is the term used to describe the field work involved in surveying a longitudinal section. The line of the section must first be set out on the ground by *ranging* in (*see* II, 4) sufficient poles or pegs to define the straights and curves. In more accurate work the setting out, chaining and pegging may be completed first using a theodolite, as described in XV, 29. Once the line has been established on the ground levelling can commence.

8. Reference to datum. Levelling should start from an established bench-mark and then, by means of backsights and foresights only, sometimes called *flying levels*, extend to a final foresight on to a firm peg marking the start of the section. The level is then set up in a suitable position from which observations may be made on to as great a part of the section line as possible.

9. Levelling the section. First a chain, or preferably a tape, is drawn out along the section line. With the tape held taut a peg is placed to mark the end of the regular interval, say 30 m, if the regular pegging has not previously been completed. The process then continues as follows:

(*a*) The staffman holds the staff on the peg at the beginning of the section and a backsight is taken and booked, noting in the remarks column that this point has *zero chainage*, being the start of the line.

(*b*) The staffman then follows the line of the tape and, depending on the accuracy and detail required, would hold the staff and call out the chainage of the following:

(*i*) Every marked change of slope.
(*ii*) Every feature crossing the section line, *e.g.* property boundaries, fences, hedges, power and telephone lines, railway lines, etc.

(*iii*) Edges of banks and, if possible, the beds or bottoms of streams, ditches, ponds, etc.

(*iv*) The back edge of pavements, the top and bottom of kerbs and the section line on the centre line of any existing road crossing.

(*v*) The underside of bridges, using the staff inverted.

(*vi*) The end of each tape length or regular interval of, say, 20 or 30 m, as required.

These *intermediate sights* are observed and booked. The chainage called out by the staffman each time is recorded in the remarks column of the field book against the appropriate level reading.

(*c*) After completing all observations along one tape length it is pulled forward along the line as before and the same process continues, the leveller noting each time the continuous chainage from the start of the section line.

(*d*) The level must be moved forward to a more convenient position after a time and the leveller will signal the need for a *change point*. The staffman will then choose a stable change point preferably on the line, but off it if necessary. After observing the foresight the instrument is moved forward to another suitable position, a backsight is taken to the change point, and the whole process continues as before.

10. Field checks. After some distance has been covered a foresight is taken on to a *permanent* change point or T.B.M., ready for the start of the observations on to the next part of the section line. The levelling work so far considered has now to be checked. This can be done in one of three ways:

(*a*) *By closing the level circuit back on to the starting benchmark.* The difference between the final sums of the backsights and foresights will indicate the accuracy of the work, as described in X, **31**.

(*b*) *By closing the levels on to another nearer bench-mark.* The observed difference in height between the two benchmarks is then compared with the known difference.

NOTE: A misclosure between the two bench-marks may indicate a disturbance of one of them and may not necessarily be due to any error in the levelling observations.

(*c*) *By using double change points.* In this method the

field book is ruled with two B.S. columns and two F.S. columns. At each set-up the H.I. is thus determined twice, the one observation checking the other. This method is similar to running a closed circuit back to the starting bench-mark, but with one set of instrument positions only. This does not form a reliable check for two reasons:

(*i*) The difference between the two foresight readings can be retained in the leveller's mind and deliberately or inadvertently applied to the following backsight readings. This will record a consistency which does not actually exist.

(*ii*) A settlement of the instrument between the pair of backsight readings and the pair of foresight readings will still show an apparent check on the readings despite a real loss of accuracy.

11. Plotting the profile. Once the field observations have been taken and checked and the field book reduced the profile drawing can be prepared. This is illustrated in Fig. 75 and is drawn up as follows:

(*a*) *Draw a datum line* chosen to plot about 5 cm below the lowest reduced level on the profile and being a multiple of 5 m above datum. This line must be clearly marked, *e.g.* datum line 35 m A.O.D.

(*b*) *Scale off the chainages* of the points at which the levels were observed along the datum line to a suitable scale and tabulate them as shown. This horizontal scale must also be noted on the drawing and in presentation work usually includes a scale bar.

(*c*) *Erect ordinates* (perpendiculars) at these points and scale off the reduced levels of each and tabulate them as shown. To make the irregularities of the ground more obvious the vertical scale is usually larger than the horizontal scale. This provides a vertical exaggeration of the profile. The vertical scale is usually five to ten times greater than the horizontal, the greater exaggeration being used on flatter land. The vertical scale must be noted on the drawing, even if it is the same as the horizontal scale. Again, in presentation work, a scale bar is usually included.

(*d*) *Join each point of reduced level plotted* with a continuous line. This line must *not* be a curve like a graph because levels are taken at points of change of slope, so the slope should be even between these points. The points are therefore joined

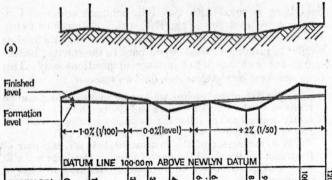

Finished level

Formation level

|← −1·0% (1/100) →|← 0·0% (level) →|← +2% (1/50) →|

DATUM LINE 100·00 m ABOVE NEWLYN DATUM

CHAINAGE (m)	0·0	12·4	30·0	38·7	48·9	60·0	67·2	84·0	90·0	108·4	120·0
REDUCED LEVELS	112·52	114·16	112·33	111·91	110·03	110·92	111·71	110·04	110·53	113·58	114·13
FORMATION LEVELS	111·60	111·48	111·30	111·30	111·30	111·30	111·44	111·78	111·90	112·27	112·50
CUT	0·92	2·68	1·03	0·61			0·27			1·31	1·63
FILL					1·27	0·38		1·74	1·37		

HORIZONTAL SCALE 1/1000 VERTICAL SCALE 1/100

(b)

Fig. 75.—*Working profile along a ground line*

(*a*) A sectional view along the ground with the staff positions marked. Note the exaggeration of the actual profile.
(*b*) The working profile, all required information of proposed and existing work being recorded as shown.

with a series of straight lines, although in presentation work this line may be drawn freehand over a lightly ruled pencil line. The resulting slight unevenness sometimes tends to improve the appearance of the drawing.

(*e*) *Represent on the profile the features* which intersected the line on the ground. Include descriptive notes, *e.g.* street names, property designations, etc.

12. Working profile. This consists of the original profile or longitudinal section with the position of the new work levels shown on it, their relation to existing ground level and any other information which may be needed during construction. This information is recorded as follows:

(a) New work is represented by two parallel lines. The lower indicates the level to which the earth is to be worked, *i.e.* the *formation level,* and the upper indicates the level of the finished construction, *i.e.* the *finished level.*

(b) The gradients of the formation level are clearly recorded as shown in Fig. 75.

(c) The formation levels at each point are calculated and tabulated as shown in Fig. 75.

(d) Where formation level is above ground level the difference between the two levels represents *fill.* Conversely, where formation level is below ground level the difference between the two levels represents *cut.* The cuts and fills at each point may be obtained by subtracting the formation levels from the profile levels, but these differences are also tabulated as shown in Fig. 75 to assist the setting out (*see* XV, 1) on site. Their tabulation also helps to prevent errors from arising in setting out.

(e) The positions of new works, bridges, culverts, etc., are shown with a reference to the drawing, which gives details of their construction.

13. Fair drawing. The profile drawings may be finished off as follows:

(a) *For professional and commercial purposes.* The drawings are simply finished in black ink only on tracing paper, tracing linen or plastic sheets so that copy prints may be obtained easily.

(b) *For presentation work and practical examinations.* Before the 1930s the practice of providing copy prints from transparencies was not established and working drawings were well presented and drawn on good-quality paper using coloured inks and washes. A convention of colours was developed for the preparation of profiles and these can, with advantage, be maintained in this type of drawing today. This colour convention is as follows:

(i) Ordinates: thin *blue* lines.
(ii) Ground and datum lines: *black* (sometimes the ground line is verged in *burnt sienna* along its underside).

(*iii*) Tabulated chainages and reduced levels: *black*.
(*iv*) Formation level line and gradients: *red*.
(*v*) Finished level line: *blue*.
(*vi*) Tabulated formation levels and depths of cut: *red*.
(*vii*) Heights of fill: *blue*.
(*viii*) Horizontal and vertical scales, scale bars, notes and titles: *black*.

14. Intersection of gradients.

The points at which the formation level intersects the existing ground level may be required. In such cases their chainage along the section line and

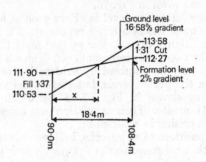

Fig. 76.—*Gradient intersection*

A detail is given of the intersection of the formation level and ground level shown in Fig. 75 between chainage 90·0 m and 108·4 m in order to calculate the intersection point.

their level will have to be calculated. In the working profile illustrated in Fig. 75 the formation level can be seen to intersect the ground level at four points.

EXAMPLE

The following is an example of the calculation of gradient intersection chainage. Consider the intersection point which occurs between chainage 90·0 and 108·4 m in Fig. 75.

Referring to Fig. 76, which illustrates this intersection in greater detail, it can be seen that the distance x required may be calculated from the similar triangles formed in the following way:

$$\frac{x}{1·37} = \frac{18·4 - x}{1·31}$$
$$\therefore x = 9·41$$

This calculation may be considerably simplified:

The total relative displacement between the gradients in moving along them from chainage 90·0 to 108·4 is 1·37 + 1·31 = 2·68. When the relative displacement, starting from chainage 90·0, becomes 1·37, intersection occurs because the actual displacement will have now reached zero. It follows, by simple proportion, that if the relative displacement of 2·68 occurs in 18·4 m, then the displacement of 1·37 occurs in:

$$\frac{18·4 \times 1·37}{2·68} \text{ m} = 9·41 \text{ m}$$

Therefore the *chainage* of the intersection point is 90·0 + 9·4 = 99·4 m (rounding off to one decimal place).

EXAMPLE

The following example shows the calculation of the gradient intersection level.

The level of the intersection point shown above to occur at chainage 99·4 m is calculated as follows:

The ground rises from level 110·53 to 113·58, a rise of 3·05 m in 18·4 m. Its percentage gradient is calculated as follows:

18·4 m occasion a rise of 3·05 m

$$\therefore \text{ 100·0 m occasion a rise of } \frac{3·05 \times 100}{18·4} = 16·58 \text{ per cent}$$

From this percentage gradient the rise in the calculated distance x will be:

$$9·41 \times \frac{16·58}{100} = 1·56$$

the rise from R.L. 110·53 to the point of intersection. Therefore the reduced level of the point of intersection is 110·53 + 1·56 = 112·09.

To prove the level calculation it should be repeated along the other gradient as follows:

The percentage gradient of the formation level is 2 per cent, therefore:

$$\text{the rise in 9·41 m} = 9·41 \times \frac{2}{100} = 0·19$$

the rise from R.L. 111·90 to the point of intersection. Therefore the reduced level of the point of intersection is 111·90 + 0·19 = 112·09 as before, proving all previous calculations, including that of the chainage of the point of intersection.

CROSS-SECTIONS

15. The interval between cross-sections. In 4 above it was explained that cross-sections extend the width of the information supplied by a longitudinal section. They should therefore be taken at intervals in such a way that there is no marked change of slope in the ground between them. This would be at right-angles to at least every level point taken on the longitudinal section. In practice this is frequently neglected, cross-sections being mostly observed at *regular intervals* of about 20 to 30 m to make calculations of volumes of earthworks (*see* XIV, 13) easier.

16. Setting out. Cross-sections are set out normal, *i.e.* at right-angles, to the longitudinal section, the right-angle being judged by eye for narrow strips such as roads and railways. Where the cross-sections needed are long, such as for reservoirs, motorway intersections, etc., or where special accuracy is needed, then they must be set out using a theodolite, a level with a horizontal circle or an optical square. If cross-sections are taken other than at right-angles to the longitudinal section, usually needed along a valley or ridge intersecting the centre line at an angle, then this angle must be measured so that its position may also be shown in the plan view.

17. Methods of cross-sectioning. The field work is basically similar to that of observing longitudinal sections. Levels are observed at changes of slope and their positions are fixed by measuring their distance from the longitudinal section line. Cross-sections are usually observed using the following equipment:

(*a*) *A level, tape and staff* are the most usual instruments.

(*b*) On steep ground, to save frequent re-positioning of the instrument, it may be more convenient to use *a theodolite, tape and staff*.

(*c*) Alternatively, where less accuracy is needed, such as on preliminary or pre-contract works, then *a hand level, tape and staff or ranging rod* may be used instead of the more accurate level.

(*d*) *A clinometer, tape and ranging rod* may be used on steep ground instead of a theodolite.

NOTE: The hand level or clinometer is seldom used today because final routes of construction projects can generally be chosen with greater precision than hitherto from aerial photographs. Also modern theodolites and levels are now so light and easy to manipulate that special hand instruments are seldom required.

18. Cross-sectioning with a level. When a level is used the cross-sectioning may be done at the same time as the main profile. Alternatively it may be carried out as the second stage of the work, the level's height being fixed and checked at each set-up by a backsight and foresight to previously heighted pegs on the longitudinal section.

(a) The level is set up and a backsight observed or the H.I. measured. The staffman follows the line of the previously pegged cross-section, or is guided forward at right-angles by an assistant, who remains on the main section controlling the tape. The staffman retains the zero end of the tape and holds the staff and tape end at each change of slope. The assistant on the main section then calls out the measured distance to each staff position to the leveller.

(b) On flat ground it may be possible to observe all the levels on one cross-section from a single set-up before moving on to the next. This makes booking easier and helps to prevent errors. However, where the ground slope is greater it may be necessary to move the instrument several times before all the levels on one section can be observed.

(c) To cut down the number of instrument set-ups it is better to observe the available positions on several cross-sections first before moving the instrument to observe the other levels on the same section lines. In adopting this method care must be taken in booking to ensure that the staff readings are properly recorded against the offset distances and that the individual cross-sections are correctly identified each time.

19. Cross-sectioning with a theodolite. On steep ground, to save having to move a level several times to cover the whole slope of the cross-sections, a theodolite may be used instead.

(a) The theodolite is set up over the previously levelled centre line peg. Its height of collimation above the peg is measured, which is equivalent to a backsight in levelling. By orienting along the centre line an accurate right-angle can be turned off for the cross-section. The chainage of the centre line peg is noted to define the particular cross-section being observed.

(b) An inclined line of sight is set on the instrument, roughly parallel to the ground, and this vertical angle is recorded. This angle of slope of the line of sight can be altered as necessary for different staff positions or for readings on either side of the longitudinal section. Errors are less likely to occur if one setting can be retained as far as possible.

(c) Staff intersections are read off as before and the distances to staff positions are taped. The tape should be held horizontally. If this is not possible the tape may be held along the line of sight, the zero end of the tape being held against the staff at the approximate height of the reading and the distance read off at the instrument against the horizontal axis. These lengths are reduced to the horizontal using the same recorded angle of slope in the formula $s = l \cos \theta$ (see II, 9).

20. Cross-sectioning field notes. The field observations are booked in the same way whichever instrument is used, except

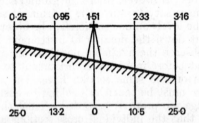

FIG. 77.—*Sketch booking of a cross-section*

This is observed at chainage 90·0, R.L. 110·53, on the longitudinal section illustrated in Fig. 75.

that with the theodolite the vertical angle must be noted each time. Booking may take one of two forms:

(a) *The sketch section*, with the readings noted thereon as illustrated in Fig. 77. This is usually adopted where the cross-sections are to be scale drawn, only without a record of reduced levels.

(b) *The level book form*, with three distance columns to denote cross-sectional distances to the right and left of the longitudinal section line as illustrated below. As a check on H.I. a foresight is shown taken on to the peg at chainage 60·0.

B.S.	I.S.	F.S.	H.I.	R.L.	Dist. L.	Chain-age	Dist. R.	Remarks
1·51			112·04	110·53		90·0		Peg
	0·95			111·09	13·2	90·0		
	0·23			111·81	25·0	90·0		
	2·33			109·71		90·0	10·5	
	3·16			108·88		90·0	25·0	
		1·12		110·92		60·0		Peg

21. Cross-sectional plotting. Unlike longitudinal sections the horizontal and vertical scales of cross-sections are usually the same. They are plotted without vertical exaggeration as this is more convenient for showing new work and for volume calculations (*see* XIV, **13**). Figures 95 and 96 give examples of cross-sectional plots.

PROGRESS TEST 11

1. What is meant by the term "sectioning"? **(1)**
2. What measurements must be taken in order to plot a section? **(2)**
3. What is the difference between a longitudinal section and a cross-section? **(3-4)**
4. What are (a) longitudinal sections and (b) cross-sections used for? **(5)**
5. What criteria govern the position of levels taken on cross-sections? **(6)**
6. Describe in detail the field work involved in running a longitudinal section. **(7-10)**
7. Describe three methods of checking the levelling observations in sectioning. **(10)**
*8. Calculate the remaining gradient intersections that occur in Fig. 75. **(14)**
*9. The following is the field sheet of a level circuit, including a section line *AB* 100 m long:

B.S.	I.S.	F.S.	H.I.	R.L.	Remarks
0·57				40·00	O.B.M. No. 1
0·41		3·27			00 m Peg A
	2·32				20
	1·84				40
0·33		2·58			60
	2·89				80
	3·16				100 m Peg B
3·97		0·97			
3·74		1·14			
		1·06			O.B.M. No. 1

(a) Reduce the levelling observations, showing all checks.

(b) Assuming a roadway is to be built to run evenly from ground level at A to ground level at B, determine the percentage gradient of this uniform formation level.

(c) Calculate the depths of cutting or amounts of filling required at every 20 m between A and B.

(d) Calculate the chainage and level of the gradient intersections of ground level with formation level.

(e) Plot this working profile to suitable horizontal and vertical scales and tabulate all data. Confirm that the scaled cuts and fills agree with their calculated values. **(11–16)**

*10. A railway line is to be regraded at a constant fall of 1/100 from A. The levels and chainages in metres of three points, A, B and C, on the line are as follows:

Point	Reduced levels	Chainage
A	82·51	500·0
B	72·51	1000·0
C	75·01	2000·0

Calculate the following:

(a) The amount by which the rail must be raised at B.

(b) The amount by which the rail must be lowered at C.

(c) The chainage and level of the point along the existing rail at which no alteration in level will take place. **(14)**

11. Explain why cross-sections should theoretically be observed at irregular intervals and why, in practice, they are usually taken at evenly spaced intervals. **(15)**

12. How are cross-sections established in relation to a longitudinal section? **(16)**

13. Describe the field work involved in running cross-sections using (a) a level and (b) a theodolite. **(18–19)**

14. Describe and illustrate two methods of booking cross-sectional observations. **(20)**

15. What is the essential difference between the plot of a longitudinal section and a cross-section? **(21)**

CHAPTER XII

TACHEOMETRY

PRINCIPLES

1. Definition of tacheometry. The word tacheometry is derived from the Greek *takhus metron* meaning a "swift measure." It is that branch of surveying where heights and distances between ground marks are obtained by optical means only, the slower process of measuring by direct taping being entirely eliminated. A *tacheometer* (or *tachymeter*) is any theodolite adapted, or fitted with an optical device, to enable measurements to be made optically.

2. The principle of tacheometric measurement. Various tacheometric methods have been developed, but all are based on one common principle.

Consider an *isosceles triangle:* the perpendicular bisector of the base is directly proportional to the length of this base. If the base length and the apex angle, called in tacheometry the *paralactic angle*, are known, then the length of the perpendicular bisector can be calculated. In some tacheometric systems the base length remains constant and the apex angle it subtends is measured in order to obtain the distance. In others the paralactic or apex angle remains constant and the varying base lengths are measured in order to obtain the respective distances.

3. Systems of tacheometry. Four tacheometric systems may be classified in accordance with their method of using the basic principle:

(*a*) *The stadia system,* in which the apex angle of the measuring triangle is defined by the *stadia hairs* on the telescope diaphragm. The base length is obtained by observing the intersection of the stadia hairs on the image of the measuring staff seen in the telescope's field of view (*see* 4–16).

(*b*) *The tangential system*, in which the apex angle subtended by a base of known length is accurately measured, usually with a single-second theodolite. In order to obtain the distance between instrument and base the *tangent* of the angle or angles observed must be used in the calculation, hence the name. The staff or bar defining the base length may be held either vertically or horizontally. When it is held horizontally this tangential system is called the *subtense system* (*see* 17–25).

(*c*) *The optical wedge or double-image system*, in which the paralactic angle is formed by refraction through a wedge-shaped prism, readings being taken to a specially designed staff (*see* 26–33).

(*d*) *The range-finder system*, in which the base line is at the observing instrument and the paralactic angle is defined optically at the point to which the measurement is being taken (*see* 34–36).

THE STADIA SYSTEM

4. General principles. In this system the diaphragm contains two additional horizontal lines known as stadia hairs, placed equidistant above and below the main horizontal cross hair. The distance between these stadia hairs is called the *stadia interval*. This stadia interval is usually a constant, providing fixed-hair tacheometry. On some instruments this interval may be altered, the movement being measured on a micrometer. It is then known as *movable hair* or *subtense tacheometry*, but this method is seldom used today because it has no special advantage, nor does it give increased accuracy, so the extra equipment cost is unwarranted.

Observations are made on to a levelling staff which acts as the variable base. In the telescope's field of view the stadia hairs subtend a certain length of the staff, which is greater the farther off the staff is held. This length of staff, called the *staff intercept*, is proportional to its distance from the instrument and so from this observed length of staff the distance between it and the tacheometer may be obtained.

5. The stadia formula. The stadia method of providing the horizontal distance between instrument and staff is illustrated in Fig. 78, which shows diagrammatically the simple case of an external focusing telescope providing a horizontal line of sight.

In Fig. 78:

f = the focal length of the object glass.
o = the outer focal point of the object glass.
i = the stadia interval ab.
s = the staff intercept AB.
c = the distance of the object glass to the instrument axis.
d = the distance from the outer focal point to the staff.
D = the horizontal distance required.

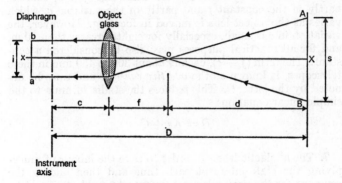

FIG. 78.—*External focusing stadia telescope*
The geometry of the stadia formula is shown.

When the telescope is in focus the image of the staff AB will be formed at ab in the plane of the diaphragm. Then a ray of light from A, which passes through o, on passing through the lens will emerge parallel to the optical axis. Similarly with a ray from B as shown. The rays here considered will form two similar triangles each with their apex at o, the base of the smaller triangle at the object glass being equal to the stadia interval i.

From these similar triangles:

$$\frac{d}{s} = \frac{f}{i}$$

$$\text{but } d = D - (f + c)$$

$$\therefore \; \frac{D - (f + c)}{s} = \frac{f}{i}$$

$$\therefore \; D - (f + c) = \frac{f}{i} s$$

$$\therefore \; D = \frac{f}{i} s + (f + c), \text{ the stadia formula.}$$

6. The stadia constants. In the stadia formula the term f/i is a constant, known as the *stadia* or *multiplying constant* and may be denoted by the letter K. The term $(f + c)$ consists partly of the constant f and partly of the variable c, which varies as the object lens is moved in focusing. However, the variation in c is small, especially for sights greater than 10 m, and for all practical purposes may also be considered a constant. The term $(f + c)$, usually about 300 to 450 mm in these telescopes, is known as the *additive constant* and may be denoted by the letter C. This reduces the stadia formula to the simple linear equation:

$$D = Ks + C$$

7. The analactic lens. In order to save the labour of multiplying the staff intercept each time and then adding the constant for the particular instrument, it would obviously be simpler if K were to be 100 and C zero. This would provide a stadia formula of $D = 100s$ and calculation would merely consist of moving the decimal point of the staff intercept reading two places to the right.

The advantage of K being 100 was realised, but, due to lack of precision in early instruments, this exact multiplying constant was seldom accurately obtained, its value being usually around 98 to 102. Most vernier instruments still in use today do not have an accurate K value of 100, but most modern tacheometers generally do.

The elimination of the additive constant was achieved by an Italian, J. Porro, in 1840, when he invented the *analactic lens*.

The inclusion of a second convex lens fixed in relation to the object glass had the effect of bringing the apex of the measuring triangle, the analactic point, into exact coincidence with the vertical axis of the instrument, as illustrated in Fig. 79. The stadia formula would now become $D = Ks$, the additive constant being entirely eliminated. Such an externally focusing telescope is known as an *analactic telescope*.

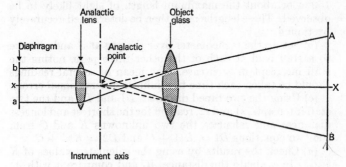

FIG. 79.—*The analactic telescope*

The inclusion of an analactic lens in an external focusing telescope has the effect of moving the analactic point on to the instrument axis.

8. The internal focusing telescope.

In modern surveying telescopes focusing is effected by means of the internal focusing concave lens, as described in VI, 2. By a suitable choice of focal lengths, and relative positioning of lenses and stadia interval, the internal focusing telescope can, for all practical purposes, be considered analactic.

The *stadia formula*, as applied to the internally focusing telescope, is very complicated. The combined focal length of the object glass and focusing lens is no longer a constant and the act of focusing alters slightly the position of the analactic point. However, the linear form of the stadia formula, $D = Ks + C$, is considered to apply, although in this case both K and C are in fact variables. The amount of variation in K and C is negligible for distances greater than 10 m and they are considered as being constants in practice as for the true analactic telescope. The errors which arise in adopting the simple formula as correct are less than 1/1000, which is the greatest accuracy that can be obtained by the stadia method.

9. Evaluation of stadia constants. In most modern surveying telescopes the stadia constant is designed to be 100 and the additive constant 0. To confirm the value of these constants or to establish the stadia constants of an old instrument the following field work should be carried out:

(*a*) Set out four pegs A, B, C and D on fairly level ground such that AB is about 10 m, AC about 100 m and AD about 150 m or about the maximum length of sight likely to be observed. These lengths must then be determined accurately by taping.

(*b*) Set up the tacheometer over the peg at A and observe to a staff held at each of the other three pegs, noting the staff intercept in each case. The mean of several readings should be taken each time to minimise observational errors.

(*c*) Using the two taped distances $D1$ and $D2$ and the two staff intercepts, $s1$ and $s2$, read off for the shortest and longest distances and calculate the two unknowns K and C from the two equations $D1 = Ks1 + C$ and $D2 = Ks2 + C$.

(*d*) Check the results by using the calculated values of K and C to evaluate the distance AC and compare it with its known taped length.

10. Stadia observations with a level. The method of obtaining distances by stadia tacheometry with a level is best illustrated by solving the problem of the following specimen question.

SPECIMEN QUESTION

A level was set up at a point A and observations which were taken to points B and C are given below. The points A, B and C all lie in sequence on one straight line. The stadia constants are 100 and 0.

Readings on to staff at B:

Bottom hair	3·252
Middle hair	2·763
Top hair	2·276

Readings on to staff at C:

	4·033
	Obscured
	2·807

Calculate the distance BC and the difference in height between B and C.

NOTE

(*i*) As the image of the staff is inverted (except in automatic levels) the bottom hair will provide the greater staff reading, as shown in the record of readings, on to the staff at *B*.

(*ii*) It is unnecessary to note the actual intersecting hair and it would not be recorded in practice. The staff readings can simply be noted one below the other as in the second set of observations.

(*iii*) In the observations to *C* the centre hair reading was obscured and will have to be deduced.

SOLUTION

In the first set of readings the staff intercept is $3 \cdot 252 - 2 \cdot 276 = 0 \cdot 976$.

NOTE: Readings may be verified as follows:

First *half* intercept is $3 \cdot 252 - 2 \cdot 763 = 0 \cdot 489$.
Next *half* intercept is $2 \cdot 763 - 2 \cdot 276 = 0 \cdot 487$.

By construction of the stadia hairs both half intervals are equal (*see* 4), so both *half* staff intercepts should be equal. The difference of 2 mm between them is small and is due to minor observational errors and proves that all three readings taken are satisfactory. A difference of more than 10 mm would indicate a gross error of observation in at least one of the readings and re-observation would be required.

In the second set of readings the staff intercept is $4 \cdot 033 - 2 \cdot 807 = 1 \cdot 226$. The obscured reading would be exactly midway between these readings, *i.e.* $3 \cdot 420$, which is proved by equal half intercept readings of $0 \cdot 613$ on either side of the deduced centre hair reading of $3 \cdot 420$. There is, of course, no observational check as explained in the note above if any one of the three readings cannot be taken.

Using the stadia formula $D = Ks + C$, K and C are respectively 100 and 0 and therefore the distance AB, obtained from the first set of readings, is $100 \times 0 \cdot 976 = 97 \cdot 6$ m. Similarly, the second set of readings results in the distance AC being $122 \cdot 6$ m. Therefore the distance BC required is $122 \cdot 6 - 97 \cdot 6 = 25 \cdot 0$ m.

The height difference is obtained in the same way as for ordinary levelling, using the centre hair readings only, $2 \cdot 763 - 3 \cdot 420 = -0 \cdot 657$. Therefore *C* is $0 \cdot 657$ m below the level of *B*.

11. Inclined sights. As height differences between staff positions and instrument increase it will become impossible to use the horizontal line of sight which so far has only been considered. In such cases a tacheometer must be used to provide an inclined line of sight and the angle of elevation or depression must be recorded. The stadia formula must now reflect the angle of inclination of the line of sight and two such cases arise:

(*a*) Where the staff is held *vertically* at the far station.
(*b*) Where the staff is held *normal* to the line of sight from the instrument.

12. Inclined sights with the staff vertical. Figure 80 illustrates an observation of an inclined sight to a staff held

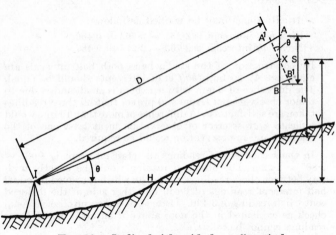

FIG. 80.—*Inclined sight with the staff vertical*

vertically. A, X and B are the readings on the staff and A', X and B' are those which would have been taken had the staff been swung about X to position it at right-angles or normal to the line of sight.

In Fig. 80:

s = the staff intercept AB.
h = the length of the centre hair reading from the staff base.

$V =$ the vertical component XY, the height of the centre hair reading above (or below) the instrument axis.

$D =$ the length of the line of sight IX.

$H =$ the horizontal distance required.

(a) *Reduction of horizontal distance.* From the ordinary stadia formula $D = Ks + C$ it can be seen that the term s in this case is the distance $A'B'$ normal to the line of sight. However, the observed value of s is the length AB, so $A'B'$ actually equals $s \cos \theta$ almost exactly. Therefore the length of the inclined sight $D = Ks \cos \theta + C$, but H, the horizontal distance actually required, obviously equals $D \cos \theta$, therefore the stadia formula now becomes:

$$H = Ks \cos^2 \theta + C \cos \theta$$

(b) *Reduction of the vertical component.* From the right-angled triangle IXY it can be seen that:

$$V = D \sin \theta$$

but

$$D = Ks \cos \theta + C$$

$$\therefore V = Ks \cos \theta \sin \theta + C \sin \theta$$

but

$$\cos \theta \sin \theta = \tfrac{1}{2} \sin 2\theta$$

$$\therefore V = \tfrac{1}{2}Ks \sin 2\theta + C \sin \theta$$

(c) *Simplified formulae.* In instruments where the additive constant is zero these formulae are simplified as follows:

$$H = Ks \cos^2 \theta$$
$$V = \tfrac{1}{2}Ks \sin 2\theta$$

(d) *Reduction of height difference.* To obtain the reduced level at the staff position where the reduced level of the instrument station is known, the height difference between the points is applied as follows:

$$\text{Difference in height} = \text{H.I.} \pm V - h$$

where H.I. $=$ the height of instrument (always positive);

$V =$ the vertical component (positive for angles of elevation, negative for angles of depression);

$h =$ the centre hair reading (always negative).

The reduced level of the instrument position I plus the difference in height equal the reduced level of the staff position S. Therefore:

$$\text{R.L.}_S = \text{R.L.}_I + \text{H.I.} \pm V - h$$

13. Inclined sights with the staff normal.

13. Inclined sights with the staff normal. Figure 81 illustrates the observation on to a staff held normal to an inclined line of sight. The same notation applies as in Fig. 80.

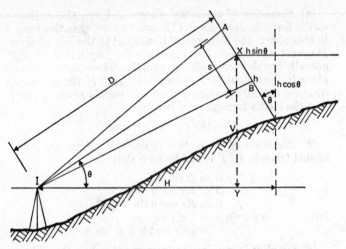

FIG. 81.—*Inclined sight with the staff normal to the line of sight*

(a) *Reduction of horizontal distance.* This time the staff reading normal to the line of sight is the actual reading and does not have to be reduced as in the previous case. Therefore:

$$D = Ks + C$$

but　　$H = D \cos \theta \pm$ (the distance from point X to the vertical through the staff base)

$$\therefore H = (Ks + C) \cos \theta \pm h \sin \theta$$

NOTE: The term $h \sin \theta$ is added for positive, uphill sights and subtracted for negative, downhill sights when the staff leans the other way. Where the value of θ is less than $10°$ the assumption is generally made that the term $h \sin \theta$ is zero.

(b) *Reduction of the vertical component.* As before $V = D \sin \theta$, therefore:

$$V = (Ks + C) \sin \theta$$

(c) *Simplified formulae*. In instruments where the additive constant is zero and the value of θ is less than 10° these formulae may be simplified as follows:

$$H = Ks \cos \theta$$
$$V = Ks \sin \theta$$

(d) *Reduction of height difference*. To obtain the reduced level at the staff position, then the height difference between the points is first reduced as follows:

$$\text{Difference in height} = \text{H.I.} \pm V - h \cos \theta$$

NOTE

(i) The notation is the same as in **12**(d).

(ii) Where θ is less than 10° the assumption is often made that $h \cos \theta = h$, the centre hair reading remaining uncorrected without great loss of accuracy.

14. Comparison of methods.

(a) *When holding the staff:*

(i) The staff can be held vertically with greater ease than in the normal position. Also, it is simpler to plumb a staff with a staff bubble than to hold the staff normal to a line of sight.

(ii) For normal holding it is usually necessary to attach a peep-sight perpendicularly to the face of the staff so that the staffman can sight towards the instrument. A sighting attachment is often not readily available.

(iii) In bush the peep-sight may well be obscured, preventing normal holding, while the upper part of the staff is still available for sighting in the vertically held position.

(iv) The normal position may also be found by swinging the staff until the lowest possible reading of the centre cross hair is obtained. However, in bush and over longer distances it is difficult to signal to the staffman that the correct position has been found.

(b) *Reduction of observations*. The vertical staff reduction formulae in **12** are simpler than the normal staff reduction formulae in **13** when the $h \sin \theta$ and $h \cos \theta$ terms are included in the normal formulae. If these terms are omitted there is little difference in the time it takes to reduce by either method. Published tables and simple computers are available for the reduction of vertical staff observations.

Only in examinations is it ever necessary to reduce observations from first principles. A simple form of tacheometric reduction table is found in Appendix VII.

(c) *Careless staff holding.* Errors of distance and elevation are very much more marked when there is a deviation from the vertical than where there is a deviation from the normal position, especially on steep sights.

(d) *Summary.* The vertical system is the more convenient and is generally preferred despite the loss of accuracy when the staff is not perfectly held, as is often the case. This loss of accuracy becomes so great on sights over 10°, even when a staff bubble is used, that the staff normal position should be resorted to if any reasonable accuracy is to be maintained. For sights inclined at more than 25° to the horizontal the vertically held staff will give results in practice which are quite unreliable.

15. Field book and reductions. Stadia observations are booked in tabular form, the actual layout being largely a matter of personal preference, and may range from six to sixteen columns. A suitable layout of ten columns is illustrated below and may be adapted for any particular requirements.

To (1)	Horizontal circle (2)	H (3)	Stadia (4)	h (5)	Vertical circle (6)	V (7)	±V−h (8)	R.L. (9)	Remarks (10)
			At Station A					30·73	H.I. = 1·35
B	316 22	141·47	3·150 / 1·730	2·440	+3 30	+8·65	+6·21	38·29	Wooden peg
1	10 25	71·45	0·72	1·36	+5 00	+6·25	+4·89	36·97	
2	97 47	102·88	1·03	1·06	−2 00	−3·59	−4·65	27·43	
3	147 42	92·42	0·93	1·35	−4 30	−7·27	−8·62	23·46	
			At Station B					38·29	H.I. = 1·39
A	136 22	141·69	3·060 / 1·640	2·350	−2 40	−6·60	−8·95	30·73	Iron peg
4	210 41	63·60	0·64	1·42	+4 30	+5·01	+3·59	43·27	
5	322 33		0·57	0·95	+2 00				
6	352 42		1·33	1·33	−3 00				
7									

NOTE

(i) The first three columns contain the information used for plotting, showing each station and its bearing and distance.

(ii) The distance AB has been obtained twice. The mean of 141·47 and 141·69, *i.e.* 141·58, provides a check on accuracy and would be used for plotting or calculation.

(*iii*) In the first observation to *B*, instead of recording the three readings one below the other, the centre hair reading is recorded in a separate column to facilitate level reductions. The centre hair reading must still be checked as the mean of the two stadia readings.

(*iv*) In the observations to the numbered points neither stadia reading has been recorded. This method must only be used by experienced surveyors whose reading ability is reliable as readings are at this stage unchecked. This speeds up observing time, however, the operation being to read first the centre hair at the vertical circle setting. The tangent screw is moved to bring the upper hair on to a whole graduation and the staff intercept is read off directly and recorded, frequently with the decimal point omitted. The slight alteration in the angle of the line of sight is insufficient to affect the reduced horizontal distance to any appreciable extent.

(*v*) The horizontal distance *H* and the vertical component *V* may be calculated from the stadia formulae:

$$H = 100s \cos^2 \theta \text{ and}$$
$$V = \tfrac{1}{2}100s \sin 2\theta$$

provided that the stadia constant of the instrument is 100 and the additive constant is 0. Alternatively these values may be obtained from tables. The tacheometric table in Appendix VII is used in the following way:

The staff intercept for $AB = 1.42$, but from the tables the value of $100(\tfrac{1}{2} \sin 2\theta)$ for $3° \ 30' = 6.09$. Therefore $V = 1.42 \times 6.09 = 8.65$. Similarly the value of $100 \cos^2 \theta$ for $3° \ 30' = 99.63$. Therefore $H = 1.42 \times 99.63 = 141.47$.

(*vi*) Column 8 facilitates reduction and contains the vertical component *V*, from which is subtracted the centre hair reading, *e.g.* in the first observation $8.65 - 2.44 = +6.21$.

(*vii*) The reduced levels of each staff position are obtained by adding the height of instrument to the known reduced level of the station and then adding, or subtracting as the case may be, the values recorded in column 8, *e.g.* in the first observation $30.73 + 1.35 + 6.21 = 38.29$.

16. Accuracy of stadia observations.

(*a*) *Accuracy of distance measurement.* Under ideal conditions it should be possible to obtain an accuracy of 0·01 per cent in distance measurement, but this is seldom achieved in practice. Using an ordinary levelling staff with

10-mm divisions practical accuracies approximate to the following:

Distance	20 m	100 m	150 m
Accuracy	± 100 mm	± 200 mm	± 300 mm

(b) *Accuracy of height measurement.* Provided that the staff is held vertically with reasonable care and angles of sighting are less than 10°, then heights should be accurate to within 0·01 per cent of the sighting distance.

NOTE: Though the distances H in column 3 in **15** and the R.L.s in column 9 are usually reduced to two decimal places to allow for rounding off, it must be realised that their accuracy is not likely to be better than 0·1 m.

THE TANGENTIAL SYSTEM

17. General principles. In this system the paralactic angle subtended by a known length of staff is measured directly. Figure 82 illustrates the method where observations are taken to an ordinary levelling staff held vertically.

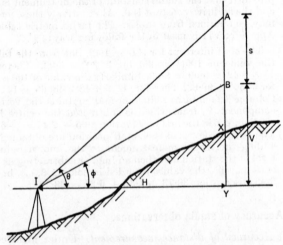

FIG. 82.—*The tangential system of tacheometry*

The distance H and the height difference between stations can be obtained from the tangents of two vertical angle observations.

The instrument is set up and the vertical circle is read on both faces to give the angle of elevation (or depression) to a whole staff graduation. This process is repeated to another whole graduation to give as large a staff intercept, s, as possible.

From the staff intercept and the two observed vertical angles θ and ϕ the horizontal distance H may be calculated as follows:

$$AY = H \tan \theta \text{ and}$$
$$BY = H \tan \phi$$
$$AY - BY = s = H(\tan \theta - \tan \phi)$$
$$\therefore H = \frac{s}{(\tan \theta - \tan \phi)} \text{ or for sights downhill,}$$
$$H = \frac{s}{(\tan \phi - \tan \theta)}$$

The difference in height between the instrument station and the staff station is found as follows:

The vertical component $V = BY = H \tan \phi$, and the height difference = H.I. $\pm V - BX$.

This calculation can be checked by using $AY = H \tan \theta$ instead, when the height difference = H.I. $\pm V - AX$.

18. Accuracy of the tangential system. The accuracy of this method is no greater than for ordinary stadia observations in practice even when angles are read with a single-second theodolite. The three reasons for this are as follows:

(*a*) The sight lines at different elevations are influenced by differing conditions of *refraction*, which affect the accuracy of the angular measurements.

(*b*) On *steep sights* non-verticality of the staff causes considerable error in the calculated distance.

(*c*) A small *displacement* of staff or bubble between the measure of the two angles can cause a large error in the calculated distance.

NOTE: The tangential system compares unfavourably with the stadia method in the speed of observations and, although it is a simple system in practice and theory, because of these points it is seldom used except as a theoretical exercise.

19. The subtense system. This is a particular form of the tangential system where the measured base is held horizontally as illustrated in Fig. 83 instead of vertically. The paralactic angle is measured with greater accuracy using the horizontal circle instead of the vertical circle. The horizontally held base is specially made for this purpose and is known as a *subtense bar* (*see* 20).

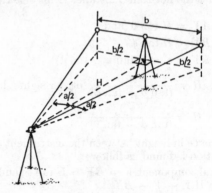

FIG. 83.—*The subtense bar*

The horizontal angle subtended by a subtense bar of length *b* is measured with a theodolite.

20. The subtense bar.

Instead of the usual graduated staff the subtense bar is a specially made instrument supported on a tripod with two sighting targets set a precise distance apart, usually 2 m. Other features incorporated in the instrument are the following:

(*a*) *A central target*. This is placed midway between the end targets for traverse angle measurement and for use in sighting with the auxiliary base method (*see* 25).

(*b*) *A sighting device*. This is fixed at right-angles to the line of the bar so that it may be positioned at right-angles to the line of sight from the theodolite.

(*c*) *A low coefficient of expansion*. As temperature affects the bar length, the subtense bar targets are usually attached to invar rods or wires, which have a low coefficient of expansion, so that their nominal distance apart remains almost constant; *e.g.* the length of the Kern invar subtense bar is guaranteed to remain constant within a tolerance of

$\pm 0\cdot03$ mm, which is too small to be measured with a single-second theodolite.

(*d*) *Illumination.* The targets may be lit from behind for night observations, which have the advantage of a less disturbed atmosphere resulting in increased accuracy in the angular measurement.

21. Calculation of distance. From Fig. 83 it can be seen that the horizontal distance

$$H = \frac{b}{2} \cot \frac{a}{2}$$

because half the bar length divided by the perpendicular bisector of the isosceles triangle is the tangent of half the measured angle *a*.

In the usual case where the bar *b* is 2 m long this means that the distance is simply the co-tangent of half the measured angle, so that no calculations are involved. To save even halving the measured angle the manufacturers supply tables giving distances in terms of the whole paralactic angle measured.

NOTE: As the paralactic angle is measured on the horizontal plane the distance obtained is always the *horizontal distance* and no slope corrections are ever necessary however far above or below the theodolite the subtense bar may be.

22. Height difference. If height differences between theodolite and bar stations are required then a vertical angle θ must be measured to the line of the bar and the vertical component calculated simply from the formula $V = H \tan \theta$. In addition the height of the theodolite above its station (H.I.) and the height of the bar above its station (H.B.) must be measured and then the height difference between stations $= +\text{H.I.} \pm V - \text{H.B.}$

NOTE: By positioning the bar at instrument height the terms H.I. and H.B. cancel each other out and the height difference between stations will be the calculated vertical component *V*.

23. Accuracy of subtense measurements.

(*a*) *Accuracy of distance measurement.* The subtense method provides the most accurate of all tacheometric systems, although errors in distance tend to increase in proportion to the square of the distance.

Assuming that it is possible to measure the paralactic angle accurately to $\pm 1''$ by taking the mean of several observations on both faces with a single-second theodolite, then the error in an individual measurement can be found approximately from the expression:

$$E = \frac{H^2}{400\ 000}$$

where E is the error and H the distance measured.

Accordingly the following errors are likely to exist:

Distance (m)	20	50	100	150	300	400	500
Error (mm)	1	6	25	56	225	400	625
Accuracy	1/20 000	1/8000	1/4000	1/2700	1/1300	1/1000	1/800

NOTE

(*i*) These figures are approximate and assume that the angle has been measured to $\pm 1''$. In the field it is often not possible to guarantee this degree of accuracy and probably a measurement to $\pm 2''$ is more likely, when the accuracies shown above must be halved.

(*ii*) For distances less than 20 m, accuracy is not increased as the formula might indicate because of the increasing error in the angle measurement due to sighting the target at an angle.

(*iii*) Accuracies of 1/20 000 can be maintained over longer distances by using geodetic-type theodolites or by repetitive observations of the angle over different portions of the theodolite circle.

(*b*) *Accuracy of height measurement.* This is about the same as for ordinary stadia observations, about 0·01 per cent of the distance up to about 150 m, after which the effects of refraction rapidly decrease accuracy.

24. Subdivided sections. If a line is to be measured using a subtense bar and the distance is such that a single observation will not provide the required accuracy, it can be measured in a number of equal sections. This will reduce the overall error of a single observation. The resulting error can be roughly judged by dividing the error of the single observation by $\sqrt{n^3}$, where $n =$ the number of sections used.

For example, in the measurement of the distance of 100 m the error is shown in **23** to be 25 mm for $\pm 1''$ accuracy. If instead the subtense bar is set up midway and the angle is measured from each end of the line to the bar in the middle then the error in the total measurement by two sections is likely to be:

$$\frac{25}{\sqrt{2^3}} = \frac{25}{2 \cdot 83} = 9 \text{ mm}$$

This shows that a measurement of 100 m can be measured to an accuracy of 1/11 000 instead of only 1/4000.

25. Auxiliary base method. Instead of subdividing a long line into several short sections as described in **24**, which entails a lot of extra work, the auxiliary base method may be used, as illustrated in Fig. 84.

It is required to measure the distance AC, which is about

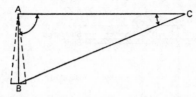

FIG. 84.—*The subtense auxiliary base*

The length AC can be obtained by measuring the length AB by subtense bar and the triangle is solved for ABC after measuring the angles at A and C. Accuracy of measurement of AC is greatly increased by measuring AB precisely by taping in catenary. This is known as the Hunter short base, first devised by Dr J. de Graaf Hunter of the Survey of India.

500 m long. With the theodolite at A and the subtense bar at B the paralactic angle is measured and the distance AB obtained. Angle BAC is also measured. The theodolite is next set up at C and the new paralactic angle ACB is measured, sighting to the central target on the subtense bar. The length AC is calculated by solving the triangle ABC in which one side and two angles are known.

The overall error in the calculated length of AC, assuming $\pm 1''$ accuracy of angular measurement, is considerably less than the 625-mm error of a single observation, being about 55 mm only. By measuring the same distance in eight equal sections, the error is likely to be ± 27 mm, but the saving in time may well compensate for this loss of accuracy, which is still of the order of 1/9000, or more than ten times greater than that of the single measurement.

THE OPTICAL-WEDGE SYSTEM

26. The Richards wedge. If the cross hairs of a theodolite are sighted on a whole graduation of a staff the line of sight can be considered to pass through this point. If a wedge of glass is placed in front of the object glass, the line of sight will appear to shift along the staff and take a new position, owing to refraction.

This shift in the line of sight can be read off the staff and, if the wedge allowed an angular deflection of 34′ 22·6″, the ratio of shift to distance from the theodolite would be 1/100. Thus by multiplying the shift measured on the staff by 100, the distance from the staff to the instrument may be obtained.

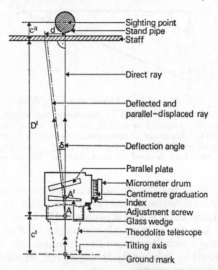

[*Courtesy of Wild Heerbrugg, Switzerland*

FIG. 85.—*The Wild DM 1 precision telemeter attachment*

A measurement is obtained between the ground mark at the theodolite to the sighting point at the base of the staff-supporting stand pipe.

27. Application of the Richards wedge principle. Various instrument manufacturers have adopted this principle. In its simplest form the wedge is incorporated in an attachment known as a *telemeter* (*see* Fig. 85, which shows the Wild

DM 1 telemeter). Here the wedge only covers roughly the centre half of the object aperture. As a result two images of the staff are produced, one shifted relative to the other. By a special division and colouring and the use of a vernier on the staff, as illustrated in Fig. 86, it can be read directly to 1 mm, or the equivalent of 0·1 m in distance. This instrument includes an optical micrometer, as described in X, **16**, which allows a precise vernier setting to be made. This additional

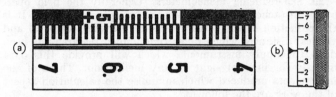

FIG. 86.—*Reading the Wild telemeter*

(*a*) The image of the staff with the vernier superimposed against it providing a reading of 50 m against the vernier index. The fifth line of the vernier is in coincidence providing a total course reading of 50·5 m. The vernier in use shows a +5 or 50 m constant, giving a total course reading of 100·5 m.

(*b*) The micrometer drum used for setting the vernier image to a whole graduation. The micrometer drum reads 0·04 m, thus providing a total distance measurement of 100·54 m.

Note that improving the micrometer reading by estimation to 0·039 as shown provides a measure to millimetres, which is beyond the capability of the instrument.

shift is read off the micrometer drum as shown to 0·1 mm, or 10 mm in distance.

28. Accuracy of double-image tacheometers. Under ideal conditions it is possible to measure a length of 100 m to ±20 mm, giving an accuracy of about 1/5000. In field conditions individual observations are probably accurate to ±50 mm in the range 20 to 150 m, although, owing to compensating errors, traverse closures of 1/3000 are readily obtainable.

NOTE

(*i*) Unlike the subtense bar the distances thus obtained are the *slope* distances of the line of sight and must be reduced to the horizontal by multiplying the observed distance by the cosine of the vertical angle of observation or by using slope tables.

(ii) Height differences are obtained using the measure of the vertical angle as in ordinary stadia measurements. Where the telemeter staff is held horizontally the vertical component $V = 100s \sin \theta$, where s is the horizontal shift along the staff. Accuracy, as in stadia measurements, is about 0·01 per cent of the sighting distance.

29. Self-reducing tacheometers. Generally the field operations of tacheometric observing are simple and direct. It is the reduction of the observations to provide horizontal and vertical distances which takes time. Much research has been done to supply instruments which will provide this data directly for lines of sight at any inclination. Three of the instruments produced which minimise the calculation aspect of the work are the following:

(a) Beaman's stadia arc which contains two scales called the H-scale and the V-scale which rotate equally with the vertical circle and are read in the same way (*see* VI, **27**) but without the micrometer adjustment.

(b) The Ewing stadia-altimeter which consists of two parts added to a normal theodolite. One is a cylindrical scale unit, mounted on top of one of the standards, and which has a drum engraved with two sets of curves, and the other part is an optical reader mounted on the telescope and moving with it near the side of the drum.

(c) Tacheometers such as the Wild RDS which allow the stadia interval to alter in proportion to the angle of the line of sight as they are engraved on a rotating glass circle inside the telescope. They eliminate the $\cos^2 \theta$ term and simplify the $\frac{1}{2} \sin 2\theta$ term to multiplication by a simple constant seen in the field of view.

NOTE

(i) These three instruments operate on different systems and, although effective in their way, have not been universally adopted and are now being superseded by self-reducing tacheometers based on the Richards wedge principle.

(ii) The moving cross hair geared to the telescope has been improved in recent years and ordinary stadia accuracy has been slightly increased by the use of specially graduated staffs. The Kern self-reducing tacheometer model DK RV is an example of such an instrument. Such tacheometers are special developments of individual manufacturers and are still basically stadia instruments with modifications.

30. Self-reducing double-image tacheometers. These are very refined instruments capable of providing directly the horizontal and, in some cases, the vertical components of a line. Details of construction vary between manufacturers and the operation of the optical and mechanical features of these instruments cannot be examined in detail here. Very broadly the general principles of such instruments are as follows:

(*a*) Instead of a single deflecting wedge, as in the telemeter, there are *two wedges*, the combined effect of which on a horizontal line of sight is to provide a lateral deflection, which will enable the distance to be read off a horizontally held staff, as in the telemeter.

(*b*) As the line of sight is inclined up or down, these two wedges, geared to the telescope, rotate in opposite directions, thus altering the amount of deflection. The effect of this *altering deflection* is always to provide a staff reading which reflects the horizontal distance.

(*c*) An *optical micrometer* is incorporated within the instrument, enabling accurate vernier settings to be made on the staff so that distances can be read off directly to 0·01 m.

31. Self-reducing vertical measurements. These are made in one of two ways:

(*a*) *Tangents.* In some instruments the natural tangents of the angles of slope are graduated on the vertical circle. These are read off directly and by multiplying with a slide-rule by the horizontal distance previously obtained, the vertical distance between the horizontal staff and the tacheometer axis can be simply calculated. In this respect these instruments are not wholly self-reducing.

(*b*) *Wedge adjustment.* In the Wild RDH the vertical component is obtained by direct observation. This is achieved by first adjusting the wedges so that no deflection takes place with a horizontal line of sight, as is necessary for distance measurement. As the telescope is then rotated in the vertical plane the wedges rotate again giving a deflection, which, when read off the horizontal staff, gives the vertical height between the telescope and the staff. For convenience the staff is usually fixed at the same height above the station mark as the tacheometer is set up above its station. Thus the reading obtained provides the actual height difference between station points.

NOTE

(*i*) Owing to the lens arrangement of self-reducing double-image tacheometers the apex of the measuring triangle does not coincide with the instrument's vertical axis. Also the apex moves as the telescope is tilted in the vertical plane. Such a telescope is not *analactic* (*see* 7) and an adjustment should be applied to the staff reading.

(*ii*) The constant part of this adjustment is usually allowed for by a displacement of the staff verniers and in the graduation of the micrometer drum. The variable part, which is always negative and varies as the versine of the angle of slope, is small enough to be neglected in most distance measurements.

(*iii*) In the Wild RDH this variable can be read off an auxiliary scale for both the horizontal and vertical measurements. It is included in this instrument because the variable for vertical measurement varies as the sine of the angle of slope and is thus large enough to affect the value. It is positive for angles of elevation and negative for angles of depression. For a vertical angle of $+20°$ the horizontal variable has the value -4 mm and the vertical variable has the value of $+25$ mm.

32. Code tacheometers. Recent developments in tacheometry include instruments in which the measured distances and angles are recorded in coded form on film. The film data are transferred to tapes and co-ordinates are determined by electronic computer. These co-ordinates can then be used for computer plotting of the points themselves. The human source of error in reading, recording and reducing observations is thus entirely eliminated.

33. Accuracy of self-reducing tacheometers. The accuracy claimed for the Wild RDH self-reducing tacheometer, for example, is as follows:

(a) *For horizontal distances.* Accuracy of ± 20 mm in 100 m.

(b) *For height differences.* Accuracy of ± 50 mm over sights of 100 m.

THE RANGE-FINDER SYSTEM

34. General principles. Strictly speaking the range-finder system is not a true tacheometric method as no staff or instrument needs to be set up at the point to which observations are being made. The base of the measuring triangle is at the instrument and the paralactic angle is defined at the forward station by obtaining coincidence of its image from both ends of the base which forms part of the instrument.

35. The range finder. This instrument consists of a tube of fixed length with two reflecting mirrors or prisms positioned at either end. The observer looks through a centrally placed eyepiece and sees the image of the object reflected from the left-hand end prism, at the same time seeing the image reflected from the right-hand end prism, the two parts of the images being displaced relative to one another. The rays of light from the right-hand side are deflected through a wedge-shaped prism, which can be moved to alter the amount of deflection. By altering the position of the wedge the two images seen in the eyepiece can be brought into coincidence. This prism carries a *range scale* which moves with it and once the images are in coincidence the range can be read off in the eyepiece. In earlier instruments coincidence was obtained by rotation of one of the end-reflecting mirrors to which the range scale was attached.

The range finder has military applications but is seldom used in land surveying, except for some reconnaissance work, because of the following reasons:

(a) The *minimum range* is normally about 250 m.

(b) The range finder is not normally fitted with a horizontal circle and *angular measurements* cannot be made so that the direction of the distance measured cannot be established. However, the Wild TM 10 range finder is an exception as it does have both horizontal and vertical circles which can be read to 6' by estimation.

(*c*) *Levels* cannot be determined.

(*d*) *Accuracy* is comparatively poor, being less than 1/1000 at the shortest range and falling off rapidly in proportion to the square of the distance to less than 1/100 at 1000 m for a 1-m base range finder.

36. The Zeiss Teletop. The range-finder principle has been applied in the Zeiss Teletop, as illustrated in Fig. 87. In this instrument a unique telescopic arrangement is fitted with both horizontal and vertical circles and a detachable base arm. A

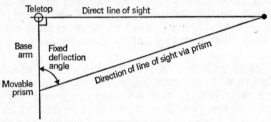

FIG. 87.—*The Teletop principle*

The direct distance from the Teletop is in proportion to the length along the base arm to the deflecting prism.

prism in a sliding carriage is fitted on this arm and provides a set angle of deflection. Two images of the object sighted are seen in the telescope's field of view, one image being reflected off the prism on the base arm. By moving this prism so that coincidence of the images is obtained, the base length of the measuring triangle, with a fixed paralactic angle, is read off the measuring bar. Depending on the deflection angle of the prism used, the slope distance can be deduced from this measure.

This instrument has many advantages but is more useful in exploration and reconnaissance work than in site or engineering surveys for the following reasons:

(*a*) It is *easily portable* in rough country. The weight of the instrument alone is only about 3 kg as opposed to the 7·2 kg of the Wild RDH.

(*b*) The *accuracy* of distance measurement is not great, being about 1/750 up to 60 m. By altering the base prism to give a 1/1000 deflection, the range can be increased, but accuracy tends to drop to about 1/100.

(c) Trees and building heights can be determined with ease, and even perpendicular distances to overhead wires can be directly obtained.

NOTE: Although the principle of the Teletop is similar to that of the range finder, there is one essential difference. The range finder has a *fixed base length* and the value of the *paralactic angle is altered* by deflection of the light rays. The Teletop has a fixed paralactic angle and it is the base length which is altered.

PROGRESS TEST 12

1. What is meant by the term "tacheometry"? **(1)**
2. Describe the basic principle upon which tacheometric measurements are based. **(2)**
3. What are the main differences between the four systems of tacheometry? **(3)**
4. Show how the stadia formula is derived for an external focusing telescope providing a horizontal line of sight. **(5)**
5. What is the effect of an analactic lens? **(7)**
6. Why is a modern internal focusing telescope considered to be analactic when it does not contain an analactic lens? **(8)**
7. How would you evaluate the stadia constants of a tacheometer? **(9)**
*8. A level with internal focusing was set up at A on the straight line ABC, B and C being on the same side of the instrument. Foliage partially obstructed the view when the following readings were taken:

Readings on to staff held at B: 2·753
                                        Obscured
                                        2·377

Readings on to staff held at C: Obscured
                                         1·956
                                         1·533

Use the following data:

(a) The stadia constant is 100 and the additive constant is 0.
(b) The reduced level of A is 10·000 m.
(c) The height of instrument is 1·450 m.

Evaluate the following:

(i) The reduced levels of B and C.
(ii) The horizontal distance between B and C. **(10)**

9. Show that $H = Ks \cos^2\theta$ and $V = \frac{1}{2}Ks \sin 2\theta$ for inclined sights to a vertically held staff when the additive constant is 0. **(11)**

10. Show that $H = (Ks + C) \cos \theta \pm h \sin \theta$ and that the difference in height = H.I. $\pm (Ks + C) \sin \theta - h \cos \theta$ for inclined sights to a staff held normal to the line of sight. (13)

11. Compare the relative advantages and disadvantages of the methods of stadia tacheometry with the staff vertical and with the staff normal. (14)

*12. Calculate from first principles the horizontal distances and the reduced levels of the staff positions numbers 5 and 6 omitted from the reduction sheet in 15, using the stadia formulae. Check your results by repeating the calculations with the aid of the tacheometric tables. (15)

13. Show that when two angles of elevation θ and ϕ are observed to graduations on a vertical staff a distance s apart then the horizontal distance to the staff

$$H = \frac{s}{(\tan \theta - \tan \phi)} \qquad (17)$$

14. Describe the main features of a subtense bar. (20)

15. Why is it unnecessary to reduce distances obtained from subtense measurement to the horizontal? (21)

16. Describe two methods by which the accuracy of subtense measurement can be maintained over longer distances. (24–25)

17. What is a Richards wedge and how does it allow distances to be obtained optically? (26–27)

18. Describe the general principles involved in self-reducing tacheometers (29–32)

19. Describe briefly the operation of the Teletop and state its special advantages. How does it differ from the range finder? (35–36)

CHAPTER XIII

CONTOURING

CONTOUR LINES

1. Definition of contours. In I, **9,** a contour line was described as a line on a map representing a line joining points of equal height on the ground. A more accurate definition is that contours are the *intersection* of level surfaces with the surface of the earth. The contour interval is the height difference between the level surfaces adopted to define the contours. These definitions satisfactorily cover the characteristics which contour lines, the map representations of contours, display. Most of the characteristics of contour lines are obvious, but some are not and these should be borne in mind if false interpretation in map reading and errors in interpolation (*see* **18**) and plotting are to be avoided.

2. Contour characteristics. The fact that steep ground is indicated where contour lines run close together and flat ground where they are widely separated enables the *relief* or ground shape to be read from a contour map. Other less obvious characteristics are as follows:

(*a*) Contours of different elevations can only *unite* to form one line or *cross* in the case of a vertical or overhanging cliff seldom found naturally. At steep cliffs the lines would have to run so close together as to be illegible. A symbol, such as the Ordnance Survey cliff marking, would normally be used instead under these circumstances.

(*b*) A single contour line *cannot split* into two lines of the same elevation. Also it is impossible for a single contour line of higher or lower value to run between two contour lines of equal value. It may be argued that a level ridge at the height of a particular contour would be indicated, but such a ridge is unlikely to exist naturally and a contour is a line of intersection. If the level surface touches the ground tangentially no contour occurs. It must intersect the ground and pass right through to leave it again, resulting in *two* separate contours, however close together, of the same elevation.

(*c*) A contour line cannot simply *end*. It must close back on itself, although not necessarily within any one map. The shore-line of a still lake forms the perfect example of a contour.

(*d*) The *steepest slope* is indicated by the normal to the contour lines, thus a water course or water-shed will run at right-angles to the contours.

3. Direct and indirect contouring. Contouring consists of the surveying and plotting of contour lines on a map or plan, which may be done in one of two ways:

(*a*) *By direct contouring*. This consists of two processes:

(*i*) *Vertical control*, which is the actual location of the contours' positions on the ground.

(*ii*) *Horizontal control*, which is the surveying of their positions to enable them to be plotted.

(*b*) *By indirect contouring*. Here the contours are not located on the ground, their positions being established from the plotted plan.

4. General principles. The following principles apply equally to both the direct and indirect methods of contouring:

(*a*) The *degree of accuracy* in locating the contours depends on the scale and use of the plan to be produced. The contour interval depends on the following:

(*i*) *Cost*. The smaller the interval the greater is the amount of work involved, which produces higher costs.

(*ii*) *Type of country*. Steep, rough country can be clearly shown by a fairly large interval, which would be inadequate for flat ground.

(*iii*) *Purpose of the survey*. A small interval is needed for detailed design and the measurement of earthworks. For topographical mapping a large interval of 10 or 20 m is often adequate.

NOTE: Practical contour intervals often adopted are for the following:

Building sites	0·5 or 1 m
Reservoirs, landscapes and town plans	1 or 2 m
Location surveys	2 to 5 m
General topographical work	5 m upwards

(b) The points surveyed should be chosen so that the contours run *nearly straight* between them. More points should be surveyed where sharp curves exist and salient points on ridge and valley lines are always important.

5. Levels without contours. On small sites and in built-up areas contour lines are often omitted as sufficient information can be obtained from the plotted levels themselves. In such areas the vertical control is usually obtained from level observations. Horizontal control is achieved by relating the staff positions to features on the ground, which have been, or are to be, surveyed and plotted. Measurements taken from fences, wall corners, etc., to the various staff positions are scaled off on the plot to locate the various spot height positions and the reduced level of the point is then recorded on the plan.

6. Uses of contoured maps and plans. Apart from the obvious use of the interpretation of the relief of an area of land shown on a map by reading the contour lines, some other uses of contoured maps and plans are the following:

(a) *Sections* can be drawn along any line which is shown in plan. The horizontal distances are marked off along a datum line where the various contour lines intersect the line of section. Each contour elevation is then scaled off along ordinates drawn at these points in the usual way as described in XI, **11**.

(b) *Intervisibility*, which means the ability to see directly between two points, can be established either by drawing a section as in (a) or by interpolating along the line being tested the heights along an even gradient. A comparison of these heights with the contour heights on the plan will show whether or not a straight line of sight intersects the ground. For true intervisibility allowance should be made for foliage and refraction.

(c) *Earthworks* can be measured. This is described in detail in XIV, **24–27**.

(d) *Contour gradients* can be traced. A contour gradient is a line on the surface of the ground which maintains a constant gradient or angle of slope. The path of such a line can be traced on the ground or on a plan if its gradient and starting point are known.

NOTE: To trace a contour gradient on a plan set a pair of compasses to a radius equal in length to the gradient multiplied by the contour interval. For example, if the gradient is to be 1 in 50 and the contour interval is 2 m, set the pair of compasses to scale off 100 m. This means that at this gradient one must go 100 m to rise 2 m.

Place the compass point on a given point on one contour line and intersect the next contour line above. The line joining these two points is 100 m long and rises 2 m, therefore it has the required gradient. The process is continued following the shortest possible route between the two points to be joined by a maximum gradient of 1:50.

THE DIRECT METHOD

7. Direct vertical control. The process in the field may be summarised as follows:

(a) Complete a checked circuit of levels from an Ordnance Survey bench-mark to establish a T.B.M. adjacent to the site but clear of any eventual construction work so that the mark will not be destroyed.

(b) Set the level to command as much ground as possible, observe a backsight to the T.B.M., deduce the height of instrument and calculate the readings to be observed for each contour.

Take the following readings as an example:

$$\begin{array}{ll} \text{R.L. of T.B.M.} & 21 \cdot 736 \\ \text{B.S. to T.B.M.} & 2 \cdot 072 \\ \hline \text{H.I.} & 23 \cdot 808 \end{array}$$

Reading on staff for 20-m contour = 3·81
Reading on staff for 21-m contour = 2·81
Reading on staff for 22-m contour = 1·81
Reading on staff for 23-m contour = 0·81

NOTE: In levelling for contouring, sights to the staff held on the ground do not require 1-mm accuracy.

(c) Taking one contour at a time, mark the required reading on the staff with a piece of tape for speed of location and direct the staffman uphill or downhill at the edge of the site until the required reading is obtained.

(d) When he is signalled to mark, the staffman places a peg marked with the contour height.

(e) The staffman then proceeds forward along the same level and holds the staff where he assumes the contour to have changed direction and the previous process is repeated.

(f) Having pegged one complete contour visible from the instrument the next one is dealt with and pegged in the same way.

NOTE: The method of pegging one complete contour each time is preferable to fixing adjacent points on several contours as this takes longer and is more liable to error.

(g) When the whole area visible from the instrument has been covered a foresight is observed. The instrument is moved to another position to cover more of the site and the same process is repeated. The instrument is moved again after this set of observations is complete, until the whole site has been pegged and a final foresight can be taken back on to the T.B.M., thus completing the level circuit.

8. Direct horizontal control. With the contours now pegged on the ground the peg positions must be surveyed to enable them to be plotted. This can be done in one of three ways:

(a) *With a chain survey.* This is suitable for small areas. The area is triangulated by a chain survey network of lines and the pegs are located by means of offsets in the usual way (*see* II, **28**).

(b) *With a control traverse.* Here more suitably positioned survey lines can be established in order to offset the pegs by running a series of traverse lines close to the peg positions (*see* IX, **3**).

(c) *With polars.* The bearing and distance from traverse stations or triangulated control points can be observed to the various peg positions. Bearings can be obtained from compass or theodolite observations and the distances by direct taping or tacheometric observations (*see* IX, **17** (*i*)).

9. Plotting. The peg positions are plotted from the data obtained from the horizontal control survey and the heights of each are recorded. Finally the contour lines are drawn as *curves* running through the peg positions denoting each contour.

THE INDIRECT METHOD

10. Indirect contouring. In the indirect method the points located do not necessarily fall on the actual contours. The points surveyed are plotted and their heights recorded and then the points serve as a basis for the interpolation of the contour positions. There are two basic systems in this method:

(*a*) The points to be surveyed are located along series of *straight lines* set out over the site to be contoured. This facilitates the horizontal control (*see* **11–14**).

(*b*) *Spot heights*, the points to be surveyed, are *scattered* over the area, being chosen to fall at salient positions of change of slope known as *representative points* (*see* **15**).

11. Horizontal control by straight lines using cross-sections. In this system cross-sections are set out at right-angles to traverse lines to cover the whole site. The staff is then held at intervals along the cross-sectional lines, the whole operation taking place as described in XI, **16–20**. The staff positions are plotted in plan along the plotted positions of the cross-sectional lines, the reduced level of each also being recorded preparatory to the contour interpolation.

12. Horizontal control by straight lines using grid squares. This is the most popular method of contouring because the process is simple to understand, it can be carried out by relatively inexperienced operators, staff positions can be re-established and it produces levels over a site in a form which allows earthworks to be simply, if inaccurately, calculated.

13. Setting out the grid. The grid may be set out in several ways, but whichever method is adopted it is never necessary to peg every grid intersection. The two following are the most common methods:

(*a*) The grid interval, say 10 m, is pegged out along one of the survey lines used for surveying the site. At each end of the grid run a right-angle is turned off and the grid interval is pegged off down each line. At the end of the whole grid rectangle the fourth side is pegged in the same way. If a central cross is also pegged out as indicated in Fig. 88, then every point can be defined by lining in two marked points at right-angles. This method is theoretically satisfactory, but not very practical owing to the large number of ranging rods needed for the whole layout. It can be done more simply by using a load of 1-m long plasterer's laths.

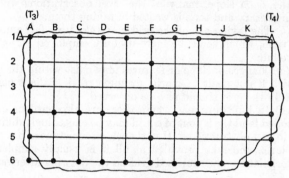

FIG. 88.—*Grid levelling*

The field book sketch of a grid layout off a survey line T_3–T_4 is shown, with the method of numbering and lettering each line to define every point. The maximum number of grid intersections which may need to be marked to define every intersection point on the ground are shown accented.

(b) A more practical method is to peg out the base line *AL* as before, using available twigs if insufficient wooden pegs are available. Then *A1A6* and *L1L6*, say 50 m each, are measured out. Line *A6L6* is then pegged as before. By ranging a tape along the line *A1A6* the staff can be held at every 10 m, the tape itself providing the line. The same process is repeated for the line *B1B6* and so on. The position at which the staff is held is noted in the remarks column of the level book each time, *e.g. D6, E6, E5* and so on. A sketch of the grid layout including the reference letters and numbers is also noted in the field book, showing its relation to the original survey lines so that the grid network can easily be plotted. After reduction of the field book the

R.L.s are noted against the appropriate grid intersections ready for interpolation.

14. Faults of grid levelling. Although popular this method has several faults which must be borne in mind when grid levelling is used for any particular survey, and they are as follows:

(*a*) A large number of levels are observed simply to complete the grid. If part of the area obviously consists of a plane, even slope, many of the level observations will be unnecessary and time is wasted in taking them.

(*b*) The laying out of the grid may take up a fair amount of time, which could be more usefully employed on actual levelling.

(*c*) Changes of slope or features may exist within the grid which if not dealt with will go unrecorded. Salient points within the grid should also be observed.

(*d*) In built-up areas where there are also gardens or in wooded land the layout of a grid may be exceedingly difficult owing to obstructions. Under such circumstances if a grid of levels must be provided at all it is usually simpler to interpolate a superimposed grid on the drawing afterwards.

15. Contouring from spot heights. This is the method most commonly adopted for larger areas. Provided the choice of the positions of the representative points is properly made, without leaving out important changes of slope, it is accurate and keeps the number of spot heights needed to be observed and plotted to a minimum.

16. Field work of spot-height contouring. The procedure involved is as follows:

(*a*) Suitable *stations* are surveyed by traversing or triangulation to command the area and the levels of these points are established by a levelling circuit from a T.B.M., the reduced level of which was established as in **7** (*a*).

(*b*) *Observations* from each station are made to the staff held at salient points. The bearing, distance and level sights to these points are recorded.

(*c*) *Bearings* are observed with a level incorporating a horizontal circle or with a tacheometer.

(*d*) *Distances* may be obtained by direct taping or by some form of tacheometry, ordinary stadia observations being most commonly used.

(e) *Height differences* may be obtained from ordinary levelling observations, but on steep ground this limits the area which can be covered from any one station. It is therefore usual to use whenever necessary a tacheometer, observing inclined sights to staff positions as described in XII, **11**.

17. Plotting spot heights. When the field book has been reduced (*see* XII, **15**), the staff positions are plotted from their bearings and distances. This is frequently done when plotting on transparent plastic sheeting by laying the sheet over a printed protractor. The sheet is then oriented and adjusted until the survey station lies at the centre of the protractor. By laying a scale from the centre point across each bearing seen through the plotting sheet the bearing is obtained and the relevant distance can be scaled off. The reduced level of the point is recorded, the decimal point frequently being used to mark the position of the spot height. When all points have been plotted and their levels recorded the drawing is ready for the interpolation of the contours.

18. Interpolation of contour lines. Interpolation is the process of locating in plan any required levels along a line joining two known levels. In Fig. 89 two points with levels of

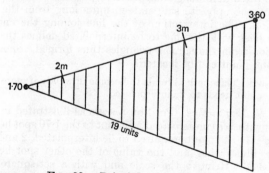

Fig. 89.—*Principle of interpolation*

The geometry of the random line graphical method of dividing a line into any required number of parts is shown.

1·70 and 3·60 m are shown plotted. It is required to locate along the line joining them the position of level 2·00 and 3·00 m.

The height difference between these points is 3·60 − 1·70 = 1·90 m. It is assumed that there is an even slope from level 1·70 to level 3·60. Therefore in travelling between them the overall rise will be 1·90 m and in travelling one-nineteenth of the distance between them the rise will be 0·10 m. If the line is divided into nineteen equal parts by the random line as shown, the first three spaces will indicate a rise of 3 × 0·1 m, i.e. 0·30 + 1·70 = 2·00 m, which is one of the points required. The next ten spaces cover the rise of 1 m from 2 to 3 m, and the final six spaces carry through to the known level of 3·60 m.

When all the required whole-metre height positions have been interpolated over the entire plan the final contour lines are drawn in as curved lines through the interpolated points, as described in **9**.

19. Interpolation aids. It is in fact cumbersome to interpolate from first principles by the method indicated in **18**. Several alternative interpolation methods exist of which the following, illustrated in Fig. 90, are the most common:

(a) *Similar triangles method.* In Fig. 90 (a) the position of the 2-m point is in the ratio of 3 to 16 along the line. Draw a line three units long from the 1·70 position and a parallel line on the opposite side sixteen units long from the 3·60 position. The intersection of the line joining the ends of these lines with the line to be interpolated defines the 2-m position from the similar triangles thus formed. Similarly the 3-m point can be located.

NOTE: This method tends to become unwieldy if more than one point needs to be interpolated.

(b) *Scaling method.* Position a scale as illustrated in Fig. 90 (b) with 1·70 units placed adjacent to the 1·70 spot height. Mark only the points required to be interpolated, 2 and 3 m in the illustration, and the value of the other spot height, here 3·60. Remove the scale and with a set-square and straight-edge run parallels from the 3·60 line, and the 2- and the 3-m position, marking just the required positions on the line being interpolated.

NOTE: This method is a simplification of the basic principle described in **18**. It is quick and needs no form of calculation, which is always a source of error.

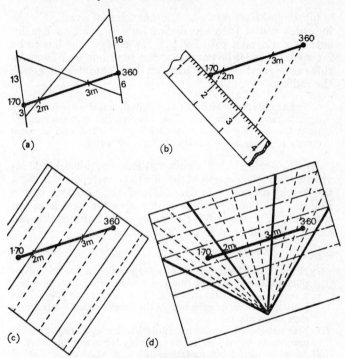

FIG. 90.—*Interpolation methods*

The plan positions of the 2- and 3-m points are located between spot heights of 1·70 and 3·60 m.

(a) Using similar triangles.
(b) Using a scale.
(c) Using an overlay of parallel lines.
(d) Using an overlay of radiating lines.

(c) *Parallel lines method.* An overlay of parallel lines ruled on tracing paper, as illustrated in Fig. 90(c), is rotated and positioned over the line until the required spacing is obtained. The interpolated points are then pricked through in the required position.

NOTE: This is an effective method, but the overlay must be prepared each time. Also the line spacing may not suit all the height differences between spot heights.

(d) *Radial lines method*. Another form of overlay is one in which radial lines are drawn from a point to equally spaced marks on a base line (*see* Fig. 90(d)). The line to be interpolated must lie parallel to the base line and to make this easier parallels to the base are drawn at intervals across the radials.

NOTE: This too is an effective method, but the overlay takes a little longer to prepare. This overlay has a greater range than the overlay for the parallel lines method and is more convenient when the contour interval is small.

(e) *Slide-rule method*. This method, not illustrated, involves scaling the length of the line to be interpolated. First the height difference is deduced and the positions of the required points are calculated by simple proportion on the slide-rule. This method is commonly used, but mistakes can easily arise and must be guarded against.

NOTE

(i) No matter which system of interpolation is used it is important always to sketch in the contour lines first, based on a rough interpolation by eye. This allows the *flow* of the contour lines to be seen before the more accurate interpolation takes place.

(ii) For small-scale work interpolation by eye may provide contour lines with sufficient accuracy for many purposes.

(iii) Another useful interpolation aid is a piece of graduated elastic, which can be stretched between spot heights to provide the spacing required.

20. Comparison of methods.

(a) *Direct contouring* is the most accurate method, but because of the excessive amount of field work it is seldom adopted except on small sites where accurate contours are required.

(b) *Indirect contouring* is most commonly used because it is the quicker method and provides contours with sufficient accuracy for most practical purposes.

PROGRESS TEST 13

1. What exactly is a contour and how does it differ from a contour line? (1)

2. Describe four characteristics of contour lines. (2)

3. What is the difference between direct and indirect contouring? (3)

4. What general principles apply to all types of contouring? (4)

5. Although levels may have been observed, under what circumstances are contour lines not usually drawn on a plan? (5)

6. What are the uses to which contour maps and plans may be put? (6)

7. What is a contour gradient and how is it plotted on a contour plan? (6)

8. Describe in detail how to perform a contour survey by the direct method. (7–9)

9. Describe three methods of horizontal control in indirect contouring. (10–13, 16)

10. What four weaknesses in the system must be borne in mind when undertaking a contour survey by grid levelling? (14)

11. Describe how a contour survey is performed using spot heights fixed from stadia observations. (15–17)

12. Describe five methods of interpolating contours. (18–19)

13. Compare the direct and indirect methods of contouring. (20)

CHAPTER XIV

AREAS AND VOLUMES

AREAS FROM SURVEY DATA

1. Area calculations. Areas of ground may be obtained from the plotted plan of a survey as described in I, **14**, but results are only as accurate as it is possible to scale off the drawings. Accuracy is greatly increased by using the measurements taken in the field. In most surveys the area is divisible into two parts:

(*a*) *The rectilinear areas* enclosed by the survey lines (*see* **2**).

(*b*) *The irregular areas* of the strips between these lines and the boundary (*see* **3**).

In order to calculate the area of the whole, each of these areas must be evaluated separately because each is defined by a different form of geometrical figure.

2. Rectilinear areas. The method of evaluating the rectilinear area enclosed by survey lines depends on the method of survey.

(*a*) If *chain surveying* is used the areas of the triangles forming the survey network are calculated from the field dimensions from the formula:

$$\text{Area} = \sqrt{s(s - a)\,(s - b)\,(s - c)}$$

where *a*, *b* and *c* = the lengths of the triangles' sides and

$$s = \frac{a + b + c}{2}, \text{ the semi-perimeter.}$$

(*b*) If *traversing* is used and the survey stations are *co-ordinated*, the computed co-ordinates are used in the area calculation as described in **4–6**.

Whichever calculation method is used *checks* must be applied to prove the area calculations. In a *chain survey network* the work must be arranged so that two different sets of the triangles forming the rectilinear figure are used in evaluating the total area, which is thus twice calculated. These two results will not normally agree precisely because the network will not be geometrically perfect owing to observational errors. If the difference is small, indicating no gross errors, the two results will be meaned to produce the final rectilinear area.

When areas are calculated from *co-ordinates* the calculation must be repeated another way to prove the result.

3. Irregular areas. Unless boundaries are straight and the corner points co-ordinated there are usually irregular strips of ground between the survey lines and the property boundaries. The areas of the irregular strips are either positive or negative to the rectilinear area and, since they are divided up by offsets between which the boundary is supposed to run straight, they are computed as a series of trapezoids. The mean of each pair of offsets is taken and multiplied by the chainage between them. Where the offsets are taken at regular intervals the trapezoidal rule or Simpson's rule for areas (*see* I, **16**) is used.

NOTE

(*i*) The field work should be arranged to overcome difficulties with corners. This is usually achieved by extending the survey line to the boundary, allowing for the triangular shape which may then occur.

(*ii*) In order to check the irregular area the calculations should be repeated by another person, or a check against gross error may be made by taking out a planimeter area of the plot.

SPECIMEN QUESTION

Calculate the area of the figure illustrated in Fig. 91. The following data were obtained from the chain survey of the site:

$$
\begin{array}{ll}
AB & 63{\cdot}0 \text{ m} \\
BC & 45{\cdot}0 \text{ m} \\
CD & 60{\cdot}0 \text{ m} \\
DA & 78{\cdot}0 \text{ m} \\
BD & 93{\cdot}3 \text{ m} \\
AC & 76{\cdot}0 \text{ m}
\end{array}
$$

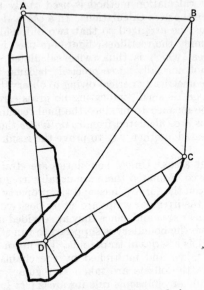

FIG. 91.—*Calculating area from a chain survey*

The figure shows the rectilinear area *ABCD*, which is calculated first; their regular strips between the chain lines and the boundary must be separately evaluated and either added or subtracted as necessary from the main rectilinear area calculation result.

AB and *BC* are straight boundaries. Offsets to the irregular boundaries are as follows:

Chainage	AD	Offset	Chainage	CD	Offset
A	0·0	0·0	C	0·0	0·0
	16·0	6·0		10·0	4·2
	33·0	7·0		20·0	6·4
	40·0	0·0		30·0	8·1
	49·0	7·0		40·0	10·3
	61·0	7·0		50·0	11·3
	68·0	0·0	D	60·0	13·2
D	78·0	11·0			
	89·0	5·0			
	93·0	9·0			

SOLUTION

The rectilinear area from $A = \sqrt{s(s-a)(s-b)(s-c)}$

The area of triangle $ACD = \sqrt{107\ (31)\ (47)\ (29)}$
$$= 2126 \cdot 3 \text{ m}^2$$

The area of triangle $ABC = \sqrt{92\ (29)\ (47)\ (16)}$
$$= 1416 \cdot 4 \text{ m}^2$$

$\therefore$ Area of $ABCD$ $= 2126 \cdot 3 + 1416 \cdot 4$
$$= 3542 \cdot 7 \text{ m}^2$$

Check:

The area of triangle $ABD = \sqrt{117 \cdot 15\ (54 \cdot 15)\ (39 \cdot 15)\ (23 \cdot 85)}$
$$= 2433 \cdot 8 \text{ m}^2$$

The area of triangle $BCD = \sqrt{99 \cdot 15\ (39 \cdot 15)\ (54 \cdot 15)\ (5 \cdot 85)}$
$$= 1108 \cdot 9 \text{ m}^2$$

$\therefore$ Area of $ABCD$ $= 2433 \cdot 8 + 1108 \cdot 9$
$$= 3542 \cdot 7 \text{ m}^2$$

Area of trapezoids on AD:

Plus	*Minus*

$\dfrac{0+6}{2} \times 16 = 48 \cdot 0$

$\dfrac{6+7}{2} \times 17 = 110 \cdot 5$

$\dfrac{7+0}{2} \times 7 = 24 \cdot 5$

$\dfrac{0+7}{2} \times 9\ = 31 \cdot 5$

$\dfrac{7+7}{2} \times 12 = 84 \cdot 0$

$\dfrac{7+0}{2} \times 7\ = 24 \cdot 5$

$\dfrac{0+11}{2} \times 10 = 55 \cdot 0$

$\dfrac{11+9}{2} \times 15 = 150 \cdot 0$

$$\begin{array}{ll}
388 \cdot 5 & \\
-140 \cdot 0 & 140 \cdot 0\\
\hline
248 \cdot 5 &
\end{array}$$

Total plus area on $AD = 248 \cdot 5 \text{ m}^2$

Area by the trapezoidal rule on CD:

$$\text{Area} = 10\left(\frac{0\cdot0 + 13\cdot2}{2} + 4\cdot2 + 6\cdot4 + 8\cdot1 + 10\cdot3 + 11\cdot3\right)$$
$$= 469\cdot0\,\text{m}^2$$

The *area of the omitted triangle* can be calculated from the formula:

Area = $\frac{1}{2}$(Base on *AD* produced) × (Perpendicular height from offset of 5 m at chainage 89·0 m).

$$\therefore \text{Area} = \frac{15}{2} \times 5 = 37\cdot5\,\text{m}^2$$

The total site area equals the sum of the individual parts, being the following:

Rectilinear area	3542·7
Irregular area on *AD*	248·5
Irregular area on *CD*	469·0
Omitted triangle	37·5
	4297·7 m²

$\therefore$ Total area = 0·4298 ha

4. Calculating areas by departures and total latitudes. Figure 92 shows a polygon, which may be of any number of sides, the area of which it is required to establish.

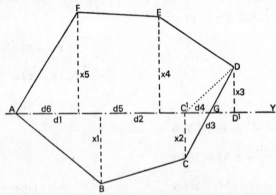

FIG. 92.—*Departures and total latitudes*

These are shown with respect to Station A of the enclosed figure *ABCDEF*. The departures of each line are shown as *d*1 to *d*6 and the total latitudes with respect to *A* are shown as *x*1 to *x*5.

(*a*) AY is parallel to the east–west axis.

(*b*) Perpendiculars are dropped to this line from each station.

(*c*) Let the total latitude of each point be $x1$ to $x5$ with respect to point A.

(*d*) Let $d1$ to $d6$ be the departures of each line.

Therefore the area A of figure $ABCDEFA$ is equal to:

$$\frac{d1 \cdot x1}{2} + \frac{d2(x1 + x2)}{2} + \frac{d4(x3 + x4)}{2} + \frac{d5(x4 + x5)}{2}$$

$$+ \frac{d6 \cdot x5}{2} + \triangle CC'G - \triangle DD'G$$

but $\triangle CC'G - \triangle DD'G = \triangle CC'D - \triangle DD'C'$

$$= \frac{d3 \cdot x2}{2} - \frac{d3 \cdot x3}{2}$$

$$= \frac{d3(x2 - x3)}{2}$$

$$\therefore A = \frac{d1 \cdot x1}{2} + \frac{d2(x1 + x2)}{2} + \frac{d3(x2 - x3)}{2}$$

$$+ \frac{d4(x3 + x4)}{2} + \frac{d5(x4 + x5)}{2} + \frac{d6 \cdot x5}{2}$$

$$\therefore 2A = x1(d1 + d2) + x2(d2 + d3) + x3(-d3 + d4)$$
$$+ x4(d4 + d5) + x5(d5 + d6)$$

If the signs are now changed throughout, which will give a negative area, the formula will agree with the normal convention of signs, thus:

$$-2A = -x1(d1 + d2) - x2(d2 + d3) + x3(d3 - d4)$$
$$+ x4(-d4 - d5) + x5(-d5 - d6)$$

This *formula* may be stated in the following way:

Twice the area of a figure equals the algebraic sum of the products of the total latitudes (or northings) of each station and the algebraic sum of the departures (or eastings) of the two lines which adjoin the station.

EXAMPLE

To find the area of the figure $ABCDEF$ of which the latitudes and departures, or ΔN's and ΔE's, are known, the formula in **4** is most easily applied in the tabulated form below:

Line	Latitude ΔN	Departure ΔE d	Station	Total latitude x	Sum of adjacent departments $d + d$	Products +	−
AB	−54·8	+64·3	A	0			
BC	+32·7	+46·4	B	−54·8	+110·7		6 066·36
CD	+48·4	+29·1	C	−22·1	+75·5		1 668·55
DE	+43·1	−17·4	D	+26·3	+11·7	307·71	
EF	+18·1	−58·6	E	+69·4	−76·0		5 274·40
FA	−87·5	−63·8	F	+87·5	−122·4		10 710·00
						307·71	23 719·31
							307·71
						$2A =$	23·411 60

$$\therefore \text{Area} = 11\ 705·80 \text{ m}^2$$
$$= 1·1706 \text{ ha}$$

NOTE

(*i*) The total latitude $x1$ of the point B with respect to A is the latitude of the line itself, −54·8 in the table above.

(*ii*) The total latitude $x2$ of the point C is the total latitude of B plus the latitude of the line BC, $-54·8 + 32·7 = -22·1$.

(*iii*) This process is continued thus:

$$-22·1 + 48·4 = +26·3 \text{ then } + 43·1 = +69·4 \text{ then}$$
$$+ 18·1 = +87·5.$$

(*iv*) The total latitude of the final point must always equal the latitude of the final line, but must be of the opposite sign. If it does not, an error of calculation has been made.

(*v*) The sum of adjacent departures is obtained by adding together the departures of the two lines on either side of the point concerned:

$$+64·3 + 46·4 = +110·7$$
$$+46·4 + 29·1 = +75·5$$
$$+29·1 - 17·4 = +11·7$$
$$-17·4 - 58·6 = -76·0$$
$$-58·6 - 63·8 = -122·4$$

(*vi*) The figures in the x column are multiplied by the figures in the $(d + d)$ column and tabulated as shown. Their algebraic sum forms *twice* the area.

(*vii*) As a check the calculation may be repeated after interchanging the columns of ΔE's and ΔN's, which has the effect of swinging the figure through 90° without altering its area.

5. Calculating areas from co-ordinates. Figure 93 shows a quadrilateral 1234 of which the area A is required. The co-ordinates of each point are E_1, N_1, E_2, N_2, etc. The area of figure 1234 = area of trapezoid $1AD4$ − trapezoid $1AB2$ − trapezoid $2BC3$ − trapezoid $3CD4$.

The areas of these trapezoids in terms of eastings and northings prove this result:

$$A = \tfrac{1}{2}(E_4 + E_1)(N_4 - N_1) - \tfrac{1}{2}(E_2 + E_1)(N_2 - N_1)$$
$$- \tfrac{1}{2}(E_3 + E_2)(N_3 - N_2)$$
$$- \tfrac{1}{2}(E_4 + E_3)(N_4 - N_3)$$

By altering the signs to suit the convention of signs in the co-ordinate system:

$$-2 \times A = (E_4 + E_1)(N_1 - N_4) + (E_2 + E_1)(N_2 - N_1)$$
$$+ (E_3 + E_2)(N_3 - N_2) + (E_4 + E_3)(N_4 - N_3)$$

This *formula* may be stated in the following way:

Twice the area of a figure equals the algebraic sum of the

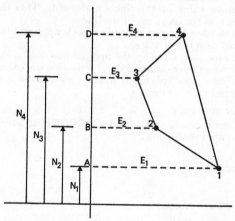

Fig. 93.—*Calculating area from co-ordinates*

The geometry of area calculation using the eastings and northings of each station is illustrated.

products of the latitudes (or $\triangle N$'s) of each line and the sum of the eastings of each end of that line.

The above expression may be expanded to produce another form of area calculation:

$$2A = (N_1E_2 + N_2E_3 + \ldots + N_nE_1) - (N_1E_n + N_2E_1 + \ldots + N_nE_{n-1})$$

which may be tabulated for a triangle, the initial co-ordinates being repeated at the end:

$$\begin{bmatrix} E_1 & \diagdown & \diagup & N_1 \\ E_2 & \diagup & \diagdown & N_2 \\ E_3 & \diagup & \diagdown & N_3 \\ E_1 & & & N_1 = 2A \end{bmatrix}$$

The oblique full lines are multiplied and the products added. The oblique pecked lines are multiplied and the products added. The difference between these two sums is twice the area.

NOTE

    (i) Half the sum of the eastings of each end of a line is the eastings value of the line's mid-point. This distance is known as the *longitude* of the line.

  (ii) The method of cross multiplication is applicable to a figure of any number of sides.

 (iii) The area calculated by the first method can be checked by reversing the co-ordinates and repeating the calculation.

 (iv) The cross multiplication method cannot be checked by reversal of co-ordinates.

SPECIMEN QUESTION

Calculate the area of the figure $ABCDEF$ of which the co-ordinates are listed below.

SOLUTION

The calculation is tabulated as shown:

Station	East-ings	North-ings	$E + E$ Double longi-tude	ΔN	Products +	Products −
A	150·0	100·0				
B	95·2	164·3	245·2	+64·3	15 766·36	
C	127·9	210·7	223·1	+46·4	10 351·84	
D	176·3	239·8	304·2	+29·1	8 852·22	
E	219·4	222·4	395·7	−17·4		6 885·18
F	237·5	163·8	456·9	−58·6		26 774·34
A	150·0	100·0	387·5	−63·8		24 722·50
					34 970·42	58 382·02
						34 970·42
					$2A =$	23 411·60

$\therefore$ Area $= 11\ 705 \cdot 8 \text{ m}^2$
         $= 1 \cdot 1706$ ha

NOTE

(i) To simplify calculations the initial co-ordinate is repeated at the bottom of the list.

(ii) If co-ordinates are large a whole-number constant would be subtracted from the eastings before summation.

(iii) The E + E column is tabulated from the eastings column thus:

$$150 + 95 \cdot 2 = 245 \cdot 2$$
$$95 \cdot 2 + 127 \cdot 9 = 223 \cdot 1 \text{ etc.}$$

(iv) The $\triangle N$ column contains normal departures or $\triangle N$'s, thus:

$$164 \cdot 3 - 100 \cdot 0 = +64 \cdot 3$$
$$210 \cdot 7 - 164 \cdot 3 = +46 \cdot 4 \text{ etc.}$$

(v) The calculation is checked either by repeating the calculation with co-ordinates interchanged or by using the cross multiplication method.

6. Machine calculation. The whole process of area calculation can be carried out on an electronic calculator from the co-ordinates without having to tabulate the intermediate calculations. The cross multiplication method can be carried out by calculator provided the area is not too large, but it cannot conveniently be checked.

7. Area problems. Areas form the basis of many calculations and general problems in surveying. Such problems can usually be solved by the application of simple mathematics and the general principles of survey calculations already covered. Four examples of such problems follow (**8–11**).

8. Cutting off an area by a line of given bearing. If an area A is to be cut off from the site $ABCDE$ in Fig. 94 (a) by a line of given bearing, the procedure required is as follows:

(a) By scaling find the approximate position of this line.

(b) Run a line from a nearby known point, say E, to intersect BC at E', the position of which has been calculated.

(c) Calculate the area A' of $EDCE'$ and from it subtract the given area A. $A' - A$ is then the area of $EYXE'$.

(d) The value of h to give the positions of X and Y can be calculated:

Since $A' - A = \dfrac{E'E + XY}{2} \cdot h$ and

$$XY = E'E - h \tan \alpha + h \tan \beta$$

$$\therefore \quad A' - A = \frac{E'E + E'E - h \tan \alpha + h \tan \beta}{2} \cdot h$$

$$\therefore \quad 2(A' - A) = 2h(E'E) - h^2(\tan \alpha - \tan \beta)$$

$$\therefore \quad (\tan \alpha - \tan \beta)h^2 - 2h(E'E) + 2(A' - A) = 0$$

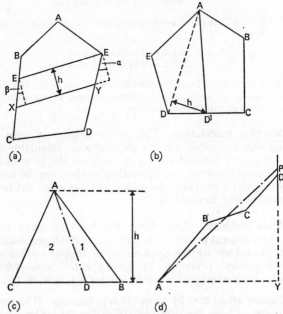

Fig. 94.—*Area problems*

(a) A given area $YDCX$ of A ha required to be cut off from the whole figure $ABCDE$ by a line YX of given bearing. The positions of X and Y are required to be calculated.

(b) A given area $ABCD'$ of A ha required to be cut off from the whole figure $ABCDE$ by a line AD' from the given point A. The position of D' is required to be calculated.

(c) In order to divide the area ABC into proportional parts the base BC need only be divided into the same proportion so that D can be located without the need to evaluate the actual areas.

(d) The boundary fence line $ABCD$ may be replaced by one line AP without loss of area from one side or other of the boundary.

NOTE

(*i*) It is always necessary to solve a quadratic equation for *h*.

(*ii*) $x = \dfrac{-b \pm \sqrt{b^2 - 4ac}}{2a}$ (an *aide mémoire* for solution of a quadratic equation).

(*iii*) The values of α and β are obtained from the bearings of the perpendiculars to the given line and the given or calculated bearings of the sides of the figure.

9. Cutting off an area by a line from a given point. Figure 94 (*b*) illustrates this case. Say an area of 10 ha is required for the figure *ABCD′* (the location of *D′* to be established). Here the method used is again to find by rough scaling the approximate position the line *AD′* will take. A nearby line is calculated between co-ordinated points, *AD*. The area *ABCD* can then be computed and the known area, here 10 ha, subtracted from it. It is then necessary to solve triangle *ADD′* using the formula ½ base × height so that it has this difference in area. From the length *DD′* obtained by solving this triangle *D′* can be located to define the figure *ABCD′* which will have the required area.

10. Dividing an area into proportional parts. Occasionally the problems covered in 7–9 require the areas to be divided into a half or some other proportion. In irregular figures it is necessary to calculate the total area first, but the area calculation is sometimes not required.

In a *triangle*, as illustrated in Fig. 94 (*c*), it is necessary to divide the area *ABC* in the proportion of 2:1. As the height *h* is common to all the triangles the areas are in fact proportional to their base lengths. If the base *CB* were 300 m, then *DB* must be 100 m to allow the line *AD* to divide the figure in the ratio of 2:1, and the areas need not be calculated.

Where the dividing line is parallel to any one side of a triangle, then similar triangles will be formed. It is useful to remember that the areas of similar triangles are proportional to the *squares* on corresponding sides (*see* **17**).

11. Calculating an equalising line. This is required where it is necessary to replace a zig-zag boundary with a straight line without loss of ground area from one side or the other.

Figure 94 (*d*) illustrates a position where the fence *ABCD* is to be replaced by a new straight fence *AP*.

To locate the position of *P* first compute the area *ABCDYA* and then calculate the distance *YP* which will give an area to the triangle *APY* the same as that of the original figure.

VOLUMES OF EARTHWORKS

12. Volume calculations. In construction works the excavation, loading, hauling and dumping of earth frequently forms a substantial part of the project. Payment must be made for the labour and plant needed for earthworks and this is based on the quantity or *volume* of material handled. These volumes must be calculated and depending on the shape of the site this may be done in one of three ways:

(*a*) *By cross-sections*, generally used for long, narrow works such as roads, railways, pipelines, etc. (*see* **13–23**).

(*b*) *By contours*, generally used for larger areas such as reservoirs, landscapes, redevelopment sites, etc. (*see* **24–27**).

(*c*) *By spot heights*, generally used for smaller areas such as underground tanks, basements, building sites, etc. (*see* **28**).

13. Volumes from cross-sections. Cross-sections are established at some convenient interval along a centre line of the works as described in XI, **15**. Volumes are calculated by relating the cross-sectional areas to the distances between them. In order to compute the volumes it is first necessary to evaluate the cross-sectional areas, which may be obtained by the following methods:

(*a*) *By calculating* from formulae or from first principles the standard cross-sections of constant formation widths and side slopes.

(*b*) *By measuring graphically* from plotted cross-sections drawn to scale as described in XI, **21**, areas being obtained by planimeter, or division into triangles or squares as described in I, **15–18**.

NOTE: The graphic measure of the cross-sectional area is most often used and provides a sufficiently accurate estimate of volume, but for railways, long embankments, breakwaters, etc., with fairly regular dimensions, the use of formulae may be easier and perhaps more accurate.

14. Calculating the cross-sectional areas of embankments and cuttings. It can be shown that the formulae for calculating the cross-sectional area of an *embankment* or *cutting* are the following, using the symbols shown in Fig. 95:

$$W_1 = \frac{g\left(\dfrac{b}{2} + hs\right)}{g - s}$$

$$W_2 = \frac{g\left(\dfrac{b}{2} + hs\right)}{g + s}$$

$$\text{Area} = \frac{W_1 W_2 - \left(\dfrac{b}{2}\right)^2}{s}$$

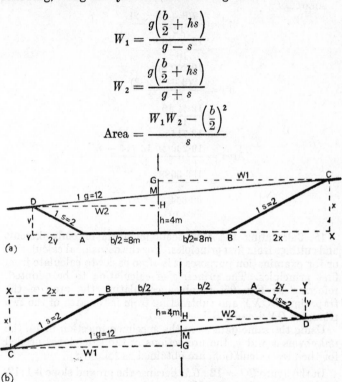

FIG. 95.—*Embankments and cuttings*

(*a*) The geometry of calculating the cross-sectional area of a cutting.
(*b*) The geometry of calculating the cross-sectional area of an embankment.

SPECIMEN QUESTION

Given the following data, apply the formulae above to provide the cross-sectional area for *either* the embankment *or* the cutting in Fig. 95, both of which have the same cross-sectional area.

Formation width $AB = b = 16$ m
Height at centre $\quad = h = 4$ m
Side slopes $\quad\quad\quad = 1:s = 1:2$
Ground slope $\quad\quad = 1:g = 1:12$

SOLUTION

$$W_1 = \frac{12(8 + 4 \times 2)}{12 - 2}$$

$$= \frac{12 \times 16}{10}$$

$$= 19 \cdot 200 \text{ m}$$

$$W_2 = \frac{12(8 + 4 \times 2)}{12 + 2}$$

$$= \frac{12 \times 16}{14}$$

$$= 13 \cdot 714 \text{ m}$$

$$\text{Area} = \frac{19 \cdot 200 \times 13 \cdot 714 - 8^2}{2}$$

$$= \frac{199 \cdot 3088}{2}$$

$$= 99 \cdot 654$$

$$= 99 \cdot 7 \text{ m}^2$$

15. Calculating the cross-sectional areas of embankments and cuttings from first principles.

For the occasional calculation or for examination purposes it is often easier to calculate from first principles. The *principle* of calculation to be adopted, referring to Fig. 95, involves calculating the area of the trapezium $DCXY$ and subtracting from it the area of the two triangles DYA and CBX.

Using the same data as in the specimen question in **14**, the unknowns x and y, the projections of the side slopes needed for the area calculation, are obtained as follows:

In the figure $GC = 12 \cdot GM$ because the ground slope is $1:12$, but $GC = 8 + 2x$ and $GM = x - 4$.

$$\therefore \quad 8 + 2x = 12(x - 4)$$
$$\therefore \quad 10x = 56$$
$$\therefore \quad x = 5 \cdot 600 \text{ and } 2x = BX = 11 \cdot 200 \text{ m}$$

Also $\quad\quad\quad DH = 12 \cdot MH$ as before

but $\quad\quad\quad DH = 8 + 2y \quad$ and $\quad MH = 4 - y$

$$\therefore \quad 8 + 2y = 12(4 - y)$$
$$\therefore \quad 14y = 40$$
$$\therefore \quad y = 2 \cdot 857 \text{ and } 2y = AY = 5 \cdot 714 \text{ m}$$

As the area $ABCD$ required = area $DYXC$ — area DYA — area BXC:

$$\text{Area } ABCD = \frac{5\cdot600 + 2\cdot857}{2}(16 + 11\cdot200 + 5\cdot714)$$

$$- \frac{2\cdot857 \times 5\cdot714}{2} - \frac{5\cdot600 \times 11\cdot200}{2}$$

$$= \frac{278\cdot354 - 16\cdot325 - 62\cdot720}{2}$$

$$= 99\cdot654$$

$$= 99\cdot7 \text{ m}^2 \text{ as in } \mathbf{14.}$$

16. Calculating the cross-sectional area of cut and fill sections. The formulae for calculating the cut and fill section illustrated in Fig. 96 are the following:

$$W_1 = \frac{g\left(\dfrac{b}{2} + hs\right)}{g - s}$$

$$W_2 = \frac{g\left(\dfrac{b}{2} - hs\right)}{g - s}$$

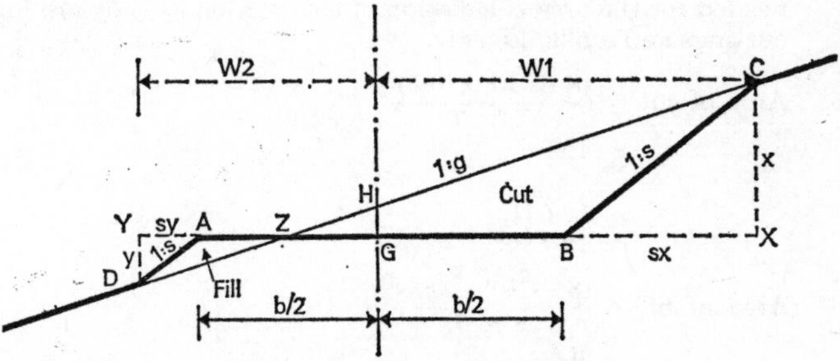

FIG. 96.—*Cut and fill section*
The geometry of calculating its cross-sectional area is shown.

Area of triangle containing the centre line = $\dfrac{\left(\dfrac{b}{2} + gh\right)^2}{2(g - s)}$ (area of *cut* in Fig. 96).

Area of triangle away from the centre line = $\dfrac{\left(\dfrac{b}{2} - gh\right)^2}{2(g - s)}$ (area of *fill* in the Fig. 96).

Given the following data apply the formulae above to provide the cross-sectional area for the *cut* and *fill* in each case:

Formation width $AB = b = 16$ m
Height at centre $HG = h = 0.5$ m
Side slopes $1:s = 1:3$
Ground slopes $1:g = 1:10$

SOLUTION

$$W_1 = \frac{10(8 + 0.5 \times 3)}{10 - 3}$$
$$= \frac{95}{7}$$
$$= 13.57 \text{ m}$$
$$W_2 = \frac{10(8 - 0.5 \times 3)}{10 - 3}$$
$$= \frac{65}{7}$$
$$= 9.29 \text{ m}$$

NOTE: While the distances W_1 and W_2 calculated may be required later for survey work on site, they are not actually needed for the area calculation of this section as they are for cuttings and embankments.

$$\text{Area of cut} = \frac{(8 + 10 \times 0.5)^2}{2 \times 7}$$
$$= \frac{169}{14}$$
$$= 12.071$$
$$= 12.1 \text{ m}^2$$
$$\text{Area of fill} = \frac{(8 - 10 \times 0.5)^2}{2 \times 7}$$
$$= \frac{9}{14}$$
$$= 0.643$$
$$= 0.6 \text{ m}^2$$

17. Calculating the cross-sectional area of cut and fill sections from first principles. As with cuttings and embankments it is often easier to calculate the cross-sectional area of cut and fill sections from first principles. The *principle* of calculation to be adopted, referring to Fig. 96, is to calculate the area of one triangle DYZ or CXZ from its base YZ or ZX

on formation level and its vertical height obtained from x or y, which are related to the side slopes. Whichever triangle is calculated first, the area of the other may be obtained from the relation of similar triangles, their areas being proportional to the squares of corresponding sides (*see* **10**).

Using the same data as in the specimen calculation in **16** the unknowns x and y needed for the calculation are obtained in the following way:

Since $HG = 0.5$ m, $ZG = 5$ m, because the ground slope is $1:10$.

$$\therefore ZB = 8 + 5 = 13 \text{ m}$$

Also $ZX = ZB + BX = 10.CX$
$$\therefore 13 + 3x = 10x$$
$$\therefore 7x = 13$$
$$x = 1.857 \text{ and } W_1 = 8 + 3(1.857)$$
$$= 13.57 \ (\textit{see } \mathbf{16})$$

Area of cut $= \frac{1}{2}ZB.CX$
$$= \frac{1}{2} \times 13 \times 1.857$$
$$= 12.071 \text{ m}^2 \text{ as in } \mathbf{16}$$

Area of fill $=$ Area of cut $\times \dfrac{AZ^2}{ZB^2}$
$$= 12.071 \times \frac{3^2}{13^2}$$
$$= 0.643 \text{ m}^2 \text{ as in } \mathbf{16}$$

NOTE

(*i*) On cuttings and embankments both side slopes are generally the same.

(*ii*) On cut and fill sections the cutting slope may be different from the fill slope in which case the correct value of s must be inserted in the formula in **16** or the area of each triangle must be separately calculated as the triangles of cut and fill are no longer similar.

18. The prismoid. In order to calculate the volume of a substance, its geometrical shape and size must be known. A mass of earth has no regular geometrical shape, but it may be assumed to take the form of a *prismoid*, the geometrical figure it most nearly approaches. The prismoid is a solid consisting of two ends which form plane, parallel figures, not necessarily of the same number of sides, which can be measured as cross-sections (*see* **12–17**). The faces between the parallel ends are plane surfaces between straight lines which join all the corners of the two end faces. A prismoid can be considered to be made up of a series of prisms, wedges and pyramids, all having a length equal to the perpendicular distance between the parallel ends.

The geometrical solids forming the prismoid are described as follows:

(*a*) *Prism*, in which the end polygons are equal and the side faces are parallelograms.

(*b*) *Wedge*, in which one end is a line, the other end is a parallelogram, and the sides are triangles and parallelograms.

(*c*) *Pyramid*, in which one end is a point, the other end is a polygon and the side faces are triangles.

19. The prismoidal formula.

$$
\begin{aligned}
\text{Let } D = & \text{ the perpendicular distance between the} \\
& \text{parallel end planes,} \\
A_1 \text{ and } A_2 = & \text{ the areas of these end planes,} \\
M = & \text{ the mid-area, the area of the plane parallel to} \\
& \text{the end planes and midway between them,} \\
V = & \text{ the volume of the prismoid and} \\
a_1, a_2, m, v = & \text{ the equivalent for any prism, wedge or} \\
& \text{pyramid forming the prismoid.}
\end{aligned}
$$

Then in a *prism* $a_1 = a_2 = m$
and in a *wedge* $a_2 = 0$ and $m = \frac{1}{2}a_1$
and in a *pyramid* $a_2 = 0$ and $m = \frac{1}{4}a_1$

Prism volume $v = D \cdot a_1 = \dfrac{D}{6}(6 \cdot a_1) = \dfrac{D}{6}(a_1 + 4m + a_2)$

Wedge volume $v = \frac{1}{2}D \cdot a_1 = \dfrac{D}{6}(3 \cdot a_1) = \dfrac{D}{6}(a_1 + 4m + a_2)$

Pyramid volume $v = \frac{1}{3}D \cdot a_1 = \dfrac{D}{6}(2 \cdot a_1) = \dfrac{D}{6}(a_1 + 4m + a_2)$

As the volume of each part can be expressed in the same terms, the volume of the whole can take the same form. Thus the prismoidal formula is expressed in the following way:

$$
V = \frac{D}{6}(A_1 + 4M + A_2)
$$

NOTE

(*i*) M does not represent the *mean* of the end areas A_1 and A_2, except where the prismoid is composed of prisms and wedges only.

(*ii*) The formula gives the volume of one prismoid of which the *end* and *mid-sectional* areas are known.

20. Simpson's rule for volumes. The prismoidal formula may be used to calculate volume if a series of cross-sectional areas, $A_1, A_2, A_3, \ldots, A_n$, have been established a distance d apart. Each alternate cross-section may be considered to be the mid-area M of a prismoid of length $2d$.

Then the volume of the first prismoid of length $2d$:

$$= \frac{2d}{6}(A_1 + 4A_2 + A_3)$$

and of the second $= \dfrac{2d}{6}(A_3 + 4A_4 + A_5)$

and of the nth $= \dfrac{2d}{6}(A_{n-2} + 4A_{n-1} + A_n)$

Summing up the volumes of each prismoid:

$$V = \frac{d}{3}(A_1 + 4A_2 + 2A_3 + 4A_4 + \ldots + 2A_{n-2} + 4A_{n-1} + A_n)$$

which is *Simpson's rule for volumes*.

NOTE

(*i*) Compare Simpson's rule for volumes with his rule for areas in I, **16** (*b*).

(*ii*) The order of the multipliers is 1424 . . . 241 as before (*see* I, **16**) and an *odd* number of cross-sectional areas are required.

(*iii*) Do not confuse the *prismoidal formula* where D or $2d$ is divided by 6 with the *use* of the prismoidal formula in Simpson's rule, where d is divided by 3.

SPECIMEN QUESTION

Calculate, using the prismoidal formula, the cubic contents of an embankment of which the cross-sectional areas at 15-m intervals are as follows:

Distance (m)	0	15	30	45	60	75	90
Area (m²)	11	42	64	72	160	180	220

SOLUTION

$$V = \frac{15}{3}(11 + 220 + 4(42 + 72 + 180) + 2(64 + 160))$$
$$= 5(231 + 1176 + 448)$$
$$= 9275 \text{ m}^3$$

NOTE

(*i*) The 15-m interval is divided by 3 as the length of the individual prismoids used is 30 m, which in the prismoidal formula is divided by 6.

(*ii*) A mass of earth, of length double the usual cross-sectional interval of 15, 20 or 25 m, is considerably different from a true prismoid so this method is not as accurate as it would be if the true mid-sectional area had been measured. This results in the use of prismoids of length equal to, instead of double, the interval between cross-sections.

21. Calculating volume from the end areas formula. It is no more accurate to use the prismoidal formula where the mid-sectional areas have not been directly measured than it is to use the end areas formula, particularly as the earth solid is not exactly represented by a prismoid. Using the same symbols as in **19** and **20** the volume may be expressed as:

$$v = d\left(\frac{A_1 + A_2}{2}\right)$$

although this is only correct where the mid-area is the mean of the end areas:

$$\left(M = \frac{A_1 + A_2}{2}\right)$$

However, in view of the inaccuracies that arise in assuming any geometric shape between cross-sections and because of bulking and settlement and the fact that the end areas calculation is simple to use, it is generally used for most estimating purposes.

NOTE

(*i*) Compare with the trapezoidal rule for areas in I, **16**(*a*).

(*ii*) The summation of a series of cross-sectional areas by this method provides a total volume:

$$V = d\left(\frac{A_1 + A_n}{2} + A_2 + A_3 + \ldots A_{n-1}\right)$$

SPECIMEN QUESTION

Calculate, using the end areas method, the cubic contents of the embankment, the details of which are found in the specimen question in 20.

SOLUTION

$$V = 15\left(\frac{11 + 220}{2} + 42 + 64 + 72 + 160 + 180\right)$$
$$= 9502 \cdot 5 \text{ m}^3$$

22. Prismoidal correction. In some circumstances where greater accuracy is required than is possible by either of the two previous methods, the *prismoidal correction* may be applied. This will produce a result approximating to the prismoidal method, where the mid-cross-sectional areas are measured, without actually having to do the calculation.

The prismoidal correction may be deduced by subtracting the volume obtained by the prismoidal method from the volume obtained by the end areas method:

Prismoidal correction = V (by end areas formula)
$$- V \text{ (by prismoidal formula)}$$

Using the same notation as before where h_1 and h_2 are the differences in height between ground level and formation level at A_1 and A_2 respectively, the prismoidal correction for cuttings and embankments is:

$$\frac{d}{6} \cdot \frac{g^2}{(g^2 - s^2)} \cdot s(h_1 - h_2)^2$$

NOTE

(i) Where the ground slope is level, *i.e.* $g = \infty$, the correction becomes:

$$\frac{d}{6} s(h_1 - h_2)^2$$

(ii) The term $(h_1 - h_2)^2$ must be positive so the correction must always be *deducted* from the area obtained by the end areas formula.

The prismoidal correction for cut and fill sections is:

$$\frac{d}{12(g - s)} \cdot g^2(h_1 - h_2)^2$$

NOTE

(i) This correction too must always be deducted from the volume obtained by the end areas formula.

(ii) Although the formula applies equally for cut or fill the appropriate value of s must be used if it differs between the cut and fill section.

EXAMPLE

This example illustrates how the application of the prismoidal correction to a volume calculated from end areas produces the same result obtained by using the prismoidal formula.

The embankment illustrated in Fig. 97 is 20 m long and has side batters or slopes of 2 vertical to 1 horizontal. The formation

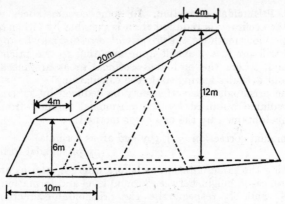

FIG. 97.—*Volume of an embankment*

The shape and size of the embankment, the volume of which is calculated in 22, is shown.

level is 4 m wide throughout and the height at one end is 6 m, its base sloping down to give a height of 12 m at the other.

To obtain the volume by the *end areas formula:*

$$V = d\left(\frac{A_1 + A_n}{2} + A_2 + A_3 \ldots + A_{n-1}\right)$$

From the height and side slopes the base at one end must be 10 m wide and at the other end 16 m wide.

Therefore $A_1 = \dfrac{4 + 10}{2} \times 6$

$= 42 \text{ m}^2$ and

$A_2 = \dfrac{4 + 16}{2} \times 12$

$= 120 \text{ m}^2$

Volume $= \dfrac{42 + 120}{2} \times 20$

$= 1620 \text{ m}^3$

Using the formula in 22:

$$\frac{d}{6} \cdot s(h_1 - h_2)^2$$

where the ground is level, the *prismoidal correction* may be calculated as follows:

$$\text{Correction} = \frac{20}{6} \times 0.5(6 - 12)^2$$

$$= \frac{20}{6} \times 18$$

$$= 60 \text{ m}^3$$

Therefore the volume by the prismoidal formula must be the volume by end areas less the prismoidal correction, thus:

$$1620 - 60 = 1560 \text{ m}^3$$

As the embankment is a regular figure its mid-area can be calculated. Its mid-height is 9 m and the base width in the middle is 13 m. Therefore the mid-cross-sectional area is:

$$\frac{4 + 13}{2} \times 9 = 76.5 \text{ m}^2$$

Using the *prismoidal formula*:

$$V = \frac{D}{6} (A_1 + 4M + A_2)$$

the volume of the prismoid is obtained thus:

$$V = \frac{20}{6} (42 + 4 \times 76.5 + 120)$$

$$= \frac{20}{6} (468)$$

$$= 1560 \text{ m}^3 \text{ as before}$$

NOTE

(*i*) The correct volume in this example is that which is obtained by using the prismoidal formula or by applying the prismoidal correction to the result obtained by the end areas formula.

(*ii*) In earth solids which do not necessarily form a true prismoid the application of the prismoidal correction will normally provide a more accurate result. This will not necessarily be the same result that would have been obtained by measuring the mid-area and by calculating the volume from the prismoidal formula, as in the example.

(*iii*) The prismoidal correction is infrequently used in practice because the prismoidal formula is only accurate for true prismoids or where the distance between the cross-sections is kept to minimum. As the cost of providing cross-sectional areas at intervals of 5 m or less is seldom warranted, Simpson's rule for volumes is seldom used except for well-defined structures, *e.g.* dam walls and bridge approaches.

23. Curvature correction. Where the centre line is curved cross-sections are usually taken radially or normal to the curve. However, *Pappus's theorem* states that if a plane area rotates about an axis in its plane, but outside its area, the volume of the solid generated is given by the product of the area and the length of the path traced by the *centroid* or centre of gravity of the area.

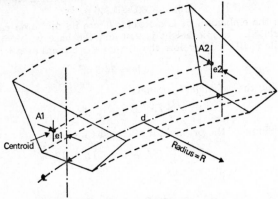

Fig. 98.—*Cross-sections on a curve*

The relation between the centre line of the construction and the path of the *centroid* or centre of gravity of the cross-sections is shown.

In considering the volume between cross-sections on a curved centre line, illustrated in Fig. 98, the volume may be taken as:

$$\frac{A1 + A2}{2} \times d$$

where $A1$ and $A2$ are the two cross-sectional areas and d is the arc distance between them along the centre line. This is only correct if the path traced by the centroid follows the construction centre line.

If the centroid is displaced distances $e1$ and $e2$ from the centre line in each case, as shown in Fig. 98, the arc distance between these points should be used for calculating the volume. The arc distance d in the centre line is equal to $R\theta$ (*see* XVI, 5) and the arc distance on the path of the centroid is:

$$\theta\left(R + \frac{e1 + e2}{2}\right)$$

where the radius of curvature is increased by the mean eccentricity of the centroid path. As $R\theta = d$ and $\theta = \dfrac{d}{R}$, the length of the centroid path is:

$$\frac{d}{R}\left(R + \frac{e1 + e2}{2}\right) = d\left(1 + \frac{e1 + e2}{2R}\right)$$

The *correction for curvature* to be applied to d is therefore:

$$d\left(\frac{e1 + e2}{2R}\right)$$

where d = the distance between cross-sections,
$e1$ and $e2$ = the eccentric distances of the centroid estimated from the cross-section and
R = radius of curvature.

NOTE

(*i*) The curvature correction may have to be either added or subtracted, depending on whether the original radius is increased or decreased, to define the path of the centroid.

(*ii*) The correction for curvature is very seldom applied in practice as the error produced by its omission is generally small, except on very short radius curves.

(*iii*) For a curve of radius 1000 m the mean eccentricity will need to be 20 m (unlikely in practice) to produce a 1 per cent error in the distance between cross-sections spaced at 20-m intervals.

24. Volumes from contour lines. Contour lines may be used for volume calculations and theoretically this is the most accurate method. However, as the small contour interval necessary for accurate work is seldom provided, owing to cost, high accuracy is not often obtained. Unless the contour interval is less than 1 or 2 m at the most, the assumption that there is an even slope between the contours is incorrect and volume calculations from contours become unreliable.

25. Calculation method. The formula used for the volume calculation is either the end areas formula or Simpson's rule for volumes, the distance d in the formulae being the contour interval. The area enclosed by each contour line is measured, usually by planimeter, and these areas $A1$, $A2$, etc., are used in the formulae as before (*see* 21). If the prismoidal method is used either each alternate contour line is assumed to enclose a mid-area or the outline of the mid-area can be interpolated between the existing contour intervals.

26. Intersection of surfaces. If any new construction is represented on a contour plan by a system of contours, then the points where the new contours cut the equivalent ground contours lie on the intersection of the new work with the ground. Thus the outline of the new work can be plotted in plan and volumes may be calculated.

Figure 99 shows the contour plan of an area with a dam wall 10 m wide on top at a level of 67 m and an access road, also 10 m wide and rising at a gradient of 1:10 from the wall. The dam has side slopes of 1:1 upstream and 1:2 downstream. The road runs through a cutting with side slopes of 1:2.

The outline of the area of fill is obtained by drawing the contours of the dam. As the top is level the contours along the side slope run parallel to it. The first contour on the upstream side at 65 m lies 2 m in plan from the edge as the slope is 1:1. The next at 60 m lies 5 m from the 65-m contour for the same reason. Similarly the other contours are drawn, those downstream being drawn 10 m apart because the slope is 1:2. By joining the intersection of each set of contours the outline of the area of fill required to form the dam wall can be drawn.

The outline of the *cutting* is obtained in a similar fashion. The 70-m contour will cross the road at right-angles 30 m away from the level section because the rise of 3 m from 67 m to 70 m at a gradient of 1:10 takes 30 m horizontally. Similarly the next contour across the road at 75 m is now 50 m away from the previous one because the rise is 5 m at a gradient of 1:10.

The contours on the *cutting slope* deviate from the road gradient in plan by 10 m in 50 m because the cutting slope contours are 10 m apart for a 5-m rise at 1:2 and the gradient must go to 50 m to rise these 5 m (*see* XIII, **6** (*d*)). They can therefore be plotted, their intersection with the ground contours allowing the outlines of the cutting to be drawn.

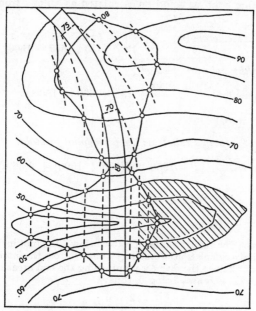

FIG. 99.—*Intersection of contoured surfaces*

This illustration shows an area contoured at 5-m intervals and how the contours of proposed works, in this case a dam wall with an access road through a cutting, shown as pecked lines, define the plan outline of the works. This also allows the volume of the earthworks to be calculated using the positions of the contour lines.

27. Volume calculations. The volume of the dam wall and the amount of cut may be obtained from the contour lines by calculating the volume of ground within the working area down to a common level surface and then calculating the new volume from the formation contour lines, the difference being the change in volume due to the works. This volume calculation is more usually carried out by using the cross-sectional method.

The *use of contours* is a practical method of calculating volumes in several cases, one of which being the calculation of water at various levels in a reservoir. For example, in Fig. 99 the volume of water which would be contained up to the level of the 60-m contour could be calculated as follows from these data:

Contour above datum (m)	50	52·5	55	57·5	60
Area (m²)	12	135	660	1500	1950

Using the end areas method:

$$V = 2{\cdot}5\left(\frac{12 + 1950}{2} + 135 + 660 + 1500\right)$$

$$= 8190 \text{ m}^3$$

Using Simpson's rule from the prismoidal formula:

$$V = \frac{2{\cdot}5}{3}\,(12 + 1950 + 4(135 + 1500) + 2(660))$$

$$= \frac{2{\cdot}5}{3}\,(9822)$$

$$= 8185 \text{ m}^3$$

NOTE: The small volume of water below 50 m (not included in the above calculation) would be estimated from the interpolated depth of 2 m at the deepest point, using the end areas formula, the lowest end area being 0, thus:

$$V = \frac{12 + 0}{2} \times 2$$

$$= 12 \text{ m}^3$$

This would then be added to either of the results above.

28. Calculating volumes from spot heights. This is a method of volume calculation frequently used on excavations where there are vertical sides covering a fairly large area, although it can be used for excavations with sloping sides. The site is divided into squares or rectangles, and if they are of equal size the calculations are simplified. The volumes are calculated from the product of the mean length of the sides of each vertical truncated prism (a prism in which the base planes are not parallel) and the cross-sectional area. The size of the rectangles is dependent on the degree of accuracy required.

The aim is to produce areas such that the ground surface within each can be assumed to be plane.

SPECIMEN QUESTION

Figure 100 shows the reduced levels of a rectangular plot which is to be excavated to a uniform depth of 8 m above datum. Calculate the mean level of the ground and the volume of earth to be excavated.

NOTE

(*i*) The mean or average level of the ground is that level of ground which would be achieved by smoothing the ground off level, assuming that no bulking would take place.

(*ii*) The mean level of the ground is the mean of the mean heights of each prism. It is *not* the mean of all the spot heights.

SOLUTION

(*a*) *Calculation from rectangles:*

Station	R.L.	Number of times the R.L. is used $= n$	Product $(R.L.) \times n$
A	12·16	1	12·16
B	12·48	2	24·96
C	13·01	1	13·01
D	12·56	2	25·12
E	12·87	4	51·48
F	13·53	2	27·06
G	12·94	1	12·94
H	13·27	2	26·54
J	13·84	1	13·84
		$\Sigma n = 16$	207·11

$\therefore$ Mean level $= \dfrac{207 \cdot 11}{16}$

$= 12 \cdot 944$ m

$\therefore$ Depth of excavation $= 12 \cdot 944 - 8 \cdot 00$

$= 4 \cdot 944$

Volume $=$ Total area $\times$ Depth

$= 30 \times 20 \times 4 \cdot 944$

$= 2966 \cdot 4$ m^3

(*b*) *Calculation from triangles.* It is usually more accurate to calculate from triangles as the upper base of the triangular prism is more likely to correspond with the ground plane than the larger rectangle. The mean level of each prism is then the mean of the *three* heights enclosing the triangle instead of *four* as before.

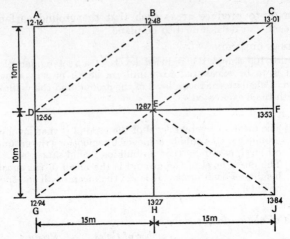

FIG. 100.—*Calculating volume from spot heights on a levelling grid*

The data shown are used in the volume calculations in **28**.

Station	R.L.	Number of times the R.L. is used = n	Product (R.L.) × n
A	12·16	1	12·16
B	12·48	3	37·44
C	13·01	2	26·02
D	12·56	3	37·68
E	12·87	7	90·09
F	13·53	2	27·06
G	12·94	2	25·88
H	13·27	2	26·54
J	13·84	2	27·68
		$\Sigma n = 24$	310·55

$$\therefore \text{ Mean level} = \frac{310 \cdot 55}{24}$$
$$= 12 \cdot 940 \text{ m}$$

$\therefore$ Depth of excavation $= 4 \cdot 940$
Volume $= 30 \times 20 \times 4 \cdot 940$
                   $= 2964 \cdot 0 \text{ m}^3$

NOTE: The diagonals forming the triangles would be noted in the field book on the grid layout (*see* XII, **13**) to conform most suitably with the ground planes.

29. Formation level involving cut and fill. Where the formation level to which an area of ground is to be excavated is not all below the ground the treatment is slightly different. The calculation of the mean level will produce a result either higher or lower than the required formation level.

If the mean level is *greater* than the formation level then excavation and carting away is needed. The volume of excavated material is not known as some of it will be needed to fill any part of the area lower than formation level.

If the mean level is *less* than the formation level then fill is needed and earth must be borrowed to raise the ground to the required level. Again the volume of some earth, which may have to be excavated and used as fill if any part of the site is higher than the required formation level, is not known.

The method of calculating the volume of the excavated earth only, the total fill required and the cart-away or borrow required, is as follows:

(*a*) Interpolate the contour line (*see* XIII, **18**) of the formation level and draw give-and-take straight lines between the grid lines following the contour line to facilitate the area calculations.

(*b*) The volume of excavation only is then calculated from the high ground on one side of the contour line. The volumes within the irregular areas formed must each be separately evaluated, as described in **28**.

(*c*) The volume of fill is similarly calculated for the area on the lower side of the contour line.

(*d*) The amount of cart-away or borrow needed, as the case may be, is obtained from a comparison of (*b*) and (*c*) above. The calculations may be checked from the mean level and volume calculation of the whole area.

NOTE: To simplify the calculations when dealing with larger areas, draw the give-and-take line following the formation level contour along the grid lines themselves. With this approach individual area calculations are unnecessary as the original rectangular grid is retained. The error produced by this more approximate method will be comparatively small. It is suitable for most practical purposes.

PROGRESS TEST 14

1. How are area calculations checked?   (2–3)

*2. Calculate the area of a triangle with sides of 64·7 m, 85·2 m and 101·7 m.   (2)

*3. Calculate the area, using Simpson's rule, between a survey line 45 m long and an irregular boundary lying wholly on one side. Offsets have been taken as follows every 5 m:

0·0; 3·2; 4·9; 7·6; 5·3; 6·2; 6·9; 5·7; 3·2; 0·0   (3)

*4. Calculate the area of the figure $ABCDE$, using the method of departures and total latitudes, given that the co-ordinate differences are as follows:

	ΔE		ΔN
		(metres)	
AB	+74·2		+173·6
BC	+21·7		−74·9
CD	−33·4		−53·2
DE	+16·7		−33·3
EA	−79·2		−12·2

(4)

*5. Calculate the area of the figure $PQRST$, using the following co-ordinates:

	E		N
		(metres)	
P	136·2		109·9
Q	210·4		283·5
R	232·1		208·6
S	198·7		155·4
T	215·4		122·1

(5)

*6. A plot of ground $ABYX$, 1·416 ha in extent, is to be set out, given the following data:

Bearing $BA = YX = 256°\ 00'\ 00''$
Bearing $AX = \qquad 150°\ 00'\ 00''$
Bearing $BY = \qquad 211°\ 00'\ 00''$

The length of AB is 228·60 m. Calculate the lengths of AX, XY and YB.   (8)

*7. The co-ordinates of a pentagonal plot of ground $ABCDE$ are as follows:

	E		N
		(metres)	
A	100·0		500·0
B	293·0		685·0
C	236·0		516·0
D	473·0		471·0
E	71·0		21·0

This area is to be divided into two equal portions by means of a straight fence AX, X being a point on DE.

Calculate the distance DX to enable the fence to be set out. (9)

*8. A triangular plot of land ABC has the following dimensions:

$$AB \quad 317 \cdot 7 \text{ m}$$
$$BC \quad 549 \cdot 4 \text{ m}$$
$$AC \quad 478 \cdot 1 \text{ m}$$

The plot is to be divided by means of a straight fence BX, X being a point on AC, such that the area of portion BXC is three-quarters that of portion ABX.

Determine the length CX to set out the fence and the length BX to find the amount of fencing required. (10)

*9. A small dyke 62 m long with vertical end faces, a top formation width of 4 m and side batters of 1:2 is to be constructed from 5707 m³ of available earth. If all the excavated earth is used, determine the height of the dyke which can be constructed.

(15, 21)

*10. Calculate the cross-sectional area of a cut section with a formation width of 20 m, where the centre line is to be 1·25 m below ground level. The side slopes are to be 1:1½ and the existing ground slopes at 1:15, transverse to the longitudinal centre line.

(16)

*11. A trench 80 m long and with end faces vertical is excavated in flat land. Subsequent to excavation, cross-sections are taken at 20-m intervals beginning at one end of the trench and ending at the other. The areas of the cross-sections are progressively 63, 71, 76, 72 and 69 m². By means of the prismoidal formula, determine the amount of excavation in cubic metres. (20)

*12. Refer to Fig. 100 and, using the following reduced levels at the corner points of the grid instead of those shown, calculate from the rectangles the volume down to a reduced level of 10 m:

$$A = 13 \cdot 97 \text{ m} \qquad B = 13 \cdot 42 \text{ m} \qquad C = 12 \cdot 86 \text{ m}$$
$$D = 14 \cdot 52 \text{ m} \qquad E = 14 \cdot 21 \text{ m} \qquad F = 13 \cdot 97 \text{ m}$$
$$G = 14 \cdot 99 \text{ m} \qquad H = 15 \cdot 03 \text{ m} \qquad J = 14 \cdot 82 \text{ m} \qquad (28)$$

CHAPTER XV

SETTING OUT

GENERAL PRINCIPLES

1. Definition of setting out. In surveying, existing features and levels are located on the ground and then plotted at a reduced scale on plan. *Setting out* is the reverse process, where the position and levels of new works already recorded on a working plan are transferred to the ground.

The accuracy of measurement required in setting out depends on the type of building work that is to take place. Where prefabricated frames and components are to be used, the setting out must be sufficiently precise for such components to fit within the tolerances laid down. Measurements must therefore be made with great care. As in surveying, the setting out must be arranged so that the work is *checked*. Every peg placed must be proved to be in its correct position within allowable limits.

2. Control. The process of setting out covers three aspects of positioning new works. These are the following:

(*a*) *Horizontal control*, in which the true relative positions of points are fixed on the horizontal plane and marked by pegs in the ground.

(*b*) *Vertical control*, in which pegs defining different levels of construction are suitably placed.

(*c*) *Works control*, in which the construction processes are controlled, *e.g.* the vertical alignment of buildings during construction and the control of embankment slopes and excavations.

3. Methods. The methods to be adopted in setting out cannot be laid down precisely. Setting out is often complicated by obstacles. The progress of construction and the restrictions imposed by plant, machinery and materials on site often prevent straightforward setting out. Each case must be dealt

334

with individually and some ingenuity is often required in over-coming difficulties. Three fundamental stages of setting out, however, are involved and are applicable in all cases:

(*a*) *Base line.* A base line is first set out from which subsidiary pegs are placed to define the new construction. The base line is often indicated on the working drawing and may be one of the following:

(*i*) The centre line of a new road, railway, pipe-line, sewer, etc.

(*ii*) The building line for domestic and smaller constructions.

(*iii*) The centre lines of columns and stancheons in large projects.

(*iv*) A line parallel to the longest construction line in the works.

(*b*) *Subsidiary lines.* These are set out from the base line and pegged. The data used should always be figured dimensions from the working drawing or calculated measurements based on plan information. Owing to obvious inaccuracies scaled dimensions are rarely used. All pegs placed must be checked and proved to have been correctly positioned.

(*c*) *Reference marks.* Since the setting-out pegs are inevitably destroyed during the course of the work a system of reference or witness marks or recovery pegs must be established so that the base line and all subsidiary pegs can be re-established at any time during the course of the work. Reference marks must therefore be located in such a way that the following conditions apply:

(*i*) That they are not likely to be disturbed.

(*ii*) That relocation of major points from them can be easily undertaken with accuracy and their position proved.

(*iii*) That if there is any possibility of the reference marks being destroyed alternative marks are still available for the main pegs to be redefined or for the reference marks to be re-established.

4. Setting-out plan. In all but minor works a setting-out plan should be prepared. This plan will show the position and description of *all* pegs set out. The linear dimensions between pegs and the angles between, or the bearings of, lines used for setting out and referencing must be recorded. In addition the reduced levels of any pegs or bench-marks to be used for vertical height control must be shown. This information is then available to others during the course of construction to verify the position of the work at its various stages and to enable any setting-out pegs to be replaced at any time.

The plans required for any construction from beginning to end include the following:

(a) *The survey plan*, prepared as a result of the original site survey.

(b) *The working plan*, produced by the designer, showing the location and form of the new construction sited on the survey plan.

(c) *The setting-out plan*, showing the relation between the recovery pegs and the pegs defining the position of the new works.

(d) *Record plans*, also known as *as-built plans* and *as-laid plans*, the latter term applicable to pipe-lines, recording any deviations from the original design and showing the new works as finally constructed. Such plans, which may consist only of revisions to the working plan, are not always completed properly.

5. Setting-out pegs. The marks used to define ground points are usually 40- or 50-mm square wooden pegs about 0·5 or 0·75 m long with a point cut at one end. These are placed reasonably accurately in position, then the precise point required is marked by a 40-mm wire nail hammered into the peg, leaving about 10 mm projecting.

Reference points and other important marks may be further secured by scooping a shallow trench around the peg and gently heaping concrete around it to keep it firm. If necessary a light railing may be erected around it to warn lorries and other vehicles to keep clear.

Permanent marks are constructed from concrete blocks set up to 1 m into the ground and built up to any required height. A brass plate with a drilled centre-mark or a pipe or other device is set into the concrete to define the precise point.

NOTE: Permanent marks are not built as often as they should be because of the time and cost involved. This shortsightedness should be overruled by the consultant engineer as permanent markers may save further extensive survey work at a later date.

6. Placing level pegs to define working levels. Assume that a peg is required to define a 5·00-m level. A level is set up and a backsight, say 1·490, is observed to a T.B.M. with an R.L. of, say, 4·042 m. The height of instrument is then 4·042 + 1·490 = 5·532. Thus when a reading on a staff of 0·532 m is taken its base will be at the required level of 5·00 m.

The following procedure is involved when positioning a peg to a specified level:

(*a*) The staff is held where the peg is to be placed and raised or lowered until the calculated reading is obtained. This indicates the approximate peg projection above ground.

(*b*) The peg is hammered down almost to the required level with frequent checks on the staff reading until it is accurately placed.

(*c*) If it is hammered down too far by mistake it cannot be lifted as it will loose stability. A nail is then placed on top and hammered down to define the reduced level as before.

(*d*) To save time in accurately positioning the top of the peg it may be left projecting above the required level. The staff is held against the peg until the calculated reading is obtained and a line defining the level is drawn across one side of the peg. For clarity this line is usually arrowed and its level chalked on the peg.

Pegs defining levels below ground have sometimes to be set out. For example, supposing earth has to be excavated to a specific level. Pegs are hammered down over the site and a level is chosen a whole number of half metres above the required level so that all pegs placed can be marked with this level above the ground surface as before. An arrow drawn pointing downwards on each peg from the level line with a note of the excavation depth required clarifies the position for others. In shallow excavations earth can be cleared up to the pegs if they project down far enough. In deeper excavations sufficient earth is left around each peg to hold it secure until the required depth is obtained all round. When a formation level is dug out by reference to the peg, the peg and mound of earth holding it is finally cleared away.

SEWERS AND DRAINS

7. Sewers and drains. A *drain* is a line of pipes and fittings, including inspection chambers, traps, gullies, etc., used for the drainage of one building and the yards and outhouses of one property. A *sewer*, on the other hand, is any piped drainage system not included in the above description. As such it may collect the drainage waste from several properties and may be private or public. Private sewers run in private land and must be maintained by the various owners whose drains lead into it. Public sewers, on the other hand, are usually laid in streets, but may cross private land. They are maintained by local authorities.

8. Gradients. Drains and sewers are laid to gradients such that the flow of water allows the drain to be self-cleansing. The old rule of thumb that 100-mm, 150-mm and 225-mm drains were laid to falls of 1:40, 1:60 and 1:90, respectively, is satisfactory for drains where the water flow is fairly low. In combined drains, which contain both foul and storm water, and where the quantity of flow is greater, shallower gradients are used. Sewers are thus laid to shallower gradients generally than drains. This is also more economical as less excavations will probably be required. The following table indicates cleansing gradients for the average flows shown:

Quantity of flow (m^3/s)	Gradient	Pipe diameter (mm)
0·001	1/40	100
0·002	1/50	100
0·003	1/80	100 or 150
0·004	1/100	100 or 150
0·005	1/120	150 or 225
0·006	1/150	150 or 225
0·007	1/160	150 or 225
0·008	1/175	225 or 300
0·009	1/180	225 or 300
0·010	1/220	225 or 300

NOTE

(*i*) The larger pipes shown above would be used for combined or storm water drains.

(*ii*) If gradients are too large the drains may become non-cleansing again.

9. Setting out the base lines. In this case the base used is the centre line of the sewer. On a block plan of the area at a scale of 1:1250 or 1:2500 the lines of existing and proposed sewers and drains are drawn. The *lines* of the new sewers are then marked on the ground by placing a peg at each manhole or inspection chamber position obtained by setting out scaled or recorded dimensions from the block plan. Manholes will be built at the following positions:

(*a*) At a maximum of every 100 m on straight runs.
(*b*) At all changes of direction.
(*c*) At all sewer junctions.
(*d*) At the head of each sewer or drain.
(*e*) At interceptors near junctions of drains and sewers. These should be within 12 m of the junction.

Once the pegs are placed and their reference numbers recorded on the block plan *line pegs* are placed every 20 or 30 m along the lines as a guide to the excavation.

10. Sections. Longitudinal sections are then run as described in XI, **1–11**, and *sections* are drawn indicating the ground profile and any features or other services crossing the path of the new sewer line to provide all information necessary for the drainage scheme design and so that the depth of excavation and any problems peculiar to the site may be evaluated and costed. On smaller sites with even slopes there may be few, if any, intermediate levels other than those at manhole positions. The reduced levels of all existing manholes and their invert levels will also be observed and recorded. An *invert level* is the level of the bottom of the inside of any pipe or channel. In manholes it is the level of the channel floor of the outgoing pipe.

From the longitudinal section *working profiles* (*see* XI, **12**) are prepared showing the gradients of drain and sewer runs and invert levels of all manholes and junctions. All gradients and levels should be *tabulated* as well as being drawn to scale.

NOTE

(*i*) The preparation of sections is desirable for most sewer runs for the proper control of the work, for costing and for record purposes.

(*ii*) Sections are not essential and are seldom supplied in the case of shallow house drains, but are desirable in larger layouts serving flats and factory buildings for the reasons given in (*i*) above.

11. Setting out subsidiary lines. The first stage (*see* **9**) of the work has been carried out when the manhole positions have

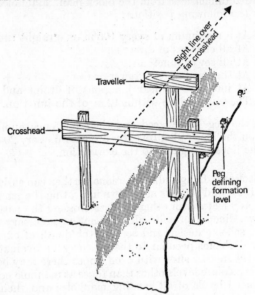

FIG. 101.—*Sight rails and travelling rod*

The illustration shows sight rails built across a drainage trench with the travelling rod being used to position pegs along the bottom of the trench at invert level parallel to the gradient of the sight line, shown dotted, across the top of the sight rails.

been pegged. The second stage does not require much work as the works have little width and it merely consists of placing pegs to mark the limits of the manhole excavations and the trench if hand excavation is to take place. On larger works machines will excavate the trench and the cutting blades will be set to provide the required width.

The third stage involves referencing the pegs which mark the final manhole positions. Where mechanical excavation is to take place reference pegs are placed in a safe position as described in **36** and their levels established. Alternatively, or for hand excavation, the *sight rails* used for establishing the gradient of the excavation are used as the reference mark, as indicated in Fig. 101. Two uprights are placed firmly in the ground clear of the manhole excavation and a cross-piece or *crosshead* is nailed between them. The peg position is plumbed up and marked on the crosshead, which can remain undisturbed during the works.

12. Excavation control. Sight rails are required in order to provide a line above ground parallel to the gradient of the pipeline below ground in order to *control* the excavation.

The *sight rails* at each end of a sewer run are fixed horizontally to their supports at a height a whole number of half metres above invert level so that the line joining the sight rails is parallel to the gradient of the sewer.

The *traveller* is a timber upright, the length from invert to sight rail, with a crosshead nailed to it for easier sighting. When its cross-piece is on the sight line over the rails then its base will be at invert level of the sewer. Using the traveller as indicated in Fig. 101 a series of pegs are eventually placed along the bottom of the trench to control the excavation. The pegs may be marked with *formation level*, usually 100 to 150 mm below invert level as the pipes generally lie on a bed of concrete or hardcore. The earth is then worked to these levels and the pegs may also be used as a guide for laying the required bed thickness.

These basic principles may be varied to suit individual contractors' practice or the excavation plant in use. Sight rails may be set up clear of the manholes or to one side of the centre line to prevent the line of sight being obscured by the machinery. Three sight rails are sometimes erected so there is at all times visual proof that the crossheads have not been disturbed.

SPECIMEN QUESTION

A sewer run 80 m long is to be laid at a fall of 1:120 from manhole F16 to manhole F17. The reduced level of the ground peg at F16 is 17·210 m and its designed invert level is 15·360 m. The reduced level of the ground peg at F17 is 17·350 m. A 3-m traveller is available. Calculate the height above each ground

peg at which each sight rail is to be fixed and the invert level of
F17.

The sight rail at F16 must be fixed at a height of 1·15 m
above the peg because the invert depth is 17·210 − 15·360
= 1·85 m. As the traveller is 3 m long and 1·85 will be its
length below the peg, 1·15 m, the balance of 3 m, will be above,
up to sight rail level.

The gradient of 1/120 indicates a fall in 80 m of:

$$\frac{80}{120} \text{ m} = 0\cdot667 \text{ m}$$

Invert level at F17 will therefore be 15·360 − 0·667 = 14·693 m.
The level of the sight rail must be 3 m above this at 17·693 m.
Therefore the height at which the second sight rail must be
fixed above the peg at F17 is 17·693 − 17·350 = 0·343 m.

13. Laying the pipes. Drain and sewer pipes are laid from
the lower end of the trench with sockets facing uphill. The
concrete bases of the manholes are first poured and the beds
for the pipes laid. The lower manhole channels are bedded
down and the upper manhole channels temporarily laid. A
side line is drawn between the two just clear of the flanges to
keep the pipe-line straight. The gradient of the pipes may then
be controlled by using one of the three following instruments:

(a) *Travelling rod.* As each pipe is laid the socket end is
adjusted for height by using a travelling rod with an iron
shoe or bracket on its base which projects into the pipe and
rests on the invert.

(b) *Straight-edge.* Using the pegs placed along the trench
with the traveller a straight-edge is laid along the invert of
each pipe length and the pipe is bedded down until the projecting straight-edge touches the peg at the invert level in
front of it. The pegs are removed as the pipe laying proceeds. This method is impracticable for long cast-iron pipes.

(c) *Boning rods.* These are short travellers, used in sets of
three, all of the same length, usually about 1 m. They are
used in deeper trenches where long travellers would be cumbersome and in shallow domestic drains. Two boning rods
are held, one at each end of the line, with their bases on a
defined gradient, such as pegs previously placed to the required levels. These two boning rods then act as temporary

crossheads as the sight line between their tops will define the
gradient between the ends of the line. The third boning rod
may then be positioned anywhere between the first two and
where its top is aligned with the sight line across the other
two its base will also be on the gradient to which the laid
pipes must be adjusted. This process is known as *boning in*.
The inverts of each pipe are either boned in or, by holding
one boning rod on the top of the first pipe at the lower end
and one on the last pipe temporarily laid at the upper end,
the tops of the pipes are boned in individually as they are
laid or jointed.

NOTE

(*i*) Pipes are often laid first, unjointed, in the trench and the
whole set is adjusted for line and gradient, jointing being
carried out afterwards.

(*ii*) The use of a top line instead of a side line to control both
gradient and line at the same time is to be deprecated
as even a taut line will sag, resulting in a dip in the pipe
line.

BUILDINGS

14. Setting out the base line. The base line adopted in
setting out a building is usually the *building line*, although on
extensive factory layouts the centre lines of buildings or runs
of machinery are sometimes used. In either case the location
of such lines is related to the physical features of the site.

The *building line* is the line of the front face of the building
as indicated in Fig. 102. Its position may be defined on the
working plan by measurements from the following:

(*a*) The property boundary.
(*b*) The edge of the road kerb.
(*c*) The centre line of the road.

NOTE

(*i*) Where there is no indication of the building line its position
must be agreed on site with the local authority building
inspector or, in inner London, with the district surveyor.

(*ii*) Where there is an obvious line of existing building frontages
this line is usually adopted as the building line.

The building line is first ranged by eye and pegs are placed
at the two front corners of the outer face of the proposed

building. Critical measurements are made from the boundary to the building corner as indicated in Fig. 102 or defined by local regulations and along the face of the proposed building with a steel tape. These accurately measured points are

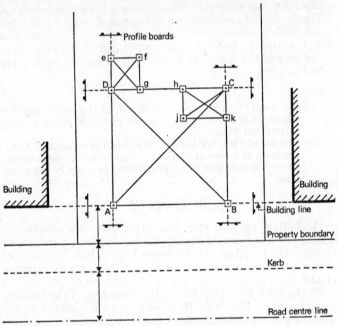

FIG. 102.—*Setting out a building*

The plan view is shown with the front of the new building set on the building line and the pegs marking the corners of the proposed building being defined by the profile boards set back clear of the eventual foundation trenches.

defined by nails hammered into the pegs. The first stage of the work is then complete.

On large sites the base lines may conveniently be set out from co-ordinate calculations. The traverse stations used in the original survey are plotted on the design plan and the precise location of the base lines may be related to them on a co-ordinate grid. The co-ordinates of salient points are calculated and the bearing and distance from nearby traverse stations are calculated (*see* IV, **14–15**) and used for setting out the points. Cross measurements must also be taken to check the placing of each peg, or the bearing and distance from another station may be observed and compared with its calculated data. This method is particularly useful on obstructed sites and for setting out boundaries of new housing and factory estates.

15. Setting out the subsidiary lines. From the two front pegs A and B angles are set out in accordance with the building plan to follow the outer face of the flank walls. This could be done with a theodolite, setting up over each peg in turn and turning off the required angle from the building line in each case. As the angle of the flank wall is most often 90° this could be set out without a theodolite using the following:

(*a*) A 3:4:5-taped triangle.

(*b*) A builder's square, which is a 3:4:5-ratio triangle made out of timber.

(*c*) An optical square (*see* II, **39**).

(*d*) A site square, which is a proprietory instrument consisting of two small telescopes fixed rigidly at right-angles on a small stand.

(*e*) A level incorporating a horizontal circle like a theodolite, but reading by vernier to about 5′ only.

When the two rear pegs C and D are placed and nail marked they are *checked* by measuring between them and by measuring the diagonals. In a rectangle the two diagonals must be equal to prove the positioning of the pegs.

After the main outline has been pegged any minor extensions or returns from the main figure are pegged and checked, such as the pegs at *e, f, g, h, j* and *k*. When the complete outline of the outer face of the building has been pegged and checked the second stage of the work is complete.

16. Setting out the reference marks. The pegs now placed will be destroyed as the foundations are excavated and a reference system must be adopted. This can be achieved by the use of *profile boards*, illustrated in Fig. 103, and indicated on the site plan (*see* Fig. 102).

Profile boards are constructed of 150- or 200-mm by 25-mm

boards supported on 50-mm square posts hammered firmly into the ground well clear of the working area. On well-organised sites the boards are all placed at one level, usually finished floor level or damp-proof course level. The advantages of this are as follows:

(*a*) They help to keep the tape horizontal when making measurements.

(*b*) They provide a level datum around the site so that less check levelling is needed subsequently.

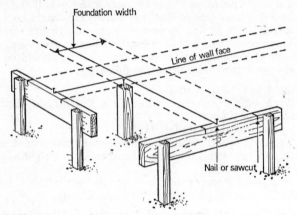

Fig. 103.—*Profile boards*

The peg positions marking the corners of the proposed building are defined by the lines drawn across between the various profile boards.

(*c*) Disturbance of the boards can easily be noted visually.

(*d*) Levels of work below ground can be controlled by travellers using the profile boards as sight rails.

(*e*) Approximate levels can be obtained by direct vertical measurements up or down from lines strung between the profile boards.

Once the boards have been placed in position all at one level lines are strung between them and positioned vertically above the nail markers defining the building outline. If the line is some distance above the peg the peg position must be plumbed upwards, using a plumb line in preference to the less accurate bricklayer's spirit level. When the lines have been accurately strung across the profile board its position is marked with a nail or sawcut so that it may be replaced at any time. The intersections of the various strung lines will then define the peg positions when they are removed for excavation. Profile boards for minor building returns or projections are not always erected or needed.

By measuring outwards along each profile board from the nail a distance equal to the projection of the foundations, the outer lines of the foundation may be defined by moving the lines to this position. Full foundation width is marked on the board and two lines strung between these points define the width of the foundation trench to be dug. Once the trench has been started the lines are removed. Alternatively the lines may be temporarily defined along the ground by means of strips of lime or sand to guide excavation.

17. Structure control. After the foundations have been laid the lines defining the building face are again strung, the building corners are plumbed down to the foundations and the brickwork or formwork correctly positioned. Sometimes both the inner and outer faces are strung which is useful in cavity work for obtaining an accurate cavity width.

NOTE

(*i*) The same process can be adopted for the erection of formwork for concrete basement walls.

(*ii*) Where there is the possibility of the profile boards being disturbed accidentally, or deliberately, as on larger sites with more plant, personnel and machinery, the lines may be extended beyond the boards to stable reference pegs concreted in and protected by railings.

18. Reference frame for setting out columns. On larger sites the principle of working from the whole to the part should be applied. The reference marks may be accurately placed first on the perimeter of a large rectangle or *reference frame* surrounding the building, the pegs defining the actual construction being placed in relation to them within the works area subsequently.

Columns are slender, vertical, structural members of stone, reinforced concrete or steel. The setting out of their positions requires care and precision. Small errors in positioning are

aggravated by the height of the structure and can impose unnecessary lateral forces on the members. The centres of
columns should be located with an accuracy of $\pm 2 \cdot 5$ mm in
relation to the design position. This can be achieved by a

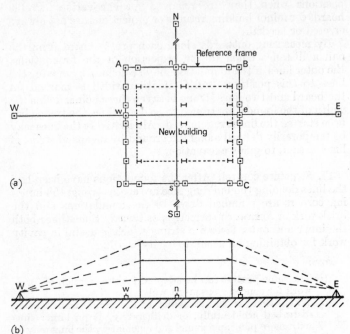

FIG. 104.—*Reference frame and vertical alignment*

(a) The plan view of the reference frame surrounding the area of the
new building with pegs placed to define the column positions.

(b) A sectional view illustrating how, by means of theodolites set up
at E and W, vertical alignment can be controlled in one direction.

surrounding reference frame, reference pegs being placed at
the spacing of the centre lines of the column positions, as
illustrated in Fig. 104. In large frames it is advisable to make
temperature corrections to maintain accuracy.

Column centres may be defined by lines or wires strung
across the framework between the appropriate reference
marks. If line tension is likely to disturb the reference marks

the lines can be carried over the marks and be fixed to stout stakes behind them. If chalked string is used, the lines may be flicked down on to the concrete to provide a fairly accurate centre line marking. Alternatively lines may be established with a theodolite, setting up at one side, sighting through to the opposite mark and, leaving the horizontal circle clamped, lowering the telescope to sight the column centres. This must be done on *both faces* to eliminate instrument errors. Pencil marks are made on either side of the column centre point on both faces and the line midway between the pairs of marks defines the centre line in one direction. The process must be repeated at right-angles from the other two sides of the reference frame.

Centre lines must be drawn on the concrete base to project beyond the outline of the column. This is done in pencil on white paint marks on the concrete. Formwork for reinforced concrete columns can then be positioned relative to these marks. By using a template corresponding to the base of steel stanchions the centre lines set out are aligned with the template centre lines, when the bolt holes required will be accurately positioned on the foundation.

NOTE: Where the site does not permit a complete reference frame to be laid out two lines positioned at right-angles are sufficient. In such cases right-angles must be turned off with a theodolite each time, lines cannot be strung and there is more chance of an error occurring in the work.

19. Vertical alignment. Vertical alignment of structures may be achieved in several ways, the suitability of each depending on the type of structure, the site concerned and the equipment available:

(a) *Centre-line axes method* (*see* **20**). This method requires the use of a theodolite, but it is simple, effective and accurate, although its use is often precluded by a lack of space surrounding the building.

(b) *Plumb-bob method* (*see* **21**). This is a traditional method often preferred even on high structures.

(c) *Optical plumbing method* (*see* **22–25**). Several proprietory devices now provide a vertically aligned line of sight.

(d) *Theodolite plumbing method* (*see* **26–28**). The theodolite may be used to establish a vertical line.

20. Centre-line axes method. Figure 104 shows the use of the centre-line axes, allied with a reference frame. If the two lines at right-angles to each other are carried up the building during construction and measurements to columns at each floor are taken off these lines the structure itself will remain vertical.

Vertical alignment is achieved in the following way:

(a) *Reference pegs* on two lines at right-angles are placed before construction, four on each line, so that the lines are not masked as the building is erected. The length between the two pegs on either side of the building should exceed twice the eventual building height to maintain accuracy.

(b) *A theodolite* is then set up over one of the outer pegs, sighted on the alignment peg near the building, and the line of sight elevated to the required floor. This is done on both faces, the mean position being marked. This process is carried out from all four outer pegs so that the centre-line axes are established on the upper floor.

(c) *Offsets* from this axis may be used to set out the base for the next floor above, all rectangular figures being checked by diagonal measurements. Alternatively the theodolite itself may be set up on each floor orienting down to the ground reference mark. Again, owing to the steepness of the sight line observations must be made on both faces.

21. Plumb-bob method. Plumb-bobs weighing 12 to 20 kg suspended on piano wire or nylon may be used. Two plumb-bob positions are needed in order to provide a base from which the upper floors may be controlled. To dampen oscillations the bob is usually suspended in a drum of oil. A glass container allows the bob to be seen hanging free. Precise setting over a mark is difficult, but by constructing a small staging above the container the plumb line's relation to index marks on the staging may be established.

Difficulties experienced in using the plumb-bob are related to the following factors:

(a) The swing set up by wind currents in high buildings.

(b) The provision of openings in floors to allow the plumb line to hang through. Service ducts may be used, but often provide an inconveniently placed base line for control measurements.

(c) Finishing trades on lower floors soon preclude the use of the bob for the full height of the building.

(d) Handling the plumb-bob apparatus is time consuming if any reasonable degree of accuracy is required.

Plumb-bobs are invaluable under certain circumstances, e.g. the accurate alignment of service pipes in high buildings, lift guides and so on.

22. Optical plumbing method. The optical plummet of a theodolite (see VI, 10) provides a vertical line of sight in a *downwards* direction which enables the instrument to be accurately centred *over* a station mark. Optical plummets are normally built into modern theodolites, but there are theodolite attachments which provide vertical lines *upwards*, allowing an instrument to be accurately set *under* a station mark, e.g. in the roof of a tunnel. Such forms of optical plumbing are short-range devices and do not provide a vertical line of sight of sufficient accuracy to control a high-rise structure.

23. Automatic optical plumbing. Special instruments are now made which provide an accurate, vertically aligned line of sight. Some require to be accurately levelled with a spirit level, but the automatic plummet with an optical compensator, like the automatic level (see X, 17), automatically ensures a vertical line of sight. There are several such instruments, but one of the better known is the Hilger and Watts *Autoplumb*. This instrument sights upwards, but also contains an optical plummet for centring over the ground station mark. The *Autoplummet* sights downwards only and is designed for mine-shaft work, boreholes, etc.

24. The Hilger and Watts Autoplumb. The Autoplumb illustrated in Fig. 105 contains two telescopes, one of which sights downwards, and the other provides the upward line of sight. The line of sight is turned vertically by means of a pentagonal prism which is mounted on pivots. It may be tilted on either side of its normal position by means of a micrometer screw. The vertical line of sight may thus be adjusted into a truly vertical position.

The *body* rotates about a vertical axis. A spring-loaded pawl engages locators on the base for setting the instrument in four positions at right-angles, which is necessary to mean out any errors in verticality and to provide two intersecting vertical planes.

The *target* consists of a 150-mm diameter disc divided into eight segments which can either be mounted on a clamp to

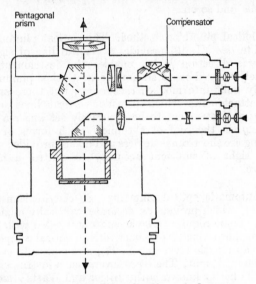

FIG. 105.—*The Autoplumb's optical system*

Once the instrument has been levelled and centred by the lower optical plumbing device the compensator provides an automatically aligned vertical line of sight through the upper telescope.

project from the side of a building or be mounted in a steel frame with four arms extending at 90° to each other. The steel frame allows the target to be laid over a sighting hole in the floor of a building. One edge of each arm is in line with the target centre so that its position may be defined by floor marks around the sighting hole.

An *alternative target* sometimes preferred, and which is more convenient for theodolite plumbing, is made by etching a right-angled cross on a sheet of firm perspex. The translucent perspex is laid over the sighting hole, the dark cross being easily discernible. The limits of the cross can then be marked in pencil on the concrete around the sighting hole.

25. Operation of the Autoplumb. The operation of the Autoplumb is as follows:

(*a*) *Mount the instrument* on its tripod over the ground mark and level up, using the plate bubble. Very accurate levelling is not needed as the sight is short, but as there is no compensation on the downward line of sight, which is at right-angles to the axis of the plate bubble, the same care must be taken as is needed in levelling up a theodolite (*see* VI, **9–10**).

(*b*) *Adjust the movable head* until the ground mark appears central on the reticule seen through the lower telescope. Rotate the instrument and check that the ground mark remains central at all four settings.

(*c*) *Set the micrometer drum* to its centre-zero. Focus the upward-sighting telescope on to the target. An assistant at the target is instructed to move it until it appears central and is bisected by the horizontal line on the reticule.

(*d*) *Depress the pawl* securing the instrument position and rotate the Autoplumb through 90° until the pawl re-engages in the next slot. The target must now be moved along the cross hair until it is again bisected by the horizontal line.

(*e*) *Rotate the instrument* through the next two positions, ensuring that the cross hair bisects the target each time.

NOTE

(*i*) To check the accuracy of the zero setting of the micrometer, position the target so that it is bisected in any one position of the Autoplumb. Rotate through 180°, when the target should again be bisected. If not, half the micrometer reading required to move the cross hair back on target is set, which will provide the required vertical line of sight.

(*ii*) The claimed accuracy of the instrument is 0·3 mm in 40 m, but in practice a vertical line of sight within 1 mm can be obtained, which is well within construction tolerances.

(*iii*) Instructions to the target holder cannot easily be given verbally from ten-storey heights or so, and either good hand signals must be agreed before observing or a two-way radio should be available for accurate target setting.

26. Theodolite plumbing method. A theodolite may be used for the vertical alignment of structures with a similar degree of accuracy as the automatic plumbing instruments. This has the advantage that the special-purpose instrument need not be made available, particularly if a theodolite is already being used on the site. The main advantage of the *Autoplumb* is that relatively unskilled persons can quickly be trained to operate the instrument to produce good results. A theodolite requires some expertise and an experienced user is required to produce reliable vertical alignments. It can be used in two ways to provide vertical alignment control, by using inclined sights described in 27 or by using the diagonal eyepiece as described in 28.

27. Plumbing by inclined sights. After the theodolite has been set up well clear of the structure and accurately levelled, inclined sights from two positions at right-angles are used in the following way:

(*a*) Sight the ground point which is to be plumbed upwards and with the horizontal movement clamped elevate the telescope to sight a scale projecting from the side of the building. Read the scale.

(*b*) Transit and again sight the ground point. Elevate the telescope and again read the scale on circle right. A vertical plane through the ground point will intersect the scale between the two readings.

(*c*) The same process is repeated from another position to provide another vertical plane to intersect the first at right-angles, when the vertical on the structure can be established.

NOTE

(*i*) In order to provide *two* plumbed points on the upper floors, *four* instrument set-ups must be made.

(*ii*) Care must be taken to transfer the plumbed point from the scale readings to an accessible station point on the structure.

(*iii*) This method can be used when no special equipment is available, but it is not always convenient owing to site obstructions and the possibility of error in defining the plumbed point at high level.

(*iv*) This method is more suited to checking the vertical alignment of existing buildings. A high point is plumbed *down* to scale readings at ground level. The position of the point can then be compared with the structure position at ground level. The process is similar to the *spire test* (*see* VI, **21**), taken in two directions.

28. Plumbing with the diagonal eyepiece. With a comparatively cheap diagonal eyepiece attachment the theodolite telescope can be positioned vertically. As the eyepiece is at right-angles to the line of sight observations can still be made through the telescope.

The following is the usual procedure:

(*a*) The theodolite is set up, levelled and optically plumbed over the ground mark. Excessive care in levelling up is not required as the vertical axis does not need to be precisely vertical. The horizontal circle is set to a reading of 0° 0′ 0″.

(*b*) The alidade bubble is accurately centred and the vertical circle is set to read zero or 90°, whichever defines the vertical line of sight.

(*c*) The target on the upper floor of the form described in **24** is positioned so that one centre line lies on the horizontal hair of the theodolite diaphragm. The limits of this line are marked on the concrete at each edge of the target.

(*d*) The instrument is turned through 180° until the horizontal circle reading is 180° 0′ 0″. The alidade bubble is again levelled and the vertical circle reading accurately set. The horizontal hair will again define a line parallel and almost in coincidence with the first, depending on the accuracy of the instrument adjustments. The target is moved on to the line of the horizontal hair once more. The limits of this line are marked on the concrete as before. A line drawn midway between these two pairs of marks will define the true vertical plane.

(*e*) The same process is repeated with horizontal circle settings of 90° and 270° to produce two more pairs of marks at right-angles to the first. The target can then be positioned so that the lines of its perpendicular cross lie midway between the four pairs of marks. The centre point of the target will then define the vertical point above the ground mark.

NOTE

(*i*) The horizontal hair must be used for alignment as the mean of C.L. and C.R. in this procedure is unaffected by any non-verticality of the vertical axis, which is not the case with the vertical hair.

(*ii*) The procedure described above will average out any index error, collimation error or graduation error of the vertical circle.

(*iii*) With an optical micrometer instrument reading direct to 20″ accuracy is almost as good as that of the Autoplumb, a position to ± 1 mm over 30 m being readily obtainable. With a single-second instrument accuracy is much increased. With a vernier theodolite, scale setting of the vertical circle is less precise and a position can only be relied on to ± 4 mm in 30 m.

ROADS AND RAILWAYS

29. Setting out the base line. The initial setting-out process involves physically pegging on the ground the centre line of the road or railway. The setting-out processes for both roads and railways are similar, except for technical differences in the actual construction works. As new roads are far more frequently built than railways the particular problems relating to road works only will be considered. The base line being the centre line of the new work, it is usually defined in one of three ways by the designer, and the setting-out process for each of the following ways that the centre line has been established must be considered:

(*a*) *Plan location only* (*see* **30**).
(*b*) *Centre-line straights ground marked* (*see* **31**).
(*c*) *Co-ordinated centre line* (*see* **32**).

30. Plan location of the centre line. If the centre line has only been drawn on an existing plan, such as on the 1:2500 Ordnance maps, the position can only be located on the ground by scaling off the map. Sometimes dimensions on the design plan may fix the intersection points of the various straights in relation to existing ground features.

(*a*) First, the *intersection points* (I.P.s) are pegged, using scaled measurements or the dimensioned tie lines from existing features. If the I.P.s are intervisible line points may be placed at regular horizontal intervals of 20 or 25 m, the pegs being lined in by the theodolite.

(*b*) Where I.P.s are not intervisible a trial line must first be run on a scaled direction. Starting from one I.P. a peg is

placed on the assumed direction to the next. A theodolite
is set up here, the back peg is observed and the telescope is
transitted (*see* VI, **13** (*h*)) to carry the direction forward
again. This operation is repeated on circle right, the true
straight lying midway between the two directions carried
forward on each face. The running chainage to each peg is
measured and reduced for slope and the alignment process
is continued until the next I.P. previously placed is reached.

(*c*) The trial line is unlikely to meet the I.P. owing to inaccuracy in the directional scaling. If the displacement is
small the designer may agree to move the I.P. on to the
established line. If the I.P. position must remain as originally placed the line must swing back on to the straight
joining the I.P.s.

(*d*) To correct alignment, the offset distance from the line
end to the established I.P. is measured, say 3·96 m. If this
has occurred over a total distance of 2962·31 m, then any
line peg a distance *d* from the start must be moved at right-
angles to the line a distance

$$d \times \frac{3 \cdot 96}{2962 \cdot 31} \text{ m}$$

All line pegs are moved by this amount in proportion to the
length *d* until the line is correctly positioned.

(*e*) The correct alignment of each straight section is
established in the same way and as each line is completed
the angle between the straights is measured, sighting to the
most distant line pegs available. Angles are measured with
a single-second instrument, the mean of at least three arcs
being taken. From these angles the *angle of deflection* of the
straights is deduced for the calculation of any curve data
necessary as described in XVI.

31. Centre-line straights ground marked. If the designer has
followed the proposed route on the ground, placing intervisible line markers to define the centre line, a traverse is run
between these marks from one I.P. to the next. As such
markers are usually placed by eye they will not be properly
aligned and the traverse angle measured at each is required to
enable the marks to be moved to the true straight between the
I.P.s.

The traverse need not be calculated in the ordinary way as

the offset corrections can be simply obtained from the fact that the departure per 100 m for 1″ is 0·0005 m approximately. The following table shows the tabulated form of calculating the offset corrections:

Line	Bearing	Chainage	Deviation	Departure
I.P.1		0		
	0° 00′ 00″			
A		600		
	359° 59′ 27″			
B		1300	−33″L	−0·099L
	0° 00′ 37″			
I.P.2		2500	+37″R	+0·222R

Line	Provisional casting	Correction	Final casting	Offset correction
I.P.1	100·000	0	100·000	0
A	100·000	−0·030	99·970	+0·030
B	99·901	−0·064	99·837	+0·163
I.P.2	100·123	−0·123	100·000	

$$\frac{0·123}{250} \times 100 = 0·004\ 92 \text{ per 100 m}$$

NOTE

(i) The angular deviations left and right of zero direction are tabulated in the fourth column.

(ii) The extent of departure that these incur is calculated by multiplying the deviation for 1″ in 100 m, 0·0005, by the distance in 100-m units and by the number of seconds; e.g. 33 × 0·0005 × 700 = 0·099, the departure of AB.

(iii) The departures for each line are added algebraically to the provisional E co-ordinate of the previous point, until the final E is obtained. To secure zero direction throughout, all E co-ordinates must be the same.

(iv) If the final point I.P.2 is to be corrected by −0·123, the whole traverse line must be swung by the proportion of 0·123/2500 m or 0·004 92/100 m. These corrections are recorded in the seventh column and applied to the provisional castings giving the actual E co-ordinates of the points surveyed.

(v) For the points to be on line all E co-ordinates must be the same as those of the two end points. The offset correction to make them so is tabulated in the final column.

(vi) Finally each original marker is offset on the ground by the amounts indicated to provide the properly aligned centre line.

32. Co-ordinated centre line. This is the ideal system where the designer provides co-ordinates of salient points on the centre line. Any point or series of points on the centre line, on straights or on curves, can be set out from a previously laid down control traverse run clear of proposed earthworks and on the same co-ordinate system. Intersection points need not be marked as the angles between straights have previously been established by calculation. The co-ordinates of every chainage point can be calculated on both straights and curves and isolated sections of the work can be set out as required. For example, a bridge structure can be set out in isolation without having to wait for the progressive setting out of the centre lines to reach that point. This method requires the control survey to be undertaken early in the design stage.

33. Centre-line chainages. Once the centre line has been aligned or ranged by one of the three methods described the pegging of the line takes place with pegs being placed along the line at continuous changes at intervals of 20 or 25 m. Pegs are numbered in 100-m units, thus:

> Chainage of origin $= 0 + 00$
> Chainage of 1st peg $= 0 + 25$
> Chainage of 2nd peg $= 0 + 50$
> Chainage of 3rd peg $= 0 + 75$
> Chainage of 4th peg $= 1 + 00$, and so on.

Additional intermediate pegs are placed at bridge centres, intersections and at the beginning and end of transitional and circular curves as described in XVI.

Broken chainages occur when it is desirable to retain the value of a provisionally designed chainage for a certain point. A constant is then applied to the chainage of a *break* point. It has both its true cumulative chainage and the new chainage from which further chainages progress.

The first stage of the work is complete when all centre-line pegs on straights and curves have been pegged and checked.

34. Setting out the subsidiary lines. The next stage of the work consists of pegging the limits of the works area:

(*a*) *Fencing limits.* These are pegged first as the contractor must provide at least temporary fencing to secure right of way and prevent trespass claims from landowners.

Fencing pegs are placed simply from a schedule of offsets from centre-line chainages. Perpendiculars are usually established by means of the *double-prism square* (*see* II, **39**). On curves the offsets are radial and this is achieved by establishing the right-angle as before off a chord between two pegs equidistant on either side of the centre-line peg from which the radial line and offset distances are being measured. A schedule of fencing pegs placed must be maintained for record and replacement purposes.

(*b*) *Top soil strip limits.* Top soil is first removed by a scraper. It is then dumped and stored for re-soiling embankments. Pegs are required as a guide to the scraper operators and are usually offset a known distance beyond the strip lines to prevent destruction by the scraper. Usually the offset distances from the centre line are scaled off the design drawings and these pegs are placed in the same way and at the same time as the fencing pegs. This provides only an approximate guide as the actual works limits are dependent on the transverse ground slope. For an accurate determination of the strip or earthwork limit the procedure of earthwork control (*see* **37**) must be adopted.

35. Levelling. Vertical control is required at all stages of the work and must be available when required. A longitudinal section may be run, as described in XI, during the design stage or design works may have been based on existing plans and air survey information.

A series of T.B.M.s must be established along the route at intervals of about 300 m to provide level control. This may be done at the time of running a control traverse or may be incorporated in a longitudinal section of the finally pegged centre line. T.B.M.s should be substantial. In open country 1·5-m angle fence posts hammered down to project about 200 mm are used. They are placed close to the fence limits to prevent damage by machinery and may be surrounded by concrete.

Cross-sections will generally be needed (*see* XI) either for further design purposes or usually to enable actual earthwork quantities to be calculated. They must be observed before any earth-moving plant starts work.

36. Setting out the reference marks. Salient centre-line points such as tangent points, road intersections and bridge control points and sufficient intervisible centre-line pegs must be referenced so that any line peg or other control point can be replaced at any time. Reference marks must be fixed clear of plants and close to the fence line is usually best. Forms of referencing will vary but generally the approach should be that even if some of the reference points themselves are destroyed it will still be possible to reinstate the point referenced.

Figure 106 illustrates a typical form of reference. Reference

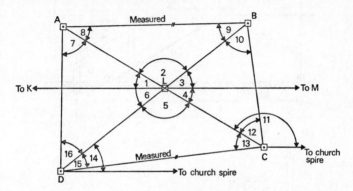

FIG. 106.—*Peg referencing*

The plan layout of an ideal reference quadrilateral for centre-line peg L is shown. This peg may be reinstated even if two of the reference pegs have also been removed.

pegs A and B are placed, the theodolite is set up at *A*, *L* is sighted and the line is projected to *C*. Similarly from *B* the line *BL* is projected through to *D*. Then all angles are measured, checked by summation and recorded. The distances *AB* and *DC* are measured for use in case any pegs are destroyed. It will often prove difficult to measure the diagonals, but they should be if an accurate measurement can easily be taken. Should two or even three of the reference points be destroyed peg L can still be replaced by the calculation of the data not directly measured originally. Under normal circumstances the peg L can quickly be replaced using two theodolites, although it can readily be replaced with one.

A necessary part of this work consists of recording the setting out data for each point on the field sketch which is filed for use each time the point has to be re-established. This serves the purpose of the *setting-out plan* mentioned in **4**.

37. Control of embankments. To keep embankments and cuttings to the correct slope, profile boards are used. These

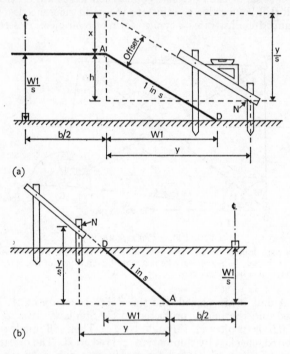

(a)

(b)

Fig. 107.—*Slope rails*

(a) The geometry and method of setting out a slope rail to guide the construction of an embankment.

(b) The geometry of setting out a slope rail to guide the construction of a cutting.

are known as *slope* rails or *batter* rails. A *batter* is the name sometimes given to slopes greater than 45°. Batter rails are generally offset a perpendicular distance from the proposed embankment slope to prevent them from being buried during the earth moving. An offset of 1 m is convenient, but may be varied to suit an individual contractor's requirements.

In order to set out the slope rail illustrated in Fig. 107(a) the following sequence of operations must be undertaken:

(a) The position of A will not yet be marked so that N is set out from the centre line a distance of half the formation width plus y or:

$$\left(\frac{b}{2} + y \right)$$

(b) Calculate x, which is dependent on the offset of the profile from the embankment slope. Where this is 1 m then:

$$x = \sqrt{1 + \left(\frac{1}{s} \right)^2}$$

For side slopes of 1 in 2, $x = 1\cdot118$ m and for 1 in 3, $x = 1\cdot054$, where an offset of 1 m is adopted.

(c) Scale the distance y from the plans or estimate the position of peg N by eye.

(d) Measure its approximate distance from the centre line and observe the level at this point and reduce the observed value of h from the given R.L. of A.

(e) From Fig. 107(a) it can be seen that:

$$h = \frac{y}{s} - x$$

(f) Divide the measured distance y by the slope s and subtract the calculated value of x from it. This provides the value h for the particular value of y used.

(g) Compare with the observed value of h obtained in (d). If the calculated value of h is smaller than the observed value the position of N has been chosen too close to A. If the calculated value of h is greater than the observed value N has been chosen too far from A.

(h) Peg N must be placed a distance y from A such that the calculated height difference from A falls about 200 to 400 mm up the peg at point N.

(i) When peg N has been conveniently placed calculate the correct value of h and using a level and staff place a nail into the side of the peg at N at the required level.

(j) The profile is set, using a template cut to suit the em-

bankment slope. A second upright is placed, the profile rests
on the projecting nail at N and is aligned by the template
levelled with a builder's spirit level and then nailed to each
upright.

NOTE

(*i*) The point at the foot of the slope D can also be pegged
using the principles detailed in (*a*) to (*j*) above as follows:

Choose the approximate position of D, measure out from
centre line and obtain the distance $W1$.

Observe the level of trial D. The level difference from A
should equal $W1/s$.

By trial and error move D until the measured height
difference times the slope s equals the measured length $W1$.
With experience this can be achieved in one or two
attempts.

(*ii*) The process of locating D, detailed in (*i*) above, also applies
to cuttings as shown in Fig. 107(*b*).

38. Control of cuttings. Batter rails for cuttings are
positioned clear of the cutting, the top edge defining the slope
of the cutting. The process is simpler than for controlling
embankments as no offsetting is usually required. The position
of the peg at N is estimated and the nail defining the required
level is placed in the following relationship:

$$\text{R.L. of N} = \text{R.L. of A} + \frac{y}{s}$$

The slope of the rail is fixed by template as before.

39. Slope rail information. Slope rails are marked in waterproof timber chalk with the following information, which is
also recorded in the field notes:

(*a*) Running chainage of centre-line point.

(*b*) Distance of peg N from centre line.

(*c*) Cut or fill; *i.e.* whether the rail defines an embankment
or cutting and the approximate amount, being the value
$W1/s$.

(*d*) The reduced level of N.

(*e*) The offset distance of the rail from the embankment
fence.

(*f*) The side slope, 1 in s.

40. Earthwork control by sight rails. Sight rails are used to control earthworks in the same way as they are used to control gradients in drainage work. Applications are varied, but the surveyor will frequently be required to set out sight rails so that works can be controlled visually by means of travellers or boning rods. Some applications are indicated in Fig. 108. Rails are frequently set level at whole numbers of half metres

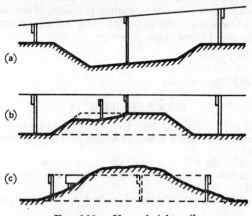

FIG. 108.—*Uses of sight rails*

(*a*) The method of controlling the cross fall to a carriageway.

(*b*) The method of controlling the amount of fill to an embankment.

(*c*) The method of controlling the lowering of ground level to a particular level or gradient.

and the travellers to be used with them are clearly marked on the crosshead, and the reduced level and the surface are defined, *e.g.* F.R.L. (finished road level). As in drainage work gradients may have to be set out to control cross falls.

In steep cuttings pegs may have to be placed at specific levels and subsequent work controlled by boning rods (*see* **13**). Finished surfaces, vertical curves (*see* XVI, **30**), cambers and kerb lines must be set out and are frequently controlled by boning rods, which are based on peg levels supplied by the surveyor, and are run from T.B.M.s on checked circuits of levels.

41. Summary. The principles of setting out described for sewers and drains, buildings and roads form the bases of nearly all the setting out problems likely to be encountered, but each site will have its own particular problems which may have to be overcome. With a little ingenuity, the use of elementary trigonometry and the adaptation of material formed on site, *every* peg required can be set out and checked by some means or other. The setting out of bridges, flyovers, dams and other civil engineering projects requires some knowledge of the structural processes involved in order to provide the requisite position of pegs, but once the required positions of the necessary setting out or works control points are known they can be set out in the usual three-stage process:

(a) *Base line.*
(b) *Subsidiary lines.*
(c) *Reference marks.*

PROGRESS TEST 15

1. How does setting out differ from ordinary site surveying? **(1)**
2. What are the three forms of *control* provided by setting out processes? **(2)**
3. Describe the three stages of all setting out work. **(3)**
4. What information is required to be recorded on a setting-out plan? **(4)**
5. What forms do setting-out pegs take and how are they placed? **(5–6)**
6. What is the difference between a sewer and a drain? **(7)**
7. What factors govern the gradients to which sewers and drains are laid? **(8)**
8. Describe the first stage of the work of setting out a new system of drains and sewers. **(9)**
9. Describe the second and third stages of the work of setting out a new system of drains and sewers. How are the centre-line points referenced? **(11)**
*10. A new sewer, 120 m long, is to be laid to a fall of 1/150 from A to B. Sight rails are erected at these points for use with a 3·5-m traveller. Use the following data:

Level reading on staff held on ground peg at A = 1·820 m.
Level reading on staff held on ground peg at B = 1·735 m.
Level reading on staff held on invert level at A = 3·950 m.
Reduced level of invert at A = 15·360 m.

Calculate the following:

(a) The height at which the rails must be fixed above the pegs at A and B.
(b) The reduced level of the invert at B. **(12)**

11. Describe the conditions under which, and how, building work is controlled by the following forms of reference mark:

    (a) Profile boards.

    (b) A reference frame.

    (c) Reference lines at right-angles. (16–18)

12. Describe in detail *five* methods of controlling the vertical alignment of high-rise structures. (19–28)

13. Describe three methods of setting out the centre line of a new road. (29–33)

14. Describe the process of pegging fencing and top soil strip limits. (34)

15. What levelling control is required for new roads? How is this supplied? For what purposes is it used? (35–40)

16. Describe a suitable method of referencing a new road centre-line control point. (36)

17. Describe in detail the method of controlling embankments and cuttings by means of slope rails. (37–38)

*18. An embankment with a formation width of 15 m and side slopes of 1 in 2 is to be controlled by means of a slope rail placed at right-angles to the centre line from a centre-line peg marking a formation level of 15·50 m. The underside of the slope rail is to be offset a perpendicular distance of 1 m from the embankment slope. A peg is placed at N at an offset distance of 17·00 m from the centre-line peg. A level of which the height of collimation has been established at 12·365 m from a backsight to a T.B.M. is used to level the base of the slope rail against peg N.

    (a) What staff reading is required for peg N to be marked at the required height?

    (b) If the reading on the staff held on the ground beside the peg N is 0·69 m, roughly how far above the ground will the nail be placed to mark the base of the slope rail? (37)

19. What information should be recorded on slope rails? (39)

20. Describe how some forms of earthwork may be controlled by means of sight rails and travellers. (40)

CHAPTER XVI

CURVES

ELEMENTS OF THE CIRCULAR CURVE

1. Circular curves. Horizontal, circular or simple curves are curves of constant radius required to connect two straights set out on the ground. Such curves are required for roads, railways, kerb lines, pipe-lines, etc., and may be set out in several ways, depending on their length and radius.

2. Definition of curve elements. Figure 109 shows two straights *EP* and *PF*, which intersect at *P*, the point of intersection. If these straights are the set-out centre lines of a proposed construction it may be necessary to connect them by means of the circular curve *AGHKB* as shown. The following terminology is used in defining the various parts of the figure:

θ = the *angle of deflection* or the *angle of deviation* of the curve.

T = the *tangent length* = $AP = PB$. Points A and B are sometimes termed *BC* and *EC*, indicating the *beginning* and the *end* of the *curve* respectively.

R = the *radius* of the curve.

L = the *arc length* of the curve from A to B.

O = the *centre* of the circle.

H = the *crown* or *apex* of the curve.

A = the first tangent point or T.P.1.

B = the end tangent point or T.P.2.

δ = the *angle of deflection* of the chord or the *circumferential angle*.

AB = the *long chord* or the *chord to the curve* of length C.

$AG = GH = HK = KB$ are equal *chords* of length c, subtending equal arc lengths a.

HM = the *height of the crown* or the *versed sine of the chord*.

368

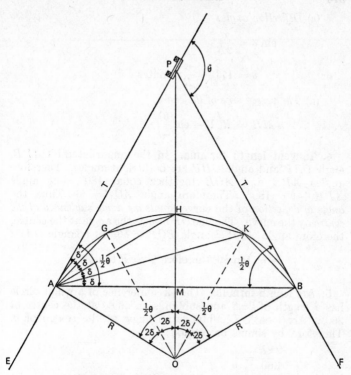

FIG. 109.—*Elements of a circular curve*
The geometry required for establishing the curve formulae is shown.

3. Curve formulae. In order to set out a curve, depending on the method to be used, the data may have to be calculated from the following formulae:

(a) *Tangent length:*
$$T = R \tan \tfrac{1}{2}\theta$$

(b) *Arc length:*
$$L = R\theta \frac{2\pi}{360} \text{ (where } \theta \text{ is in degrees)}$$

or
$$L = R\theta \text{ (where } \theta \text{ is in radians)}$$

(c) *Deflection angle:*

$$\sin \delta = \frac{c}{2R}$$

or $$\delta = 1718 \cdot 9 \, \frac{c}{R} \text{ minutes}$$

(d) *The versed sine of the chord:*

$$MH = R\left(1 - \cos \frac{\theta}{2}\right)$$

4. Tangent length formula. In the quadrilateral $OAPB$, angle OAP and angle OBP are both right-angles. Therefore angles APB and AOB together equal 180°, but angle $APB + \theta = 180°$. Therefore angle $AOB = \theta$. Thus the *angle of deflection* of the curve *equals the angle subtended at the centre* by the curve. The line OP bisects the angle at the centre, therefore angle $AOP =$ angle $BOP = \frac{1}{2}\theta$. In triangle OAP:

$$\frac{T}{R} = \tan \tfrac{1}{2}\theta, \text{ therefore } T = R \tan \tfrac{1}{2}\theta$$

5. Arc length formula. The circumference of a whole circle has a length of $2\pi R$ and subtends an angle at the centre of 360°. Arc length L subtends an angle at the centre of θ. Therefore, by simple proportion:

$$\frac{2\pi R}{360} = \frac{L}{\theta}$$

$$\therefore \; L = R\theta \cdot \frac{2\pi}{360} \text{ (where } \theta \text{ is in degrees)}$$

or $$L = R\theta \text{ (where } \theta \text{ is in radians)}$$

NOTE: $\dfrac{2\pi}{360}$ is a factor which converts degrees into radians, for example:

$$30° \times \frac{2\pi}{360} = \frac{\pi}{6} = 0 \cdot 5236$$

need not be calculated, but can be looked up in tables of circular measure or radians.

6. Deflection angle formulae. The following is the proof that angle BAP, the angle of deflection of the long chord AB, is equal to $\frac{1}{2}\theta$, half the angle of deflection of the curve:

Consider triangles PMA and OAP:

angle APM = angle APO and
angle PMA = angle OAP = 90°

Therefore the triangles are similar and angle MAP = angle BAP = angle $AOP = \frac{1}{2}\theta$.

Therefore the *deflection angle of the long chord is half the angle of deflection of the curve.* This property is used in (*b*) below.

(*b*) In order to derive formulae which give the value of δ,

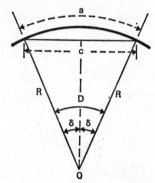

FIG. 110.—*Degree of curve*

The relationship between the degree of curve D and the radius R is shown.

the angle of deflection of the setting out chords c, let AG, GH, HK and KB be equal chords of length c and join G, H and K to A as shown in Fig. 109.

The angles AOG, GOH, etc., subtended at the centre by these equal chords are themselves equal. These angles subtended at the centre are each twice the circumferential angles δ of these chords, *i.e.* the angles they subtend at the circumference at A.

In **6** (*a*) it was shown that angle MAP, the angle between the tangent and the chord, is half the angle subtended at the centre by the chord. In the same way the angle PAG between the tangent and the chord AG is half the angle it subtends at the centre, but it subtends at the centre the same angle as the other equal chords, which has the value

2δ. Therefore the first angle of deflection of the first chord is also δ, the same value as the circumferential angles of the other chords.

Therefore *all deflection angles of equal chords from the tangent are equal.*

(c) The value of δ may be calculated in two ways:

(i) Figure 110 shows part of the whole curve subtended by one of the short chords c. Using the previous notation it can be seen that the chord c subtends an angle 2δ at the centre. In the bisected triangle thus formed:

$$\sin \delta = \frac{\frac{1}{2}c}{R} \quad \text{or} \quad \sin \delta = \frac{c}{2R}$$

(ii) From the formula $L = R\theta$, it can be seen from Fig. 110 that:

$$a = R2\delta$$

$$\therefore \quad \delta = \frac{a}{2R} \text{ radians}$$

$$\therefore \quad \delta° = \frac{a}{2R} \times \frac{360}{2\pi}$$

$$\text{or} \quad \delta = \frac{a}{2R} \times \frac{360}{2\pi} \times 60 \text{ minutes}$$

$$\therefore \quad \delta = 1718 \cdot 9 \frac{a}{R} \text{ minutes}$$

$$\text{or} \quad \delta \doteqdot 1718 \cdot 9 \frac{c}{R} \text{ minutes}$$

NOTE: Where the radius R is twenty times greater than the chord length c, the difference between the arc length a and the chord length c is small enough to be neglected.

7. The versed sine formula. The perpendicular from the centre of the long chord to the crown of the curve is MH. It is known as the versed sine of the chord and its length may be calculated from the formula derived below:

$$OM = R \cos \tfrac{1}{2}\theta$$
$$MH = R - OM$$
$$= R - R \cos \tfrac{1}{2}\theta$$
$$= R(1 - \cos \tfrac{1}{2}\theta)$$

NOTE: A *versine* is $(1 - \text{cosine})$, hence the name of this length.

8. Degree of curve. A curve may be defined by its radius, but in setting out such curves the deflection angles of the chords are nearly always odd numbers of minutes and seconds of arc. To simplify this a curve may also be defined by its *degree of curve*.

The degree of curve requires specific definition. In some cases it is the angle subtended at the centre of the circle by a *chord* 100 ft long, the definition adopted in setting out American railways; in others it is the angle subtended at the centre by an *arc* 100 ft long. Both curve definitions have been used in setting out in Great Britain, but it is the *arc* definition which is now generally accepted.

Under the metric system the degree of curve definition generally adopted is the angle subtended at the centre by an *arc* of 100 m. Different organisations may adopt a different basis for the degree of curve, so it is important always to define the exact terms when calculating by this method.

9. Relation between radius and degree. Referring back to Fig. 110, if the arc length a is 100 m and it subtends an angle D, *the degree of curve*, at the centre, then:

$$RD = 100$$

$$\therefore R = \frac{100}{D} \times \frac{360}{2\pi} \text{ (where } D \text{ is in degrees)}$$

$$\therefore R = \frac{5729 \cdot 58}{D} \text{ (where } D \text{ is the degree of curve)}$$

Thus for a 2° curve the radius is 2864·8 m and the circumferential angle is 1°. If 20-m chords are to be used for setting out then the deflection angle for each will be one-fifth of 1°, which is 12′ for each chord.

NOTE

(i) Check this value of 12′ by calculating δ from the formula in **3**(c).

(ii) Not only is the derivation of δ simplified, but tabulating the bearings and setting the theodolite readings is easier and less liable to error.

(iii) A curve with a design radius of 2500 m differs very little from one of radius 2864·8 m in practice, but the setting out is simpler. It is therefore sensible to design on the degree of curve instead of on the radius for large radius curves.

SETTING OUT CIRCULAR CURVES

10. Methods of setting out a curve. Curves may be set out in a variety of ways, depending on the accuracy required, its radius of curvature and obstructions on site. Methods of setting out are as follows:

(a) *Using one theodolite and a tape* (*see* **11–15**). This method can be used on all curves, but is necessary for long curves of large radius unless they are set out by co-ordinates.

(b) *Using two theodolites* (*see* **16**). This method can be used on smaller curves where the whole length is visible from both tangent points and two instruments are available.

(c) *Using tapes only by the method of deflection distances* (*see* **17–18**). This method is used on smaller curves if no theodolite is available or if there is an obstruction to sighting.

(d) *Using tapes only by the method of offsets from the tangent* (*see* **19**). This method is used for minor curves only.

(e) *Using tapes only by the method of offsets from the long chord* (*see* **20**). This method is used for short radius curves.

(f) *Using the optical square* (*see* **21**). This method is used for small curves if the diameter of the circle can be set out.

(g) *Using co-ordinates* (*see* **22**). This method is preferred for most road curves, particularly when obstructions prevent traditional setting out methods.

11. Using the theodolite and a tape: location of tangent points. Before the curve can be set out the tangent points must first be located on the ground. For any particular pair of straights there is only one point on each straight for a curve of given radius or degree to leave the first tangentially in order to join the other tangentially. These tangent points cannot be scaled off a plan with sufficient accuracy and they must be located by field observations. The tangent points are represented in Fig. 109 by the points *A* and *B*. The method of locating these tangent points is summarised in (*a*) to (*h*) as follows:

(*a*) Set up the theodolite near *A* and extend straight towards *P*.

NOTE: Having located the two straights and defined their position with ranging rods, peg out the first straight up to the approximate position of A. Set up the instrument there and produce the line (by transitting on both faces) on to a profile board, ruling the line in pencil through P, the position of which is estimated from the line of ranging rods on the straight BF.

(*b*) Set up on the straight BF and produce it to meet the line at P.

NOTE: The theodolite is moved to some convenient point on the other straight and this line is produced as before to meet the pencil line ruled on the profile board at P.

(*c*) Mark the intersection of tangents at P.

NOTE: The point of intersection, P, of the two straights is thus found and accurately marked with a nail on the board at P.

(*d*) Measure angle EPF and obtain angle θ.

NOTE: The theodolite is set up over the peg at P and the angle P is observed. By subtracting the angle thus obtained from $180°$ the angle of deflection of the curve θ is found.

(*e*) Calculate tangent length PA.

NOTE: The tangent length is calculated from the formula $T = R \tan \frac{1}{2}\theta$ (*see* **4**).

(*f*) Place pegs at A and B on the lines.

NOTE: From P measure the lengths PA and $PB = T$ and line in the points A and B on the straights with the theodolite still set up at P. Mark the pegs at A and B distinctively as representing tangent points. This can be done by painting the peg or by placing three pegs, the centre one representing the tangent point.

(*g*) Set up at A and measure angle PAB, which should equal $\frac{1}{2}\theta$.

NOTE: This checks the equality of the tangent lengths, both of which may, however, be in error by the same amount through an error in measuring θ or in the calculation of T.

(*h*) Complete the chaining of the first straight to A.

NOTE

(*i*) The chaining of the first straight is completed by measuring the distance from the last chain peg and noting the actual chainage of the tangent point A.

(*ii*) In many cases the intersection points *P* may have been previously marked on the ground. In such cases the field work consists of pegging the straights and measuring θ without having to locate the intersection by the method described above.

12. Using one theodolite and a tape : location of points on the curve. After the tangent points have been pegged as described in **11**, the points on the curve must be located. The interval between chainage pegs on the curve should be measured along the actual arc. As chords are used in locating the pegs the difference in length should strictly be calculated as they are slightly shorter than the arc distances. This would be done in precise work, *e.g.* underground railways. In most practical cases where *R* exceeds twenty times the chord length this difference is negligible.

The tangent point *A* will seldom fall exactly at a peg interval. Since the chainage must be continuous, the chord *AG* to the first point on the curve may be shorter than the regular chord length which is *c*, usually equal to the peg interval (*see* XV, **33**) or half the peg interval if additional pegs are needed to mark the curve clearly on the ground. There will generally also be a *sub-chord* at the end of the curve. Let these sub-chord lengths be denoted by *c′* and *c″*.

The method of locating the points on the curve is summarised in (*a*) to (*k*) as follows:

(*a*) Obtain the first sub-chord $c' = c - EA$.

NOTE: Assuming *E* is the position of the last chainage peg on the straight, then $EA + c' = c$ and as *EA* has been measured and *c* is known the length of the sub-chord can be obtained.

(*b*) Calculate δ for chord length *c*.

NOTE: This can be calculated from $\sin \delta = \dfrac{c}{2R}$ or $\delta = 1718{\cdot}9 \times c/R$ minutes.

(*c*) Calculate δ′ for the first sub-chord.

NOTE: This can be calculated in the same way as for δ, but for flat curves it can be obtained with sufficient accuracy from

$$\delta' = \frac{c'}{c} \cdot \delta$$

(d) Calculate the final sub-chord and its δ''.

NOTE: Calculate from θ and the radius the length L of the curve ($L = R\theta$). Then the chainage of $A + L$ = chainage of B. The amount by which the chainage of B exceeds an exact number of peg intervals, plus the initial sub-chord, is the length of the end sub-chord c''.

(e) Draw up a table of deflection angles to the various points.

NOTE

(i) This will take the following form:

1st deflection angle to $G = \dfrac{c'}{c} \cdot \delta = \delta''$

2nd deflection angle to $H = \delta' + \delta$
3rd deflection angle to $K = \delta' + \delta + \delta$

(ii) The final deflection angle to tangent point B must equal $\frac{1}{2}\theta$, allowance being made for the sub-chords, i.e.:

$$\tfrac{1}{2}\theta = \delta' + \delta + \delta + \ldots \delta + \delta''$$

(f) From A set out δ' for the line AG.

NOTE: The instrument is set up at A and P is sighted at a reading of 0° 00′ 00″ and the horizontal circle is clamped with the lower clamp. The first deflection angle δ′ is set on the vernier or optical micrometer using the upper clamp and tangent screw only, so that the line of sight is along AG.

(g) Place G a distance of c' m from A on line AG.

NOTE: The zero of the tape is held at A and the distance c' marked with a peg, which is then moved on to the line AG as defined by the theodolite sighting.

(h) From A set out δ′ + δ for the line AH.

NOTE: This is the second deflection angle PAH obtained from the table in (e).

(i) Set out $GH = c$.

NOTE: The zero of the tape is now held at G and the chord length or peg interval along the tape is marked with a peg, which is moved on to the line AH as given by the theodolite.

(j) Repeat the same process to set out the remaining pegs.

NOTE

(i) Continue until the last peg on the curve has been placed and measure the remaining distance to B which should

equal the calculated length c'' of the final sub-chord.
Also set out the final deflection angle, which should pass
through tangent point B, indicating no disturbance of
the instrument.

(*ii*) As a final check on the accuracy, locate point B by the
deflection angle and sub-chord c''. If this position does
not coincide with the tangent point B, the distance
between the two is the actual error of tangency. If this
is large, indicating an error, the whole process must be
repeated. Where calculations are inaccurate by a few
millimetres in the final placing of the pegs, it is usual to
adjust the last few pegs to secure tangency. In accurate
tunnel work the degree of precision must, of course, be
greater.

(*k*) The first chainage peg on BF will be $c - c''$ from B.

NOTE: Having calculated the distance of the first chainage
peg F on the second straight, chaining may be proceeded with
after moving the instrument to B or some other convenient
point on this straight.

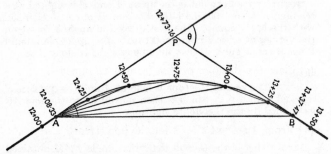

FIG. 111.—*Setting out a circular curve*
The illustration shows how sub-chords arise.

SPECIMEN QUESTION

Two straights AP and PB intersect with an angle of deflection
of 12° 20′ as illustrated in Fig. 111. They are to be connected
by a circular curve of radius 600 m. The chainage of the intersection point is $12 + 73·16$. Calculate the setting-out data
required to peg the curve at a continuous chainage with pegs
at 25-m intervals.

SOLUTION

(a) *Calculate the tangent lengths from* $T = R \tan \frac{1}{2}\theta$:

$$T = 600 \tan 6° 10'$$
$$= 600 \times 0{\cdot}108\ 046$$
$$= 64{\cdot}83 \text{ m}$$

(b) *Calculate the arc length from* $L = R\theta$:

$$L = 600 \times 12° 20' \times \frac{2\pi}{360}$$
$$= 600 \times 0{\cdot}215\ 26$$
$$= 129{\cdot}16 \text{ m}$$

(c) *Calculate the chainages:*

Chainage of P = 12 + 73·16
Less T =   64·83
Chainage of A = 12 + 08·33
Add L =   129·16
Chainage of B = 13 + 37·49 m

(d) *Calculate the sub-chords.* The last peg on the straight is at chainage 12 + 00, therefore the next peg must be at chainage 12 + 25. There is still 8·33 m on the straight to the tangent point, so there will be 25·00 − 8·33 = 16·67 m along the curve to the first peg on the curve. Thus 16·67 m is the length of the first *sub-chord*.

As the curve length is 129·16 m and the first sub-chord is 16·67 m there is 129·16 − 16·67 = 112·49 of arc left. Four 25-m standard chords make up the next 100 m, leaving a final sub-chord of 12·49 m. The measure of the arc distance by these chords is sufficiently accurate for most practical purposes, although theoretically the measured distance is shorter than the arc distance.

(e) *Calculate the deflection angles from* $\delta = 1718{\cdot}9\ \dfrac{c}{R}$:

$$\delta = 1718{\cdot}9 \times \frac{25}{600}$$
$$= 71{\cdot}62'$$
$$= 1° 11{\cdot}62'$$
$$= 1° 11' 37{\cdot}2''$$

(i) The initial sub-chord is 16·67 m so its deflection angle will be in the proportion of:

$$\frac{16{\cdot}67}{25} \times 1° 11{\cdot}62' = 47{\cdot}76'$$
$$\therefore\ \delta' = 47' 45{\cdot}6''$$

(*ii*) The final sub-chord is 12·49 m so its deflection angle will be in the proportion of:

$$\frac{12\cdot49}{25} \times 1° \; 11\cdot62' = 35\cdot78'$$

$$\therefore \; \delta'' = 35' \; 46\cdot8''$$

(*g*) *Tabulate the deflection angles.* The deflection angles are tabulated as follows (*see* **12** (*e*)):

Instrument at $A = 12 + 08\cdot33$

To peg at	Chord length	Bearing ° ′ ″
P		00 00 00
		+ 47 45·6
12 + 25	16·67	00 47 45·6
		+ 1 11 37·2
12 + 50	25	1 59 22·8
		+ 1 11 37·2
12 + 75	25	3 11 00·0
		+ 1 11 37·2
13 + 00	25	4 22 37·2
		+ 1 11 37·2
13 + 25	25	5 34 14·4
		+ 35 46·8
B = 13 + 37·49	12·49	6 10 01·2 = $\frac{1}{2}\theta$ (*check*)

NOTE: There are always likely to be minor rounding off errors such as the 1·2″, which is negligible. To keep these errors to a minimum the calculation is always carried out to 0·1, but the observed bearings are rounded off to 1″ for more accurate work and frequently to 10″ or even 20″, depending on the theodolite being used for setting out.

13. Obstructions to setting out. Obstructions on site may prevent normal setting out in a variety of ways. Most problems of this kind can easily be overcome if setting out is by means of co-ordinates, but two common problems which often arise are the following:

(*a*) Where the *intersection point* is inaccessible (*see* **14**).

(*b*) Where there are *obstructions to sighting the deflection angles* to every point on the curve from the initial tangent point (*see* **15**).

14. The inaccessible intersection point. It may not be possible to measure θ at the intersection point if it is inaccessible, *e.g.* on mountain roads. By setting out a line such as XY in Fig. 112, and by measuring its length and the angles α and β, the triangle XPY can be solved for the lengths PX and PY and θ can be deduced. The tangent points can then be located from X and Y and the curve set out in the usual way.

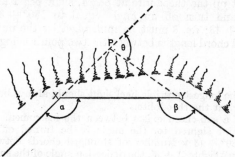

Fig. 112.—*An inaccessible intersection point*

The illustration shows how angle θ is obtained when it cannot be measured directly.

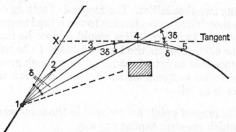

Fig. 113.—*Obstructed deflection angles*

The theodolite is re-oriented when it has to be set up at a curve point in order to continue the setting out of subsequent points on the curve.

15. Obstructions to sighting the deflection angles. Where obstructions prevent the sighting to every peg on the curve the following procedure must be adopted as illustrated in Fig. 113:

(a) Pegs 2, 3 and 4 have been placed turning off deflection angle δ each time. Peg 5 cannot be placed from peg 1 owing to an obstruction.

(*i*) Triangle 1X4 is isosceles therefore angle X14 = angle 14X = 3δ.

(*ii*) The angle between the chord 1–4 produced and the tangent X4 produced is also 3δ and the angle δ is required to be turned off this tangent to locate peg 5.

(*iii*) An angle of 180° + 4δ is required to be turned off the line 4–1 in order to locate the direction 4–5.

(*b*) Set up the theodolite at peg 4, sight peg 1 at a zero setting and turn off an angle equal to $180° + δ(5 − 1)$ $= 180° + 4δ$; *i.e.* δ must be multiplied by the number of standard chord lengths between the two points being sighted to.

NOTE

(*i*) The longest possible backsight should always be used to orient the theodolite.

(*ii*) If a sub-chord exists between the instrument and the point sighted to, the angle to be turned off will be 180° + (δ × Number of standard chords between the pegs sighted) + δ′, the deflection angle of the sub-chord.

(*iii*) The rule for obtaining the angle applies between any two pegs on any one circular curve.

16. Using two theodolites. The method of setting out curves using two theodolites saves having to use a tape to position the curve pegs, but two theodolites would seldom be made available due to cost. This method is only likely to be used if it is almost impossible to tape because of very rough ground. The procedure to be adopted in setting out a curve using two theodolites is as follows:

(*a*) *The tangent points* are located in the same as described in **11**, which requires taping anyway.

(*b*) *Deflection angles* are calculated and tabulated for the first tangent point (*see* specimen question in **12**). An equivalent set is also tabulated as though the curve were to be set out from the other tangent point.

(*c*) *Both theodolites* are set up, one at each tangent point, and the curve pegs are located at the intersection of their lines of sight for each tabulated setting.

17. Deflection distances method: location of tangent points. Before the curve can be set out the tangent points must first

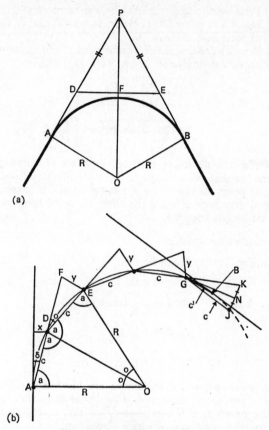

FIG. 114.—*Deflection distances*

(*a*) The method of locating the tangent points *A* and *B* of a curve by direct taping without measuring the angle of deflection at *P*.

(*b*) The method of setting out points on a curve by deflection distances only, without using a theodolite.

be located on the ground. These can be located without measuring the angle of intersection, as would be necessary if a theodolite were to be used in setting out the curve. The procedure is illustrated in Fig. 114 (*a*) and is described as follows:

(a) Produce the two straights by eye to meet at P.

(b) Select any pair of intervisible points, D and E, on each tangent such that $PD = PE$.

(c) Measure DE and mark its midpoint F and measure PF.

(d) From the similar triangles PDF and POA:

$$\frac{PA}{OA} = \frac{PF}{FD}$$

so that $T = PA = \frac{PF}{FD} \cdot R$

18. Deflection distances method: location of curve points. After the tangent points have been located as described in **17** the initial point on the curve is located at the intersection of two taped distances, x being the offset from the tangent and c the chord length adopted.

To calculate the offset x:

From Fig. 114 (b) it can be seen that:

$$x = c \sin \delta$$

but $\qquad \sin \delta = \dfrac{c}{2R}$ (*see* **6**(c))

$$\therefore \; x = c \times \frac{c}{2R}$$

$$= \frac{c^2}{2R}$$

Subsequent points on the curve are located at the intersection of two taped distances, y being the deflection distance from the previous chord produced its own length and c the chord length from the previously placed peg.

To calculate the deflection distance y:

Triangles DFE and ODE are similar because both are isosceles and angle $FDE = 180° - 2a =$ angle DOE.

$$\therefore \; \frac{y}{c} = \frac{c}{R}$$

$$\therefore \; y = \frac{c^2}{R}$$

To check the setting out at B, the final tangent point, where GB is a sub-chord, set out K and J as for a whole chord. Bisect JK at N, then GN is the tangent to the curve at G. From GN set off the perpendicular offset to equal $GB^2/2R$, and its distance from B will indicate the error of tangency.

19. Offsets from the tangent method. This is useful for short curves and there is no need for equal chords. Distances are measured along each tangent and offsets from these points are set out to define the curve as shown in Fig. 115 (*a*).

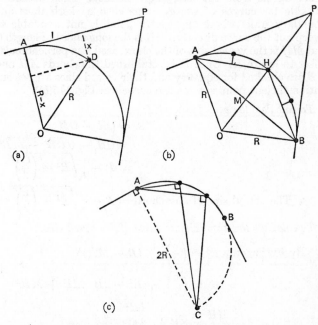

FIG. 115.—*Setting out small curves*

(*a*) The setting out of a curve using tapes only by the method of deflection distances.

(*b*) The setting out of a curve using tapes only by the method of offsets from the long chord.

(*c*) The setting out of a curve using an optical square.

By Pythagoras $R^2 = (R - x)^2 + l^2$

$$\therefore \ R^2 = R^2 - 2Rx + x^2 + l^2$$

$$\therefore \ x = \frac{l^2}{2R} + \frac{x^2}{2R}$$

but where l is less than $\frac{R}{20}$ the second term can be neglected, thus:

$$x \doteqdot \frac{l^2}{2R}$$

20. Offsets from the long chord method. This method is suitable for curves of small radius such as kerb lines and boundary walls where the centre point is not available to sweep out the curve directly. AB is the long chord of length C and MH is the versed sine of the chord used as a perpendicular offset to locate H. Once H is established the chords AH and HB are checked for equality and their versed sines are set out until sufficient points define the curve (*see* Fig. 115(*b*)).

To calculate the versed sine MH:

$$MH = OH - OM$$

$$= OH - \sqrt{OB^2 - MB^2}$$

$$= R - \sqrt{R^2 - \left(\frac{C}{2}\right)^2}$$

$$\therefore \ \text{The versed sine of any chord} = R - \sqrt{R^2 - \left(\frac{c}{2}\right)^2}$$

To calculate the approximate value of the versed sine:

By Pythagoras $R^2 = \left(\frac{c}{2}\right)^2 + (R - MH)^2$

$$R^2 = \left(\frac{c}{2}\right)^2 + R^2 - 2R \cdot MH + MH^2$$

$$MH = \frac{c^2}{8R} + \frac{MH^2}{2R}$$

$\therefore$ The versed sine of any chord $\doteqdot \dfrac{c^2}{8R}$, but this should not be used unless c is less than $\dfrac{R}{20}$.

21. Using the optical square. Figure 115(*c*) indicates how an optical square may be used for setting out a circular curve.

Once the tangent points have been located and the radius is known a perpendicular is set out from one tangent point equal to $2R$. Ranging rods are placed at A and C and the observer moves round the curve marking points where A is in coincidence with the image of C.

22. Using co-ordinates. The use of co-ordinates is ideal for setting out long radius curves. Normally a traverse will have been run along the route to survey detail and if the straight-line pegs, tangent points and curve pegs have all been co-ordinated they can be placed and checked from the traverse stations. Although used in the calculations, intersection points do not need to be marked on the ground.

TRANSITION CURVES

23. Principle of transition curves. The centrifugal force acting on a vehicle as it moves along a curve increases as the radius of the curve decreases. A vehicle moving from the straight—with no centrifugal force acting upon it—into a curve

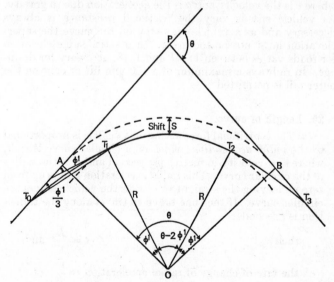

FIG. 116.—*The transition curve*

would suddenly receive the maximum amount of centrifugal force for that radius of curve. To prevent this sudden lateral shock on passengers in the vehicle a *transition* curve is inserted between the straight and the circular curve (*see* Fig. 116). The radius of a transition curve varies from infinity at its tangent with the straight to a minimum at its tangent point with the circular curve. The centrifugal force thus builds up gradually to its maximum amount.

24. Super-elevation. The centrifugal force tending to thrust a vehicle sideways on a curve is resisted by the friction between the wheels and the surface. If the outer edge of the surface is raised or *super-elevated* the resultant forces tend to reduce the frictional force necessary to hold the vehicle on the surface. At a particular slope α the frictional force necessary can be eliminated where:

$$\tan \alpha = \frac{v^2}{gR}$$

where v is the velocity and g is the acceleration due to gravity. As vehicle speeds vary the frictional resistance is always necessary and as a vehicle may stop on the curve the super-elevation must not be too great. In practice super-elevation for roads varies between $1:14\frac{1}{2}$ and $1:48$, necessary for drainage. In railways a maximum of a 150-mm lift or cant on the outer rail is permitted.

25. Length of curve.

(*a*) The centrifugal force acting on a vehicle is proportional to the *radial acceleration*, which on a circular curve is v^2/R, where $v =$ velocity in metres per second and R is the radius of the circular curve. This radial acceleration builds up from zero on leaving the straight to v^2/R as the vehicle enters the circular curve. If the time taken to travel along the transition is t seconds:

then $$t = \frac{L}{v} \quad \text{and}$$

the rate of change of radial acceleration $= \dfrac{v^2}{R} \div t$

(b) The *permissible limit* of the change of rate of radial acceleration generally accepted is that given by W. H. Short in the *Journal of the Institution of Civil Engineers* (Vol. CLXXVI). He defines the "comfort limit" as being 1 ft/sec³, above which a marked sideways throw will be noted. In S.I. units this may be taken as 0·3 m/sec³.

(c) *The length of transition* may be obtained from these considerations. The rate of change of radial acceleration:

$$= \frac{v^2}{R} \div \frac{L}{v}$$

$$= \frac{v^3}{RL}$$

If this value is 0·3 m/sec³:

then $$0 \cdot 3 = \frac{v^3}{RL}$$

$$\therefore \ L = \frac{v^3}{0 \cdot 3 R} \ \text{m}$$

and where $$V = \text{km/hr instead of } v = \text{m/sec}$$

then $$L = \frac{0 \cdot 0715 V^3}{R} \ \text{m}$$

NOTE: In practice the length of transition curve would be rounded up to the nearest 10 m so that a curve of even length would be adopted.

26. Spiral formulae.

Transition curves may be *spirals*, *parabolas* or *lemniscates*, but the spiral only is now generally adopted. The equation defining the spiral is:

$$\phi = \frac{l^2}{2RL}$$

where ϕ is the angle of deflection between the straight and the tangent to the transition at a distance l along the transition curve. L is the total length of transition adopted to reach a minimum radius R of the circular curve.

(a) *Deflection angles.* The deflection angle to any point on the transition is $\phi/3$, the total deflection being $\phi'/3$, where:

$$\phi' = \frac{L^2}{2RL} = \frac{L}{2R} \ \text{radians}$$

The deflection angle in degrees to any point on the curve is:

$$\delta = \frac{l^2}{6RL} \cdot \frac{180}{\pi} \text{ degrees, or}$$

$$= \frac{l^2}{6RL} \cdot \frac{180}{\pi} \cdot 60 \text{ minutes}$$

$$= \frac{l^2}{RL} \cdot \frac{1800}{\pi}$$

$$= 572{\cdot}958 \frac{l^2}{RL} \text{ minutes}$$

(b) *Shift.* When transition curves are included between a circular curve as in Fig. 117, the circular curve is *shifted*

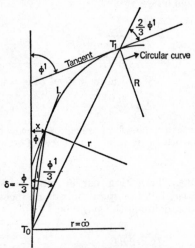

Fig. 117.—*Transition curve detail*

from its original position by a reduction S in its radius. The original curve of radius $(S + R)$ is replaced by two transition curves and a circular curve of radius R. The original tangent point A is now moved back to T_o. The amount of this shift is calculated from the formula:

$$S = \frac{L^2}{24R}$$

(c) *Tangent length*. The tangent length of the original curve (*see* 4) may be calculated from:

$$PA = (R + S) \tan \tfrac{1}{2}\theta$$

The length $A - T_o$ from the original tangent point to the new is equal, for all practical purposes, to half the length L of the transition curve. Therefore the new tangent length becomes:

$$P - T_o = (R + S) \tan \tfrac{1}{2}\theta + \frac{L}{2}$$

(d) *Circular curve length*. The length of the original circular curve is $(R + S)\theta$ (*see* 5). The amount of the deflection angle of the curve used by the transition curves is $2\phi'$, so that $(\theta - 2\phi')$ remains and the length of the circular curve is now $R(\theta - 2\phi')$ or $R\theta - L$.

(e) *Offsets*. The length x (see Fig. 117), being the offset from the tangent, may be used to locate points on the transition curve. It can be shown that:

$$x = \frac{l^3}{6RL}$$

27. Setting-out transitions. It is normal to set out transitions using deflection angles from the tangent point, or by deflection distances for short transitions, in the same way as for circular curves.

The deflection angles for transitions are not equal as are those for circular curves. The chord length used is often *half* that used on the circular curve. In practice the *setting-out data* are usually extracted from tables which relate to various design speeds. The only calculations needed are for the tangent lengths using the observed deflection angle θ.

Once the *tangent points* have been established the transitions are set out from both tangent points to T_1 and T_2, the limits of the circular curve. Then from T_1 or T_2 the direction of the tangent to the circular curve is obtained by turning off $\tfrac{2}{3}\phi'$ (*see* Fig. 117) from the chord to the transition and the circular curve deflection angles are set out as before.

28. Setting-out calculations. If the tabulated data are not available the length of the transition must first be obtained from the formula in 25 (c). This forms part of highway design and is dependent on traffic speed, available space and the radius to be adopted. The setting out surveyor will be provided with the transition length and the radius or degree of curve. With this information and the observed deflection angle θ, the following calculations are needed before setting out the pegs:

(a) *Shift*. This is calculated from:

$$S = \frac{L^2}{24R}$$

The radius $R = \dfrac{5729 \cdot 58}{D}$, if only the degree of curve is given.

(b) *Tangent lengths*. This is calculated from:

$$P - T_o = (R + S) \tan \tfrac{1}{2}\theta + \frac{L}{2}$$

This distance will be taped back from the intersection point and the two tangents T_o and T_3 pegged.

(c) *Deflection angles*. The deflection angles for 10-, 15- or 20-m chords are calculated from:

$$d = 572 \cdot 958 \, \frac{l^2}{RL} \text{ minutes}$$

where l is the continuous chainage along the transition. For small angles of deflection the summation of the chord lengths may be taken to equal the lengths l.

The final deflection angle to locate T_1 is $572 \cdot 958 \dfrac{L}{R}$ minutes, and ϕ' is three times this value.

(d) *Length of circular curve*. This is obtained from $R\theta'$ in the usual way, where:

$$\theta' = (\theta - 2\phi') \text{ and}$$
$$2\phi' = 57 \cdot 2958 \, \frac{L}{R} \text{ degrees}$$

NOTE: If $2\phi'$ is greater than θ it is not possible for the transitions to be contained within the straights. Longer transitions leading to a curve of smaller radius will have to be used.

SPECIMEN QUESTION

Calculate the setting-out data for a 75-m transition curve to connect an 8° circular curve joining two straights with an angle of deflection of 20° 00′, using 15-m chords.

SOLUTION

(a) *To calculate the radius and shift:*

$$\text{Radius } R = \frac{5729 \cdot 58}{D}$$
$$= \frac{5729 \cdot 58}{8}$$
$$= 716 \cdot 20 \text{ m}$$
$$\text{Shift } S = \frac{L^2}{24R}$$
$$= \frac{(75)^2}{24 \times 716 \cdot 20}$$
$$= 0 \cdot 327 \text{ m}$$

(b) *To calculate the tangent lengths:*

$$\text{Tangent } T = (R + S) \tan \tfrac{1}{2}\theta + \frac{L}{2}$$
$$= (716 \cdot 20 + 0 \cdot 33) \tan 10° + 37 \cdot 5$$
$$= 163 \cdot 84 \text{ m}$$

(c) *To calculate and tabulate the deflection angles and deflection distances:*

$$\delta = 572 \cdot 958 \frac{l^2}{RL} \text{ minutes and } x = \frac{l^3}{6RL} \text{ m}$$
$$= \frac{572 \cdot 958}{716 \cdot 20 \times 75} l^2$$
$$= 0 \cdot 010\ 67\ l^2$$

Chord	l	l^2	δ	x
15	15	225	2′ 24″	0·010
15	30	900	9′ 36″	0·084
15	45	2025		0·283
15	60	3600	38′ 24″	
15	75	5625	60′ 00″	1·309

NOTE: *Either* the deflection angles *or* the deflection distances are calculated and used for setting out. In many cases, where the distances are short they form the more convenient setting out method.

(d) *To check the final deflection angle and calculate ϕ':*

Final $\delta = 572 \cdot 958 \dfrac{L}{R}$ minutes

$\qquad = 572 \cdot 958 \dfrac{75}{716 \cdot 20}$

$\qquad = 60'$

$\qquad = 1° 00''$, which checks the final deflection angle calculated and tabulated in (c) above

$\therefore \quad \phi' = 3° 00'$ (from **26** (a))

$\therefore \quad 2\phi' = 6° 00''$

but $\quad 2\phi' = 57 \cdot 2958 \dfrac{L}{R}$ degrees (from **28** (d))

$\qquad = 6° 00''$, which checks the above value.

(e) *To calculate the length of the circular curve:*

θ, consumed by both transitions, $= 2\phi' = 6°$

$\therefore \quad L$ curve $= 716 \cdot 20 \times (20° - 6°) \times \dfrac{2\pi}{360}$

$\qquad = 716 \cdot 20 \times 0 \cdot 244\ 35$

$\qquad = 175 \cdot 00$ m

29. Setting out curves containing a transition. To illustrate this procedure the following describes the process of setting out the curve, the details of which are found in the question above:

(a) *Setting out the transitions.* The first transition is set out from T_o. The other tangent point T_3 is set out along the second straight the same distance from P as T_o, equal to 163·84 m. The final transition is then set out between T_3 and T_2 as before.

(b) *Setting out the circular curve.* Assuming 15-m chords are to be used, there will be eleven 15-m chords and one 10-m sub-chord to make up the arc of 175 m. The standard deflection angle will be:

$$\frac{15}{100} \text{ of } 4° = 36'$$

and for the sub-chord:

$$\frac{10}{100} \text{ of } 4° = 24'$$

Set up at T_1 (see Fig. 117), sight T_o and swing through $180° + \frac{2}{3}\phi' + \delta$ to sight to the first peg on the curve, completing the setting out to T_2 in the usual way for circular curves. This initial angle is $180° + 2° + 36' = 182° 36' 00''$.

NOTE: In practice transition curve data are tabulated for various design speeds and degrees of curve, and apart from the calculation of the tangent length from the tabulated shift and radius and the measured angle of deflection all the deflection angles would be directly available to the field surveyor.

VERTICAL CURVES

30. Summit and valley curves. Wherever two gradients intersect it is necessary to smooth out the profile so that there is a gradual change from one gradient to the other. On hills such vertical curves are known as *summit* curves and in valleys they are known as *valley* curves or *sags*. The curve normally adopted for vertical curves is the simple parabola, which has the equation $y = mx^2$, where y is the offset from the tangent at a distance x along it from the tangent point and m is any suitable constant.

31. Gradients. To simplify calculations gradients are usually expressed as a percentage. A 1:50 gradient is the same as a 2 per cent gradient. It represents a rise of 2 m in a horizontal distance of 100 m. Also gradients rising to the right are considered positive, falling to the *right* negative. The *grade angle*, as a percentage, is the algebraic difference between the gradients. If a $+2$ per cent gradient meets a -3 per cent gradient at a summit the grade angle is $+5$ per cent.

NOTE: Where two equal gradients meet, the vertical curve is *symmetrical*. Where the gradients differ the curve is *unsymmetrical*. Generally, in both cases the tangent lengths adopted are equal.

32. Length of vertical curves. The two principal factors governing the length of vertical curves are the following:

(a) *The centrifugal effect* caused by the rate of change in the gradient. The larger the grade angle, the greater must the length be to reduce the rate of change of gradient. A standard minimum radius of 1000 m is used on vertical curves to prevent discomfort from the centrifugal force. The horizontal distance from beginning to end of a parabolic vertical curve of this minimum radius is ten times the grade angle as a percentage.

(b) *Sight or vision distances* needed for vehicles to give

them time to stop on seeing obstructions over the brow of a summit curve. Sight distances on one-way dual carriageways need be less than on two-way roads, where vehicles are approaching each other at speed. Sight distances depend on the following factors:

(*i*) The speed of vehicles.

(*ii*) The thinking distance, *i.e.* the distance travelled during the time of a driver's reaction, usually one second.

(*iii*) Stopping distance, which depends on the road surface and braking efficiency.

(*iv*) The height of the eye above the road, usually taken to be 1·1 m. In sports cars the eye height is obviously less than 1·1 m, but this is compensated for by greater braking efficiency.

(*v*) A safety margin added to the calculated sight distance.

33. Curve length and sight distance. Where the grade angle or speeds are low, the length of the vertical curve needed is often less than the sight distance. As speeds or the grade angle increase the lengths of vertical curves must also be increased until the rate of change of gradient becomes the ruling factor and curve lengths become longer than is necessary for sight only.

The actual length of curve to be adopted in any particular case forms part of the highway design, and is now generally extracted from published tables, which take into account the factors described in 32.

34. Properties of the parabola. In Fig. 118 the properties of the parabolic vertical curve are illustrated.

(*a*) The *vertical* through P, the intersection point of the gradients, bisects the chord AB. Also on the vertical $PD = DC = e$.

(*b*) The *tangents* $AP = BP = l$.

(*c*) *Offsets* from the tangent AP are proportional to the squares of the distances from A. Similarly offsets from PB are proportional to the squares of distances from B.

NOTE: These offsets should be perpendicular to the tangent, but in practice it is sufficiently accurate to measure them vertically.

(d) The *high point*, H.P., or *low point*, L.P., in symmetrical curves is at D in the centre. In unsymmetrical curves it lies at a distance X from A (*see* **35** (*b*) and **36**).

(e) For most *practical purposes* it is sufficient to consider the length $2l$ along both tangents as being equal to the following:

    (*i*) The length L of the curve.
    (*ii*) The chord AB.
    (*iii*) The horizontal projection of $AB = H$.

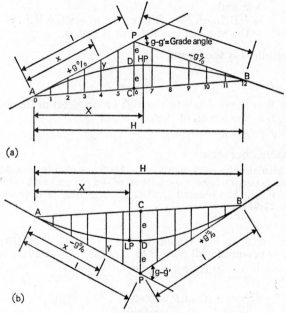

(a)

(b)

FIG. 118.—*Vertical curves*

  (*a*) The geometry of a vertical summit curve.
  (*b*) The geometry of a vertical valley curve.

35. Setting-out data. To calculate the setting-out data of a vertical curve the following information must be known:

  (*a*) The *design length* of the vertical curve.
  (*b*) The *gradients* of the intersecting slopes and the *reduced*

level of at least one known point or the reduced levels of sufficient points for the gradients to be calculated.

The formula needed is:

$$y = e\left(\frac{x}{l}\right)^2$$

where x = the length from the beginning or end of the curve in any units such as metres or chord lengths,

      l = the half length of the curve in the same units as x,

      y = the vertical ordinate in metres from the tangent at x and

      e = $\frac{1}{2}$(R.L. of P − R.L. of C), where the R.L. of C is the mean of the R.L.s of A and B.

Also required is the formula:

$$X = \frac{gL}{g - g'}$$

where X = the distance to the high or low point of the curve,

      L = the length of the curve and

g and g' = the gradients.

SPECIMEN QUESTION

Calculate the setting-out data by 25-m chords of a 300-m summit curve where two gradients of +2 per cent and −1·6 per cent meet. The reduced level at the beginning of the curve at A is 27·94 m.

SOLUTION

Referring to Fig. 118(a), the rise from A to P in 150 m is +3·00 m and the fall from P to B in 150 m is −2·40 m. Also:

$$
\begin{aligned}
\text{R.L. of } A &= 27\cdot94 \\
& +3\cdot00 \\
\text{R.L. of } P &= 30\cdot94 \\
& -2\cdot40 \\
\text{R.L. of } B &= 28\cdot54 \\
\therefore \text{R.L. of } C &= \frac{27\cdot94 + 28\cdot54}{2} \\
&= 28\cdot24 \\
\therefore CP &= \text{R.L. of } P - \text{R.L. of } C \\
&= 30\cdot94 - 28\cdot24 \\
&= 2\cdot70 \\
\therefore e &= 1\cdot35 \text{ m}
\end{aligned}
$$

Now in the formula $y = e\left(\dfrac{x}{l}\right)^2$,

$e = 1\cdot35$,

$x =$ distance along the tangent in units of 25-m chords and

$l = 6$, also in units of 25-m chords.

$$\therefore y = 1\cdot35 \left(\dfrac{x}{6}\right)^2$$

$$= \frac{1\cdot35}{36}\, x^2$$

$$= 0\cdot0375x^2$$

From the above data the relation between y and x may be tabulated as follows:

Chainage (1)	Chord No. (2)	$y = 0\cdot0375x^2$ (3)	(4)	R.L. on tangent (5)	R.L. on curve (6)
0 + 0	0	0	0	27·94	27·94
0 + 25	1	$0\cdot0375 \times 1^2$	0·0375	28·44	28·40
0 + 50	2	$0\cdot0375 \times 2^2$	0·150	28·94	28·79
0 + 75	3	$0\cdot0375 \times 3^2$	0·338	29·44	29·10
1 + 00	4	$0\cdot0375 \times 4^2$	0·600	29·94	29·34
1 + 25	5	$0\cdot0375 \times 5^2$	0·938	30·44	29·50
1 + 50	6	$0\cdot0375 \times 6^2$	1·350	30·94	29·59
1 + 66·67	High point				29·61
1 + 75	7		0·938	30·54	29·60
2 + 00	8		0·600	30·14	29·54
2 + 25	9		0·338	29·74	29·40
2 + 50	10		0·150	29·34	29·19
2 + 75	11		0·038	28·94	28·90
3 + 00	12		0	28·54	28·54

NOTE

(i) Column 1 records the running chainage through the curve.

(ii) Column 2 records the number of chords used as units of measure.

(iii) Columns 3 and 4 record the calculation of y from the formula using the factor 0·0375.

(iv) The factor 0·0375 may also be calculated from the expression:

$$a = \frac{g - g'}{2n}$$

where $g - g' =$ the grade angle per unit chord and

$2n =$ twice the number of chords used.

Take the following as an example:

$g = +2$ per cent or $+0.5$ per chord.
$g' = -1.6$ per cent or -0.4 per chord.

$\therefore$ grade angle per chord length $= +0.9$.

$$\therefore a = \frac{0.9}{24}$$
$$= 0.0375 \text{ as before.}$$

(v) Column 5 records the reduced level along the tangent at each chord length by adding the rise per chord $(+0.50)$ to each preceding level up to P, then by subtracting the fall per chord (-0.40) on the second tangent down to B.

(vi) Column 6 records the reduced levels on the curve obtained by subtracting column 4 from column 5. Except in very precise work levels to 0.01 m are sufficient.

36. High point calculation. The high point is frequently required to be pegged in order to arrange road drainage details. Using the data of the specimen question above its chainage and reduced level are calculated as follows:

(a) *To calculate chainage:*

$$x = \frac{gL}{g - g'}$$
$$= \frac{2 \times 300}{3.6}$$
$$= 166.67 \text{ m from } A \text{ or } 133.33 \text{ m from } B.$$

(b) *To calculate y:*

$$y = 1.35\left(\frac{133.33}{150}\right)^2$$
$$= 1.35 \times (0.889)^2$$
$$= 1.067 \text{ m}$$

(c) *To calculate the reduced level:*

R.L. at high point chainage on tangent $BP = $ R.L. of B $+ \left(\text{length} \times \dfrac{g'}{100}\right),$

$$= 28 \cdot 540 + (1 \cdot 33 \times 1 \cdot 6)$$
$$= 30 \cdot 673$$
$$\therefore \text{ R.L. on curve} = 30 \cdot 673 - 1 \cdot 067$$
$$= 29 \cdot 606, \text{ which has been inserted in}$$
the tabulated results of the solution
to the question above.

NOTE: The levels of the chainage pegs on the vertical curve would usually be supplied to the surveyor and would not have to be calculated by him. These calculations would be carried out by the designer in the office, the final levels being recorded on the working profile for use on site.

PROGRESS TEST 16

1. Derive the following formulae:

   (a) $T = R \tan \frac{1}{2}\theta$.

   (b) $L = R\theta$.

   (c) $d = 1718 \cdot 9 \dfrac{c}{R}$ minutes.

   (d) $R(1 - \cos \frac{1}{2}\theta) =$ the versed sine of the chord.   **(1–7)**

2. How may a circular curve be defined by its degree? What is the relation between radius and degree of curve? **(8–9)**

*3. Tabulate the deflection angles required to set out a 10° curve with 30-m chord lengths commencing at the initial tangent point with a chainage of 0 + 00. The angle of deflection of the curve is 14° 18′ 00″. **(9, 12)**

*4. A circular curve is to be set out using one theodolite and a tape. Calculate the setting-out data if the curve has a radius of 1000 m and pegs are to be placed at a continuous chainage every 20 m. The angle of deviation of the curve is 11° 25′ 00″ and the chainage of the intersection point is 10 + 73·62 m. **(12)**

*5. A circular curve is to be set out with pegs at every 25 m, continuous chainage between two straights intersecting at chainage 7 + 36·27 with an angle of deflection of 27° 00′ 00″. The radius of the curve is to be such that the minimum distance of the curve from the intersection point of the two straights is 25 m.

   Calculate the following:

   (a) The radius of the curve.

   (b) The chainage of the initial and final tangent points.

   (c) The deflection angles.

   (d) The sub-chord lengths. **(12)**

6. How is the problem of an inaccessible intersection point overcome? (14)

7. Describe the procedure to be adopted if there is an obstruction blocking the sight line of a deflection angle. (15)

8. Describe four methods of setting out a circular curve without using a theodolite. (17–21)

*9. Calculate the mid-offset from the long chord of a circular curve of 10-m radius to join two kerb lines meeting at 90°. What is the difference between its accurate value and its approximate value calculated from $c^2/8R$? (20)

10. Why are transition curves sometimes inserted between straights and circular curves? (23)

11. What is super-elevation and why is it needed? (24)

12. State the formulae used to calculate the following:

(a) Transition deflection angles.
(b) Shift.
(c) Tangent length.
(d) Transition deflection distance.
(e) Length of the circular curve. (26)

*13. Calculate the deflection angle and deflection distance omitted from the table in the specimen question in 28. (28)

*14. Two 100-m transition curves are to be inserted between a circular curve of radius 1000 m and two straights intersecting at an angle of deflection of 23° 48′ 00″.

Calculate and tabulate the following:

(a) The tangent lengths.
(b) The deflection angles for 20-m chords on the first transition only.
(c) The length of the circular curve. (28)

15. What is the difference between summit and valley curves and why are they needed? (30)

16. What information and formulae are necessary in order to calculate the setting-out data of a vertical curve. (34–35)

*17. Design a sag 250 m long to be set out by 25-m chords to suit two gradients of −3·4 per cent and +2·6 per cent. The reduced level of the intersection point is 22·60 m. What is the level and chainage of the low point? (35, 36)

CHAPTER XVII

AERIAL SURVEYING

PRINCIPLES

1. Photogrammetry. Photogrammetry is that branch of surveying in which maps and plans are prepared from measurements taken off photographs.

Terrestrial photogrammetry is the term used when maps and plans are prepared from photographs taken from ground stations.

Aerial photogrammetry is the more usual method of map preparation, where photographs taken from aircraft are used instead.

Apart from map making there are many other uses to which aerial photographs are put. *Photointerpretation*, as distinct from photogrammetry or map making, forms a major part of aerial surveying providing a vast amount of specialised information.

2. Air survey cameras. Air photographs are taken by *air survey cameras* of various types, photographing on glass plates or, more usually, on film. Contact prints, varying in size from about 140 mm to 230 mm square, the most common size, may be reproduced on glass or paper and may be in *monochrome*, *colour* or *false colour* (*see* **26** (*f*)).

Camera *lenses* may be *super wide angle*, with an angle of view of about 120°, *wide angle* up to 95°, *normal* at around 60° and occasionally *narrow angle* at 40° or less. Super-wide-angle lenses are now being more frequently used as they provide an economically larger air cover at lower flying heights. Lower flying heights allow greater accuracy in heighting, thus permitting a closer contour interval on resultant maps. Focal lengths vary with camera types from 88 to 635 mm. The most common focal length is about 153 mm, *e.g.* the 90° wide-angle lens Wild Aviogon.

Cameras are carried on special *mountings* to dampen vibration and to reduce the effects of aircraft pitch and drift.

An *instrument box* is attached to the camera recording on each film exposure some or all of the following:

(*a*) The time of exposure.

(*b*) The date of the survey.

(*c*) A spirit level, which is not, however, an accurate indication of the actual tilt owing to the centrifugal forces acting on the camera, but is indicative of the steadiness of the flight.

(*d*) A digital counter, numbering the photographs in sequence.

(*e*) The flying altitude, read from a pressure altimeter.

Fiducial or *collimating marks* appear on all air photographs in various forms. They consist of crosses or lines positioned at the four corners or in the middle of each edge of the photograph such that the line joining them will intersect at the *photo-centre* or *principal point*. In many cases the principal point is itself marked by a fine cross.

NOTE: At the time of exposure the film must lie absolutely flat inside the camera. This is achieved either by applying tension momentarily or by forcing it flat by air pressure or a vacuum.

3. Air photographs. There are two kinds of air photograph:

(*a*) Verticals, where the camera axis is approximately vertical. Verticals form the most usual type of picture because they produce the most accurate map and have the following *advantages*:

(*i*) Variation in scale over the area of the photograph is minimised. The photograph *approximates* to a map.

(*ii*) Information can be transferred to a map comparatively easily.

(*iii*) Few areas of ground are hidden.

A minor *disadvantage* is that the landscape is presented from an unfamiliar viewpoint, but with training the information depicted can be interpreted and understood.

(*b*) Obliques, where the camera axis is deliberately tilted. There are *high* obliques which include an image of the horizon, and *low* obliques where the horizon is not seen but the camera is tilted in excess of 3°.

Obliques are used under special circumstances, one of them being the ability to photograph enemy territory by flying along the border without actually crossing it. The *advantage* of oblique photographs is that they present the area from a more familiar viewpoint and features are more easily recognisable, *e.g.* building elevations, hill profiles, tree types, etc.

The *disadvantages* are the following:

(*i*) Important detail may be hidden in *dead* ground behind buildings and hills.

(*ii*) The scale varies considerably over the photograph and distances cannot be scaled, even approximately.

(*iii*) The preparation of maps from obliques is a slow, laborious task and consequently expensive.

4. Scale. The scale of a photograph is the average relationship between ground distance and photograph distance over

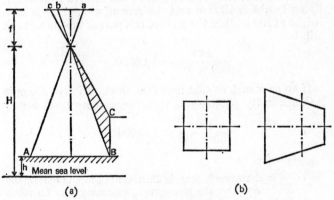

FIG. 119.—*Scale distortion*

(*a*) Height distortion: the perpendicular side of a building such as the line *CB* would not appear on a map, but it is shown as a horizontal line *cb* on the photograph.

(*b*) Tilt distortion: the square on the left would appear as a square only on a vertical photograph. If the camera were tilted the square would have the shape, shown on the right, in the photograph.

the area of the photograph. In Fig. 119 the length *AB*, on *perfectly flat ground*, a height *h* above M.S.L. (*see* X, **4**), is represented by the line *ab* on the *vertical* photograph. The scale of the photograph is therefore ab/AB and, by similar triangles, if the flying height H and focal length f of the camera are known, scale also equals $f/H - h$.

NOTE

    (i) This scale relationship is only correct if the picture plane is perfectly parallel to flat ground.

    (ii) The scale of the photograph is dependent on flying height, and the required photograph scale is dependent on the scale of the map to be produced from it (*see* 9).

5. Picture distortion. The scale of an air photograph is subject to distortion. Distortion may be caused by two factors:

(*a*) *Relief*. If the area of ground being photographed varies in height then the scale of the photograph will vary in proportion to the difference in height. For example, in Fig. 119 (*a*), if the focal length of the camera is 150 mm, flying height is 1000 m and the ground along AB is at a height of 100 m, then the scale of this part of the photograph will be:

$$\frac{150}{900 \times 10^3} = 1 : 6000$$

If an area such as that near C at an elevation of 250 m is included in the photograph, then the scale here will be:

$$\frac{150}{750 \times 10^3} = 1 : 5000$$

NOTE

    (i) This alteration in scale is illustrated in Fig. 119 (*a*) by the distance cb on the photograph, assuming C to be vertically above B.

    (ii) The elevational view of the vertical CB is also depicted on the photograph. This has the effect of making all structures appear to fall outwards radially away from the centre of the photograph, as shown in Plate 11 (reproduced by courtesy of Hunting Surveys Ltd. and which shows an area of central London around Piccadilly Circus).

(*b*) *Tilt*. If the picture plane is tilted at the time of exposure the image is distorted, as indicated in Fig. 119 (*b*). A square on the ground will take up the shape shown because of the tilt distortion. Unless it is known that the photograph was tilted at the time of exposure it may be wrongly assumed that the picture shape properly represents the ground shape of the feature.

NOTE: The distortions produced by the effects of relief and tilt can be ignored in small-scale plotting from air photographs in the following cases:

(i) Where the ground relief does not exceed one-tenth of the flying height.

(ii) Where the angle of camera tilt does not exceed 3°.

6. Stereoscopic pairs. The effect of the distortions existing in a single photograph may be eliminated to a large extent by taking stereoscopic pairs. Figure 120 illustrates how this occurs.

The *true plan relationship* of the three points numbered 1, 2

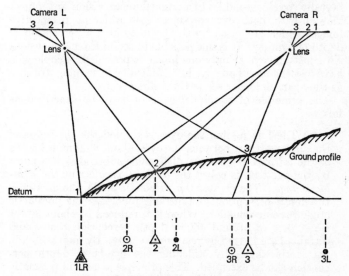

FIG. 120.—*Reconstruction from photograph images*

The ground profile may be reconstructed by recreating the position of the photographing cameras at a smaller scale. This is the principle of the Multiplex.

and 3 is indicated. The photograph from camera L positions these points at 1, 2L and 3L, a distorted relationship. Similarly, the photograph from camera R positions these points at 1, 2R and 3R, another distorted relationship.

The true plan positions may be located by reconstructing the situation at the time of taking the pictures. By projecting rays from the images on each picture as shown, their intersection will locate the positions of the points required in their true relationship, both horizontally and vertically. The plan position can then be obtained by plumbing vertically down to the datum surface or plotting table.

This reconstruction is obviously dependent on the relative positions of the points as depicted on the plane of each photograph. This illustrates the principle of *stereoscopy* (*see* 7) and forms the basis of the *Multiplex stereo-plotter* (*see* 23).

7. Stereoscopy. This is derived from the Greek and means literally "seeing solid." In normal human vision any object viewed with both eyes produces two different perspective images which are fused by the brain to give a perception of depth or solidity. It is not possible to see in three dimensions with just one eye as only one image is provided. People who have lost the use of one eye have difficulty in judging distance as they can no longer see in three dimensions.

The principle of stereoscopic vision may be described as follows:

(a) The line joining the eyes is termed the *eye-base* and the distance apart between the eyes, about 65 mm, is known as the *interocular* distance. The angle subtended at a point by the eye-base is called the *angle of parallax* or the *paralactic angle*. The greater the paralactic angle, the greater is the depth perception. As distances increase the paralactic angle becomes smaller. When it is reduced to about 30″ at a distance of around 450 m depth perception ceases and distances are judged by relative size only. By increasing the paralactic angle, by widening the eye-base, depth perception can be extended. This principle is used in prismatic binoculars, range finders and mirror stereoscopes.

(b) The principle of stereoscopic vision may be explained as follows. In viewing a three-dimensional object such as a box, each eye sees a different aspect of the box, the two

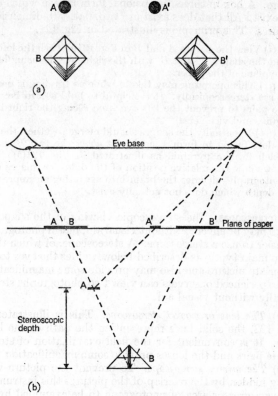

(a)

A B   A'   B' Plane of paper

Eye base

Stereoscopic depth

(b)

FIG. 121.—*Stereoscopic vision*

(a) Plan representation of a dot and a pyramid from two different viewpoints.

(b) Sectional view showing how the two plane views can provide a three-dimensional effect.

images seen being fused by the brain to provide a perception of the solidity of the box. If instead of viewing the box itself two flat pictures of it are seen, each taken from a slightly different position, looking at one picture with one eye and the other picture with the other eye, then the brain is deluded into providing the same impression of depth as before. A box in three-dimensional form is seen which does not exist. All that does exist are two, flat, two-dimensional pictures. This principle is illustrated in Fig. 121.

(*i*) View the shapes A and B in Fig. 121(*a*) with the left eye and the shapes A' and B' with the right eye, focusing below the plane of the paper.

(*ii*) This operation may take a while as training is needed to see stereoscopically. It is helpful to hold a card between the pairs to prevent the left eye from seeing the right-hand figures and vice versa.

(*iii*) Eventually the shapes should merge together, the two A dots fusing to form a single dot *above* the two B shapes which form a pyramid as illustrated in Fig. 121(*b*). This shows how the relative position of the dots—or images on a photograph—deludes the brain into accepting an impression of depth which does not actually exist.

8. Stereoscopes. The stereoscopic viewing of the shapes in Fig. 120 may be effected without visual aid, but in photographs it is easier to use a stereoscope. A stereoscope, of which there are two main types, as described below, guides the eyes to the appropriate picture and also may provide some magnification. Some experienced observers can view two photographs stereoscopically without visual aid.

(*a*) *The lens or pocket stereoscope.* This is illustrated in Fig. 122, the solid lines representing the path of the light rays. It is convenient for the field examination of stereoscopic pairs and the lenses provide some magnification.

(*b*) *The mirror stereoscope.* To prevent the picture view being hidden by the overlap of the pictures this instrument allows a greater area of photograph to be examined by increasing the eye-base, as shown in Fig. 123.

NOTE

(*i*) It is necessary to focus the eyes *below* the plane of the photographs for a stereoscopic viewing.

(*ii*) The eye-base must be parallel to the line joining the images or two overlapping plane images will be seen. Rough orientation can be obtained by trial and error.

(*iii*) If the principal point of each photograph is plotted on the other and joined by a line, representing the flight path of the aeroplane, and these are aligned parallel to the eye-base, the correct viewing position will be achieved. This process is called *base lining*.

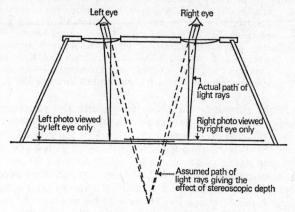

FIG. 122.—*Lens stereoscope*

The light rays from the two separate photographs to the eyes are refracted and magnified by the lenses, allowing the brain to assume that the photographs viewed are three-dimensional.

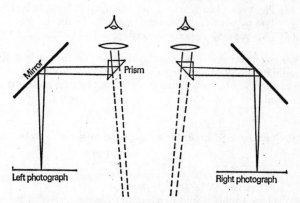

FIG. 123.—*Mirror stereoscope*

The paths of light rays in a mirror stereoscope, which has the effect of widening the eye-base and allowing a greater area of each photograph to be examined, are shown.

(*iv*) The photographs should preferably be positioned so that shadows on the photographs fall towards the observer as though formed by the light source illuminating the pictures. If this is not done a kind of *pseudoscopic vision* may occur. Pseudoscopic vision, where hills appear as valleys and vice versa and tall buildings look like shafts entering the ground, occurs when photographs set up for stereoscopic viewing are each rotated through 180°.

9. Flight planning. In order to provide the stereoscopic pairs of photographs necessary for the preparation of maps and for three-dimensional viewing every part of the ground to be surveyed must be photographed at least twice. This is achieved by flying in strips, photographs being taken with a 60 per cent fore and aft overlap to secure the 50 per cent minimum needed for stereoscopic viewing. Each strip or series of photographs overlaps adjacent strips by 30 per cent on average to ensure that no part of the ground is left unrecorded. This process is illustrated in Fig. 124.

The *flying height* is dependent on the following factors:

(*a*) The scale of the map or plan.
(*b*) The contour interval to be plotted.
(*c*) The type of country, flat or mountainous.
(*d*) The type of camera, *i.e.* focal length of lens, to be used.
(*e*) The type of plotting equipment to be used.
(*f*) The type of aircraft available.

Average flying heights may be deduced from the fact that the scale of the photographic cover should approximate to the scale of the map to be produced if simple plotting methods are to be used.

NOTE

(*i*) For a scale of 1 : 10 000 where a 150-mm lens is to be used:

$$1 : 10\ 000 = \frac{0 \cdot 150}{H - h}$$

so that $H - h = 1500$ m (*see* **4**).

(*ii*) Where sophisticated plotting machines are used it is more economical to increase flying height. For map scales of 1 : 10 000 a flying height of between 3800 and 6000 m is used, the lower flying heights being necessary for close contouring over flat terrain.

(*iii*) Some examples of mean flying heights, suitable for a camera with a lens of 153-mm focal length, are as follows:

Scale of map	Mean flying height
1:5000	3000 m
1:2500	1500 m
1:1250	750 m
1:500	375 m

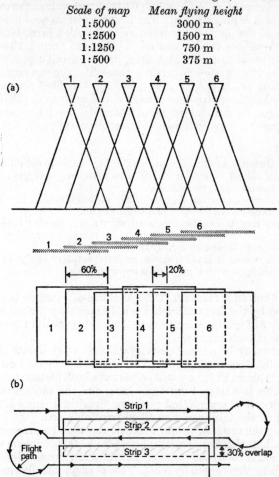

FIG. 124.—*Strip photography*

The principle of flight planning for photographic cover is shown. The way the photographs are planned to overlap in a fore and aft direction is shown in (*a*), with the lateral overlap indicated in (*b*).

10. Uncontrolled mosaics. A mosaic consists of a series of contact prints arranged to provide an overall picture of the area under survey. A photograph of average scale in the centre of the area is first selected. The boundary of an area near the middle of the picture is marked and cut with a razor blade at an angle to give it a feather edge. The next print is then cut and feathered to fit the first along lines of detail and is either taped to it or pasted down on a base. The process continues as further prints are cut and mounted. Cut lines are chosen to fall along irregular lines of dark detail, such as the shadows of hedges, to conceal as far as possible the joins between photographs. Finally the whole assemblage is re-photographed.

NOTE

   (*i*) Owing to picture distortions it is impossible to get all points of detail to match across joins between photographs, *i.e.* the mosaic is uncontrolled.

  (*ii*) A mosaic cannot replace a map as detail cannot be wholly matched and height distortions exist.

 (*iii*) A mosaic can be produced with much greater ease and speed than a map and provides much information that cannot be shown clearly on a map.

 (*iv*) A mosaic is invaluable for an interpretative study, in conjunction with a map, on a regional basis.

11. Controlled mosaics. The usefulness of a mosaic is much reduced by the fact that detail is only roughly matched along the edges of prints owing to variations in height and tilt of the camera at each exposure.

Prints may be *rectified* photographically to eliminate as far as possible the effects of tilt. The picture is projected on to a tilting table on which control points have been plotted to scale. The table is adjusted until the images of the control points coincide with their plotted position. Sensitised paper is then placed on the table and a rectified print obtained.

Using the rectified prints a mosaic can then be prepared as before, but with less disparity between prints, producing what is termed a *controlled* mosaic. Rectification *cannot* eliminate scale distortion caused by relief. Thus even a controlled mosaic is bound to contain some duplication or omission of detail and local displacement of features.

A controlled mosaic is usually completed by trimming the surplus photograph area around the edges and borders are glued on containing a title and other informative notes. Usually a scale grid is superimposed and place names and other data may be added. Finally the whole is rephotographed to provide a *photo-map*.

NOTE: The rectification principle may be adopted as a process for plotting detail. By projecting the image of a photograph on to an existing map and adjusting the photograph so that its image coincides with map detail, other detail from the photograph not included on the map may be sketched in. An instrument specifically designed for this is the Zeiss Aero-sketchmaster. An epidiascope can be used in the same way by projecting an image of an air photograph on to a map.

12. Terminology. Figure 125 illustrates the terminology of air photograph geometry. In the figure the camera is tilted, the plane of the picture forming an angle θ with the ground plane.

(*a*) *Plumb points.* The vertical through the optical centre of the lens intersects the ground and picture planes at V and v respectively, termed the ground and photograph *plumb points*.

(*b*) *Principal points.* The camera axis, the perpendicular to the picture plane through the optical centre of the lens, intersects the ground and picture planes at P and p respectively, termed the ground and photograph *principal points*. The principal point of the photograph is defined by the *fiducial* marks (*see* 2).

(*c*) *Isocentres.* The line bisecting the angle between the lines joining the plumb points and the principal points intersects the ground and picture planes at I and i respectively, termed the ground and photograph *isocentres*.

NOTE

(*i*) Points such as i and I and v and V, which are on any ray through O, the optical centre of the camera lens, are known as *homologous points*.

(*ii*) Triangles iOp and IOV are similar since angle ipO and angle IVO are both 90° and angle iOp = angle IOV. Therefore the line IOi joining the isocentres makes the same angle, $90 - \theta/2$, with both the picture and ground planes and triangle iDI is therefore isosceles (*see* **13** (*b*)).

(d) *Principal plane.* The principal line through v and p when produced meets the ground plane at D. The vertical plane through these points intersects the ground along the ground principal line through V and P. The isocentres i and I lie also on this vertical *principal plane*.

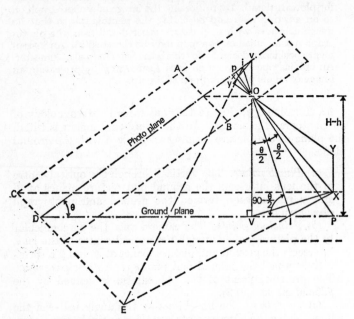

Fig. 125.—*Relation between picture and ground*

The geometry of the relation between a tilted photograph and a horizontal ground plane is shown.

(e) *Horizon trace and plate parallels.* The horizontal plane through O intersects the photograph plane along the *horizon trace* AB. Any horizontal line parallel to this on the negative is called a *plate parallel*.

13. Radial assumption. It is shown below that in a tilted photograph distortions due to height are *radial* from the *plumb point* and distortions due to tilt are *radial* from the *isocentre*.

(*a*) *To prove that height distortions are radial from the plumb point.* The displacement of *y* (*see* Fig. 125) the image of *Y*, with respect to *x*, the image of *X*, lies along the line *yxv* since *Y* is *vertically* above *X*, so that *Y*, *X*, *V*, *O*, *v*, *x* and *y* are all on the same vertical plane intersecting the photograph negative along *yxv*. Thus all distortions due to height radiate from *v*, the plumb point.

(*b*) *To prove that tilt distortions are radial from the isocentre.* In Fig. 125 $Op = f$, the focal length of the lens. Therefore:

since angle $\quad pOi = $ angle $iOv = \dfrac{\theta}{2}$

$$Oi = \frac{f}{\cos \dfrac{\theta}{2}} \quad = f \sec \frac{\theta}{2}$$

and $\quad OI = \dfrac{H - h}{\cos \dfrac{\theta}{2}} \quad = (H - h) \sec \dfrac{\theta}{2}$

The scale at the isocentre, and anywhere along the plate parallel through *i*:

$$= \frac{Oi}{OI}$$

However, $\quad \dfrac{Oi}{OI} = \dfrac{f \sec \dfrac{\theta}{2}}{(H - h) \sec \dfrac{\theta}{2}}$

$$= \frac{f}{H - h}$$

which is the scale of a vertical photograph. This does not apply at any other plate parallel.

The line *ix* produced cuts the intersection of the ground and photograph planes at *E* forming a triangle *iDE* on the photograph plane. Similarly *XI* produced cuts the intersection of the ground and photograph planes at, say, *E'*, forming a triangle *IDE'* on the ground plane. *E* and *E'* are the same point because any line and its projection meet on the axis of projection.

Now angle $iDE = $ angle $IDE' = 90°$, and $iD = ID$, since triangle *iDI* is isosceles (*see* 12 (*c*)). Therefore triangles *iDE* and *IDE'* are congruent, thus angle $pix = $ angle PIX.

Points *X*, *I*, *x* and *i* are all on one plane and from the equal angles subtended by homologous points at the same level as the ground and picture isocentres it can be seen that scale distortions due to tilt radiate from the isocentre.

For simple, practical plotting, where the tilt of the photograph does not exceed 3°, it can be assumed that the plumb point and isocentre coincide with the principal point. As this point is defined by the fiducial marks a mark exists on the photograph from which distortions can be assumed to radiate. By drawing rays from the principal point through features depicted on the photograph it can be assumed that the true plan positions lie somewhere along these radiating lines. This property of the vertical photograph forms the basis of graphical mapping and is known as the *radial assumption*.

If in any pair of overlapping photographs a system of rays to identical points on each photograph is drawn radiating from the principal points, they would be identical to the corresponding system of rays at the *homologues* of the principal points on the ground. If these two systems of rays were correctly oriented with respect to each other, the rays to corresponding points would intersect in pairs to provide a number of points in their correct, relative plan position. This process is called *radial line plotting*.

NOTE

(*i*) The scale of such a plot would be defined by the distance between the principal points on the plot.

(*ii*) The method of intersection adopted is similar to plane table intersection (*see* Fig. 50), in which the base *AB* is the equivalent of the base line between the plotted positions of the principal points.

(*iii*) The orientation of the two photographs is only possible if the photograph centre or principal point of each appears on the other. This provides the base line.

PLOTTING FROM AIR PHOTOGRAPHS

14. Single overlap plotting. The principle of radial line plotting (*see* **13**) may be used if the plan positions of at least three well-placed points in each photograph are known, when the positions of the principal points may be *resected* and marked on the plan using the tracing paper method (*see* VIII, **11**).

The base line formed by joining the two plotted principal points is traced on to another sheet. The photographs are base lined (*see* **8** (*b*) (*iii*)) and one end of the traced base is laid over its equivalent principal point on the photograph and the bases aligned. From the principal point rays are drawn on the tracing paper through the features to be plotted. The process is repeated on the next photograph, the intersection of the rays providing the correct positions of the features to be plotted to the map or plan scale.

The positions of the features are now transferred to the map by tracing or pricking their positions through the oriented overlay on the map.

NOTE

(*i*) This graphical radial line plotting method may be used wherever the plan positions of several ground points are known, *i.e.* where a good distribution of *ground control* is available.

(*ii*) It is most useful in revising old maps where existing detail on the maps may be identified on the photographs to control the individual resections.

15. Radial line plotter. This plotting instrument, illustrated in Plate 12 (reproduced by courtesy of Rank Precision Industries Ltd.), uses the principles outlined in **13**.

(*a*) The picture pair are viewed through a mirror *stereoscope* for greater accuracy in defining points of detail. Plotting takes place from a stereoscopic pair which are mounted on small photograph tables and carefully base lined. A weighted pin is then passed through their principal points.

(*b*) The centre pin in each photograph also passes through a radial line engraved on a perspex *cursor* which can be rotated about the photograph. As the prints are viewed through the stereoscope the two radial lines can be rotated until each passes through the point of detail it is required to plot.

(*c*) When it is being used for plotting, the instrument rests on the map itself. A linkage mechanism, which can be adjusted for scale, connects the two cursors together and to a pencil in such a way that the pencil point represents the map position of the point being plotted. Apart from plotting individual points, by moving the pencil so that the point of intersection of the two radial lines follows a line of detail, such as a road, any detail can be drawn.

NOTE

(*i*) One drawback of radial line plotting is that intersections near the base line are very acute and consequently weak.

(*ii*) The radial line plotter is used for map revision and for plotting detail between control provided by a slotted template (*see* 18).

16. Principal-point radial line plotting.

Where there is insufficient ground control to locate each principal point individually a *principal point* or *Arundel* plot is used to control a strip of photographs.

(*a*) The prints are base lined by plotting the position of the principal points of each print on adjacent prints as indicated in Fig. 126.

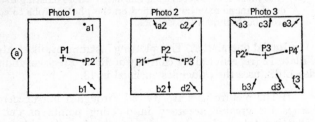

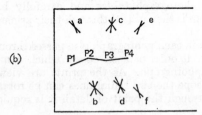

Fig. 126.—*Principal-point radial line plotting*

(*a*) Three photographs of a strip with radial lines drawn through points of ground detail which appear on adjacent prints.

(*b*) The Arundel plot on tracing paper of the principal points, showing the radial line method of intersecting and plotting the points indicated in the photographs in (*a*).

(b) Two well-defined points of detail are chosen on each print above and below the photograph centre and marked by pin pricks. These *minor control points* or *pass points* are then identified in turn on the adjoining photographs, each pair appearing on three consecutive prints as indicated in Fig. 126.

(c) The first base line $P1-P2'$ and point $a1$ and the radial through $b1$ are traced on a strip of tracing material large enough to accommodate the whole strip.

(d) The trace is laid over the second photograph. The base line $P1-P2$ is aligned until the radial through $a2$ passes through the plotted position of a. This governs the scale of the plot, a being known as the *scale point*. The radials are traced through $b2$, $c2$ and $d2$. The point $b2$ will now be plotted to the adopted scale. The direction of base $P2-P3$ is then traced.

(e) The process is repeated over the third photograph. Align the base $P2-P3$ until the radials through $a3$ and $b3$ pass through the plotted positions of a and b. If tilts are large some discrepancy in positioning may occur which would require adjustment, but with small tilts minor discrepancies are ignored.

(f) The process is continued with subsequent photographs until the whole strip has been dealt with and all principal points have been plotted to scale and in their correct relationship.

17. Reduction to scale. The Arundel traverse or plot described in **16** produces a plan plot of principal points to a scale approximating to that of the first photograph.

(a) In order to provide a map to a known scale *ground-control points* must be surveyed and their positions identified on the photographs. These ground control points are also plotted by radial intersection on the Arundel trace. At least two are required near the end of each trace, but the greater the density of ground control the more accurate will the final plot be.

(b) *A base grid* is drawn to the required scale and the ground-control points are plotted on it. If X and Y are the ground-control points for the first strip a comparison between the scaled distance XY on the Arundel trace with the known distance XY indicates the extent of adjustment required to make the trace fit the base grid. This may be effected graphically or by scaling and calculation.

(c) *Subsequent strips* must also fit the base grid, and a similar process of plotting and adjustment of the next strip of principal point base lines is effected. The lateral overlap between strips must also fit; *i.e.* minor control points plotted from one strip must coincide with the same point plotted from the adjacent strip.

(d) Not all the minor control points originally used will be convenient for lateral adjustment and additional *lateral control* points may have to be chosen. The co-ordinate differences between the positions of pass points plotted from adjacent strips are scaled and mean adjustments are applied to each principal point traverse to eliminate as far as possible all discrepancies.

(e) Once the principal points of each photograph have been finally established detail *plotting* can be undertaken by either of the methods outlined in **14–15**.

18. Slotted template. The graphical plotting described in **17** is laborious and may be simplified by a graphical–mechanical or slotted template method illustrated in Plate 8 (reproduced by courtesy of Hunting Surveys Ltd.).

(a) Every photograph is base lined and minor control points are chosen as before. Each print is then placed on the upper table of a *radial secator* or template cutter.

(b) A *template* of rigid transparent plastic is placed on the lower table and a centre hole, equivalent to the principal point, is punched through it. Radial slots are then cut in the template passing through the equivalent positions of the adjoining principal points and the minor control points chosen on the photograph. A *slotted template* is thus prepared for every photograph covering the area.

(c) When all templates have been cut they are assembled over a plotted base grid. The templates are joined by means of studs with a central hole through which each point can eventually be plotted. The studs fit the photograph centre hole and radial slots exactly. Referring to Fig. 125 again, studs would be placed in the holes at $P1$, $P2$, etc., and in the slots at $a1$ and $b1$ in the first template. The second template is placed over it so that the slots at $a2$ and $b2$ fit over the studs already placed. The stud at $P2$ can slide in the slot through $P2'$. The process of fitting the templates together is continued, all points being capable of radial adjustment along the slots.

(*d*) The studs representing the position of control points are mounted over pins projecting from the base grid plot and the surrounding assembly is pushed to accommodate it, the studs sliding radially in three slots.

(*e*) On completion the assembly is allowed to rest over-night to give the templates time to settle. Then all the studs are pricked through with pins. The control points and principal points are referenced on the map as the templates are individually removed.

NOTE: To make assembly and adjustment of the templates easier it is usual to cut off unnecessary parts of each template, rounding off all corners. In large assemblies the templates may be waxed so that they slide easily to take up their positions of equilibrium.

19. Heighting. Figure 127 illustrates the principles of parallax heighting. They are as follows:

(*a*) If two prints are set up for stereoscopic viewing the three-dimensional space model will appear to form on the intersection of assumed rays from O_1 and O_2 through the images of points X and Y, as shown.

On print 1 the images of X and Y appear at x_1 and y_1. On print 2 they appear at x_2 and y_2. These points have moved in relation to the principal points.

The total movement of each is:

y_1 to $P_1 + P_2$ to $y_2 = p_y$, the parallax of y,
x_1 to $P_1 + P_2$ to $x_2 = p_x$, the parallax of x.

Triangles $O_2y_1'y_2$ and O_1O_2Y are similar:

$$\therefore \frac{B}{p_y} = \frac{H - h_y}{f}.$$

$$\therefore p_y = f \cdot \frac{B}{H - h_y}, \text{ the parallax of } y.$$

Similarly, $p_x = f \dfrac{B}{H - h_x}$, the parallax of x.

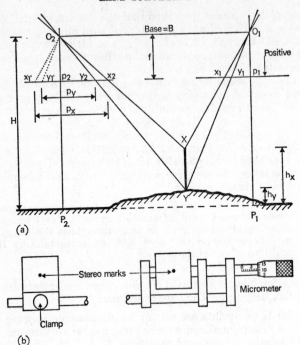

FIG. 127.—*Parallax heighting and parallax bar*

(a) The relationship between height, such as XY, and the difference of parallax, p_y and p_x, of the images of X and Y on two photographs.
(b) The parallax bar used for measuring differences in parallax.

(b) The *height difference* between X and Y may be found in the following way from the parallax of their images:

The difference in parallax between x and y is:

$$p_x - p_y = f \cdot B\left(\frac{1}{H - h_x} - \frac{1}{H - h_y}\right)$$

$$= f \cdot B\left(\frac{h_x - h_y}{(H - h_x)(H - h_y)}\right)$$

$$\therefore \ h_x - h_y = \frac{p_x - p_y}{f \cdot B}(H - h_x)(H - h_y)$$

Where h_x and h_y are small in relation to the flying height H, the difference in height between X and Y:

$$\doteqdot \frac{p_x - p_y}{f \cdot B} \cdot H^2$$

where $(p_x - p_y)$ is the difference in parallax, which may be obtained from reading a parallax bar.

(c) Alternatively, and more accurately, the height difference between X and Y may be found using the same formula, but including the absolute parallax of $x = p_x$, thus:

$$h_x - h_y = \frac{p_x - p_y}{p_x} (H - h_y)$$

If H is known and Y is a heighted ground-control point then $(H - h_y)$ is known. The expression $(p_x - p_y)$ is obtained from the parallax bar measurements and the parallax of y is obtained from the photographs by direct measurement to 0·1 mm parallel to the base line. The absolute parallax of x, p_x, or the absolute parallax of any other point of which the height is required, is obtained by adding the appropriate parallax bar reading to it. In practice all points on an overlap would be heighted from one point of known height.

20. Parallax bar or stereometer.
Two glass graticules marked with a small dot are held in frames attached to a rigid bar as shown in Fig. 127. The left-hand frame can be clamped at any distance along the bar to suit the separation of the photographs necessary for stereoscopic viewing. The right-hand frame can be moved over a range of about 13 mm by means of a micrometer reading to 0·01 mm.

(a) The two marks are superimposed over any selected point on each photograph and fused stereoscopically so that they become one. By rotating the micrometer the right-hand mark is moved horizontally, parallel to the eye-base. The fused mark will appear to move vertically or *float* and is adjusted to lie at the level of the selected point. The two marks will then have the same parallax as the selected point. The micrometer reading at which this occurs is observed and recorded. This reading is *not* the absolute parallax of the point.

(b) Another point is now chosen and the floating mark is moved again until it rests at the new level. Again the micrometer is read, the difference between the readings being the *difference in parallax* of the two points.

(c) The height differences between any points may be calculated from their difference in parallax using either of the formulae in **19**, but the results will only be approximate or *crude* because the principles apply to truly vertical photographs only and flying heights are approximate. If ground-control points, of which the level and position are known, appear on the photographs, by measuring the length between them on any one photograph the flying height may be obtained with reasonable accuracy from the following formula:

$$\frac{\text{Ground distance}}{\text{Photograph distance}} = \frac{H - h_m}{f}$$

where h_m is the known mean height of the two points and f the focal length of the camera lens. The flying height H should be obtained from the mean results taken from the photographs of a stereoscopic pair.

NOTE: If five ground-control points exist on the overlap the crude heights may be adjusted to minimise the effects of aircraft tilt producing results which may be as good as those of more elaborate stereo-plotting machines (see *Heights from Parallax Measurements* by Professor E. H. Thompson, published by the Photogrammetric Society, London).

SPECIMEN QUESTION

An air survey is carried out at a photographic scale of 1:20 000. A camera with a wide-angle lens of focal length 150 mm is used with a 230-mm square format and 60 per cent overlap. Find the difference in height between two points with parallax bar readings of 5·13 and 6·34 mm respectively.

SOLUTION

$$\frac{f}{H} = \frac{1}{20\ 000}$$

$$\therefore \qquad H = 0{\cdot}150 \times 20\ 000$$

$$= 3000 \text{ m flying height}$$

$$\text{Also } \frac{0{\cdot}4 \times 230}{B} = \frac{150}{3000}$$

$$\therefore \qquad B = \frac{0 \cdot 4 \times 230 \times 3000}{150}$$

$$= \frac{276\,000}{150}$$

$$= 1840 \text{ m, the air base length.}$$

Now, $\quad h_x - h_y = \dfrac{0 \cdot 006\,34 - 0 \cdot 005\,13}{0 \cdot 150 \times 1840} (3000)^2$

$$= \frac{0 \cdot 001\,21 \times 9 \times 10^6}{276}$$

$$= 39 \cdot 5 \text{ m, the height difference.}$$

21. Airborne profile recorder. The ground-control points necessary for the preparation of accurate maps must be heighted to provide vertical control. The reduced levels of such points can be obtained by spirit levelling or, more usually over large areas, by trigonometrical levelling. Where ground control is sparse, height control may be effected by an *airborne profile recorder*. This instrument uses radar to bounce signals off the ground back to the receiver in the aircraft producing an accurate profile of the ground elevation along the flight path.

22. Plotting machines. Air survey plotting machines are many and varied but all use the common principles of the stereoscopic viewing of rectified projections of pairs of photographs, with a kind of parallax measurement being taken for heighting by positioning a "floating" mark on a three-dimensional space model. The two instruments to be briefly considered here as examples of some basic types are the following:

(a) *The Multiplex* (see **23**).
(b) *The Wild Autograph* (see **24**).

23. The Multiplex. This instrument is shown in Plate 10 (reproduced by courtesy of Williamson Manufacturing Co. Ltd.). The basic principle used here is that of the *anaglyph*. The image of one photograph is projected in red on to a plain white surface and the image of its overlapping pair is projected in blue-green. These images are viewed with red and blue-green spectacles and a three-dimensional anaglyphic model is seen similar to that in Fig. 120. The apparatus consists of the following:

(a) *A range of projectors*, each of which represents a camera station. The air photograph is reduction printed on a glass *diapositive* about 65 mm square. A diapositive is a transparent, positive print. It is inserted in the projector with an appropriate colour filter. The projectors may be adjusted individually to alter scale and rectify the projected images to fit each other exactly.

(*b*) *A horizontal map table*, below the projectors, on which the map is drawn.

(*c*) *A bar*, which supports the range of projectors and which is capable of adjustment relative to the map table for orientation of the total integrated model to the map control.

(*d*) *A tracing table*, which consists of a white disc about 100 mm in diameter which forms the reflecting surface on which the images of the photographs are viewed. It is mounted on a vertical support on a movable stand which holds the plotting pencil. In the centre of the tracing table is a point of light vertically above the plotting pencil. The tracing table can be raised or lowered so that the floating mark can be placed in contact with the space model surface. The pencil point will then define the plan position of the point on the model. Contours are traced by setting the table to a specific height and placing it so that the mark is in contact with the model surface. By moving the tracing table the mark can be guided along a contour by keeping the mark at all times touching the model surface. The pencil will then trace the plan route of the mark following the contour. Variations in height of the floating mark can be read off a scale graduated in millimetres which is attached to the tracing table support.

24. The Wild A7 Autograph. This plotting machine, illustrated in Plate 9 (reproduced by courtesy of Wild Heerbrugg, Switzerland), is a universal, first-order instrument. It is called universal because it can be used for *aero-triangulation* as well as for detail plotting. Aero-triangulation or *bridging* is the process of linking a series of stereo models which are not individually ground controlled and thus provide a reliable control for each overlap. Once this has been done a second-order or inferior instrument can be used for detail plotting from the now controlled stereoscopic pairs.

The A7 uses 230-mm-square diapositives which are positioned horizontally on two viewing tables lit from above. These photographs are viewed through a pair of binoculars and a long train of optics, the left eye viewing one and the right eye the other, thus producing a *space model* in the field of view.

The *viewing optics* terminate in a scanning lens at the end of a *space rod*, a mechanical rod which takes up the same relative position within the perspective model as the light ray from a point of detail on the ground to its photograph. One space rod serves each diapositive and the intersection of their centre lines defines the position of a ground point as do the light rays in Fig. 120.

In order to rectify the projection of the diapositives these space rods are mechanically adjusted until their relative positions provide the proper intersection of small bundles of light rays to form an oriented and adjusted scale space model.

A *diaphragm* behind each scanning lens carries the heighting mark, equivalent to the mark of the parallax bar. These half marks fuse together to form the floating mark in the field of view.

Two hand wheels move the scanning-space rods once they have been relatively adjusted, which has the apparent effect of moving the photographs relative to the floating mark in the field of view. This X and Y movement of the space rods results in different points of detail being defined in their proper plan position. Instead of the intersection point of the rod centre lines being physically defined, as the equivalent light rays on the Multiplex are, these rods are mechanically connected to a plotting table, the Y and X movements of the rods imparting a $\triangle N$ and $\triangle E$ movement respectively to the plotting pencil.

Heighting, or the Z movement, is carried out by the rotation of a footwheel which brings the floating mark to the ground surface of the space model. Variations in height can be read off a graduated scale adjusted to suit the particular scale and the photographs being used.

The spatial X, Y and Z co-ordinates, or *eastings*, *northings* and *reduced level*, can be numerically recorded for every point defined on the plotting table by means of a suitable read-out or print-out attachment connected to the machine.

USES OF AIR PHOTOGRAPHY

25. Photointerpretation. Apart from map making air photographs have a great number of applications, many of which are based on utilising the information recorded on the photograph.

In order to extract this information *photointerpretation* is necessary. This process demands great skill as, apart from a knowledge of photogrammetry, the photointerpreter must be a specialist in the subject for which data are being evaluated.

(*a*) *Identification.* In the preliminary stage photographs are examined to identify features and this may be done by examining the following:

(*i*) Single photographs or mosaics.
(*ii*) Stereoscopic pairs.
(*iii*) Comparisons of photographs with existing maps.
(*iv*) Photographs on the ground.

(*b*) *Significance.* Having identified features it is necessary to deduce their significance and application. A few of the professional men involved in this aspect are the following:

(*i*) *The town planner*, for the extent, environment, space, etc., for development.
(*ii*) *The engineer*, for site suitability, etc.
(*iii*) *The estate manager*, for economic development, property valuation, etc.
(*iv*) *The geologist*, for strata, rock formation, existence of minerals, etc.
(*v*) *The botanist*, for plant life, agricultural development, etc.
(*vi*) *The archaeologist*, for the pattern of historic formations, etc.

26. Identification. The identification of a single feature is often simple. The analysis of the mind's assessment process will help in identifying many features which cannot always be easily recognised. The following seven factors aid identification:

(*a*) *Size.* The size of an object is often relevant. In order to estimate size the approximate scale of the photograph should be known and rough measurements may be taken. When viewing stereoscopically, heights of unknown objects can be compared with those of known features and with the aid of a parallax bar can sometimes be measured.

(*b*) *Shape.* Two objects of roughly the same size may be identified by *shape*. For example, the outline shape of a church is usually different from that of another building of similar size. Regular-shaped objects are usually man-made.

(*c*) *Shadow.* Shadow can be a hindrance as large shadows

from hills and buildings can obscure detail. This can be overcome now by electronic printing which can vary light intensity in the printing of one photograph. They are useful in the following ways:

(*i*) Shadows cast give an indication of an object's profile.
(*ii*) Shadow comparison gives an indication of relative heights.
(*iii*) Shadows of trees assist in specie identification.
(*iv*) Camouflaged buildings cast shadows.
(*v*) Flat features, such as paved areas, cast no shadows.

(*d*) *Pattern*. The pattern formed by some features aids identification. Take the following as examples:

(*i*) The seasonal pattern of wheat stooks in a field.
(*ii*) The regular pattern of an orchard.
(*iii*) The obvious layout of a modern housing estate.
(*iv*) The pattern of paths across common land.

(*e*) *Site or location*. The location of a feature helps identification in that the long building located beside a railway line is probably a station or an isolated building in a field without proper road access is likely to be a barn.

(*f*) *Tone*. The tonal range in monochrome photographs extends from white, through all shades of grey to black. The use of colour photography assists in identification as contrasts are more apparent. In many instances infra-red false colour is useful; *e.g.* foliage may appear magenta in complete contrast to surrounding ground and water or even dead foliage, which appears green. In this way crop diseases may be located early. False colour film also shows a great amount of underwater detail not possible with other emulsions.

(*g*) *Texture*. A very coarse texture will normally give rise to a lot of internal shadow and thus a dark tone. For example, green foliage, although light in colour, due to the shadows formed by leaves, will appear dark. Alternatively dark black earth when wet will reflect more light and may appear lighter in tone.

NOTE: Interpretation is based on the power of deduction, but this must not be taken too far. A train on a railway line indicates that the line is likely to be in use. The opposite obviously cannot be construed; *i.e.* that because there is no train the line is not in use.

27. Comparison between the map and air photograph. The air photograph is a picture of the land at an instant of time showing every detail, although distorted by perspective. The map shows only essentials, details are simplified by the use of conventional symbols and, as it takes time to produce, it is out of date by the time it is published. The following table covers some of the essential differences between the two:

Item	Air photograph	Map
Relief	There is no indication on a single photograph. A stereo pair give full information except in thickly wooded areas.	This is indicated by contours, spot heights and symbols. Full details between contour lines are not known.
Drainage	Natural drainage is obvious on a stereo pair.	Drainage does not show up, except for main waterways.
Buildings	The size and distribution of buildings are apparent but building functions are not shown, although they may be deduced in many cases.	Building distribution and functions of some, *e.g.* churches, public houses, etc., are shown.
Roads and railways	These can be easily located and identified, but can be concealed in wooded areas. Pavements can be seen and the number of railway tracks counted. Public and private land is not distinguishable.	Roads, paths and railways are exaggerated in width for clarity. Road class and metalling are indicated, except in larger scales.
Names	There are no road or place-names.	Road names are recorded on larger scales. Place-names are shown.
Boundaries	The demarcation of boundaries does not appear. Fences and hedges may be distinguished.	Boundaries are shown by symbols. The lines of property boundaries are shown on larger scales.
Trees	The true density of woodlands and orchards appears. From tone and	Types are shown by symbols, but show deciduous, fir, and orchard only. Species

Item	Air photograph	Map
Trees (*cont.*)	shadow, species may be established. The height and quantity of timber can be evaluated.	and quantity are not shown.
Crops	Standing crops may be identified by experts.	These are not shown.

28. Applications of air photography. The applications of air photography, apart from the provision of topographical maps and plans, are almost unlimited. In nearly all cases the applications relate to the collation of information necessary for the planning of future developments. They are therefore primarily related to town and country planning and specialist uses among all professions concerned with land use. The following is by no means an exhaustive list of some of the present applications of air survey:

(*a*) *Ecological and geographical surveys*. This involves an examination of the changes in the natural environment due to the influence of man. Scientific and economic data can be provided to further the development of both developed and underdeveloped countries.

(*b*) *Road and rail links*. The suitability of road and rail links may be examined from the point of view of construction, availability of materials and planning to suit environmental development.

(*c*) *Reservoirs*. The selection and survey of catchment areas and reservoir sites are facilitated by the examination of stereoscopic pairs of photographs.

(*d*) *Land drainage and soil erosion*. Air photographs provide the information needed for the planning of land drainage, irrigation and flood prevention. The lines of existing land drains can be located on the photographs, although invisible on the ground. Also the extent of salt damage from sea flooding can be ascertained from the photographs and they can be useful for land reclamation in low lying areas.

(*e*) *Reconnaissance*. For large-scale engineering and redevelopment projects reconnaissance can be undertaken to a large extent from air photographs. This can be done without the land-owner's knowledge, preventing land speculation, unwarranted objections or profit taking. For example, the location of road routes or routes for electric power lines and the selection of pylon positions can be undertaken by stereoscopic examination.

(*f*) *Navigation*. The survey of estuaries for navigational purposes may be undertaken from the air under certain circumstances.

(*g*) *Traffic surveys*. Air photographs taken at peak traffic periods can show bottlenecks and provide planning data for new routes. Photographs taken before and after the layout of new road junctions, road/rail crossings, traffic islands, etc., can illustrate changes in traffic flow. Individual junctions may be covered for this purpose by suspending a camera with a wide-angle lens to take photographs at regular intervals over a time period.

(*h*) *Land utilisation*. Land utilisation maps are prepared from air photographs. Air photographs will show the existence of unauthorised developments and show the increase in size of quarries, gravel pits and brick-fields.

(*i*) *Geological studies*. The location of oil and mineral deposits can often be obtained from air photographs. Also the movement of sand dunes can be studied. Often geological faults are apparent on air photographs and not on the ground.

(*j*) *Other uses*. Some other uses to which air photographs have been put are the following:

(*i*) Surveys after earthquakes evaluate the extent of damage and the amount of rebuilding required.

(*ii*) Crop diseases can be located before becoming apparent on the ground.

(*iii*) Stock maps can be prepared for quantities of standing timber.

(*iv*) Pollution effects from industrial waste on land and water can be studied.

(*v*) Oblique photographs are used to illustrate the effect of large new developments and construction on surrounding areas to lay audiences, who would not have the training to appreciate vertical photographs, although these could provide more information.

29. Digital ground model. This process known as D.G.M. or D.T.M., standing for digital terrain model, is a process whereby the ground shape may be stored in a computer instead of in a map form or a three-dimensional model. From stereoscopic pairs a large number of heighted points are established and their X, Y, Z co-ordinates are fed into a computer. Any new construction details, such as those for a new road, may be programmed and fed into the computer. The computer is then capable of interpolating the levels along the intersecting surfaces of the ground with the new formation. This is done in several positions until the pre-established conditions are satisfied and the new work is aligned in the most economically viable position.

NOTE: Three-dimensional models are often constructed from polystyrene from the contour lines provided by air survey plotting machines. The contour lines are followed by a tracer, which is connected by an adjustable pantograph to a drill. This cuts a block of the material into a true ground shape.

30. Orthophotographs. The effect of tilt may be removed with a rectifier (*see* **11**). Where ground height alters in the area photographed the scale distortion due to relief (*see* **5**(*a*)) can now be eliminated by sophisticated electronic equipment, producing *orthophotographs*. They are produced by scanning narrow strips across the stereoscopic model formed from overlapping pairs of vertical air photographs. From height analysis the correct plan position for all points on the photographs are produced and a new photograph is compiled from one of the stereo pairs. The result is a photo-map with the planimetric accuracy of a normal map. Because of the scanning process straight line features with height variation have a slightly jagged appearance due to the correction process occurring in the width of the scanning lines.

NOTE: Orthophotographs are particularly useful in certain cadastral survey systems where photogrammetric techniques are found to be more suitable than ground survey methods, see *Cadastral Surveys within the Commonwealth* by P. F. Dale, published in 1976 by HMSO.

31. Other ways of taking air photographs. For interpretative purposes photographs are taken from balloons or model aircraft or cameras can be suspended from high buildings or purpose-built for existing towers. In the future the use of satellite photography will probably become available for domestic use instead of for primarily military purposes.

PROGRESS TEST 17

1. What is the difference between *photogrammetry* and *photo-interpretation*? (1)

2. What are the main differences between air survey cameras and ordinary domestic cameras? (2)

3. What are the advantages and disadvantages of the two types of aerial photograph? (3)

4. What are the two major causes of scale distortion in air photographs? (5)

5. What is *stereoscopy* and why is it applied in photogrammetry? (6–7)

6. How and why are the two types of stereoscope used? (8)

7. How are air photographs spaced in order to secure stereoscopic cover? On what do flying heights depend? (9)

8. Describe how controlled and uncontrolled mosaics are prepared. In what way do mosaics differ from a map? (10–11)

9. Define the terms *principal point, principal plane, plumb point* and *isocentre*. (12)

10. What is the *radial assumption*? (13)

11. How may data be added to an existing map, using the radial assumption? (14)

12. Describe the use of the radial line plotter. (15)

13. Describe the process of plotting a principal point traverse. (16–17)

14. Describe the use of the slotted template. (18)

*15. In a stereoscopic pair of vertical air photographs the distance scaled between two principal points is 88·9 mm. The flying height above ground was about 2500 m. The camera's focal length was 150 mm. A television mast appearing on both photographs was observed with a parallax bar, the readings at top and bottom being 3·14 and 5·49 mm respectively. Calculate the approximate height of the mast. (19–20)

*16. Two ground-control points, 3026·5 m apart at a mean level of 327 m, appear on a stereoscopic pair of photographs. The distance between them was scaled on each photograph at 106·3 and 107·1 mm. The focal length of the lens used was 150 mm.

The parallax bar reading of control point Y with a reduced level of 305·6 m was 4·36 mm and for another point X was 7·19 mm. Calculate the approximate reduced level of X. The absolute parallax of Y was scaled and found to be 86·2 mm. (19–20)

17. What is an airborne profile recorder? (21)

18. Describe briefly the difference in operation of the Multiplex and the Wild A7 plotting machines. (22–24)

19. Name six of the professions which make use of air photointerpretation. In what way is it useful to each? (25)

20. What seven factors should be considered in the process of identification of features appearing in air photographs? (26)

21. What are the essential differences between maps and air photographs? (27)

EXAMINATION TECHNIQUE

THE only way to develop a sound examination technique is to practise. The Progress Tests in this book are designed for this purpose. The student can check his answer with the text, and those questions which are marked with an asterisk are answered in Appendix IV. A thorough knowledge of the subject, combined with a practical ability in using the instruments and a familiarity with examination conditions, can alone ensure success. It is most important that the student should be confident of his ability—in his subject and in dealing with examinations.

Questions should first be read slowly and understood. The easier questions must always be answered first. Generally two or three can be answered in less than their allocated time, providing more time for any which require more thought. *Never* spend more than the allocated time on the first two questions in any paper. If a mistake has been made by tackling a question which is taking too long, leave it and start the next. It may be possible to return to the troublesome question later.

Calculations must be properly laid out as has been shown in the text, all stages of the work and the values of functions and logarithms being neatly recorded. Rough, untidy calculations may contain a slight error and so produce a wrong answer. If an examiner cannot see easily where a calculation slip has occurred he can only mark the work as wrong, instead of allowing credit for knowledge of method. In practical survey calculations all work must be shown to be checked correct. This process of checking should become a habit and ought to be carried into examinations as far as available time allows.

EXAMINATION PAPERS

A SELECTION of recent examination questions is given below. Unless otherwise stated, thirty-six minutes per question are allowed. The answers to some of these questions are given in Appendix III.

The following are from the papers for the degree of B.Sc. from the University of Birmingham, first examination, 1969, for the schools of Geology, Geography and Civil Engineering:

1. (a) Given the following abstracts from a tacheometric field book, compute the horizontal distances to and reduced levels of the spot shots "fence," "stream" and "road" to 0·1 m in each case. The theodolite used had a multiplication constant of 100 and no addition constant.

At: *P*5 Height of peg: 278·95 m
Height of instrument: 1·74 m

To	Stadia	Axial hair	Vertical angle
Fence	1·00 2·34	1·10	83° 40′
Stream	1·00 3·68	2·30	101° 00′
Road	1·000 1·825	1·41	89° 20′

(b) Describe a method you would use to determine the multiplication and addition constants of an old external-focusing telescope.
(*See* XII, **4–16.**)

2. (a) The area is required of a strip of land between a straight fence, 80 m long, and a stream. Given the following offset measurements from the fence to the stream, in metres, compare the areas of this strip of land as computed by Simpson's rule and the trapezoidal rule, to the nearest square metre. Express each of these areas in hectares, to four decimal places.

Distance	0	10	20	30	40	50	60	70	80
Offset	17·4	28·1	33·8	37·3	38·0	37·3	33·3	29·6	22·0

(*See* XIV, **3–5.**)

(b) Describe how you would test and adjust the plate bubble of a theodolite. (*See* VI, **19.**)

3. A straight of bearing 220° 18′ is to lead into a left-hand circular curve of radius 100 m at TP1. Pegs are to be placed on the curve at 25-m intervals, measured along the arc of the curve, from a nearby traverse station E6. Given the following co-ordinates, compute the bearings and distances from the traverse station to the first two points on the curve, correct to the nearest minute and 0·01 m respectively (four-figure tables may be used).

	Y (*metres*)	X
TP1	2579·34	3468·81
E6	2544·27	3432·06

(*See* XVI, **1–12, 22.**)

4. A gradient of +1 per cent is to be connected to a gradient of −2·2 per cent by means of a 100-m vertical curve having equal tangents. Calculate the reduced levels along the curve at 25-m intervals, if the reduced level of the beginning of the curve is to be 78·46 m.

If the formation width is to be 8·00 m, and the side slopes are to be 1 in 3, using Simpson's rule compute the total volume of excavation between beginning of curve and end of curve, to the nearest 100 m³, given the original ground levels below. Neglect curvature correction in respect of the vertical curve.

Distance	$BC = 0$	25 m	50 m	75 m	$EC = 100$ m
Ground level	79·98 m	80·76 m	80·54 m	81·32 m	78·10 m

(*See* XVI, **30–36.**)

5. A distance T1–T2 was measured by means of a subtense bar. Ten determinations of the subtended angle were made, as shown below. If the survey was at a mean altitude of 1000 m above mean sea level, and if the bearing T1–T2 is 345° 01′ 23″, compute the co-ordinates of T2.

Reject any subtended angle you consider to be too much in error. The radius of the earth may be taken to be $6·373 \times 10^6$ m.

Co-ordinates of T1:	$Y = 210·987$	$X = 654·321$
Subtended angle:	1° 46′ 49·3″	1° 46′ 49·6″
	52·8	53·0
	50·1	50·9
	51·4	51·5
	41·2	50·7

(*See* XII, **20–21,** VII, **13.**)

6. Given:

	Y (*metres*)	X
T3	578·432	1215·136
T4	625·914	1153·678

(a) Compute the bearing and distance T3–T4 to 1″ and 0·001 m respectively.   (*See* IV, **14–15**.)

(b) T3 and T4 are two towers on either side of a deep valley. It is desired to suspend a light cable between them, at a tension of 98·06 newtons. 100 metres of the cable have a mass of 10 kg. A theodolite was set up 1·763 m beneath T3, and vertical angles to T4 were observed as follows:

$$\text{FL} \quad 92° \ 27' \ 34''$$
$$\text{FR} \quad 267° \ 32' \ 44''$$

Compute the length of cable required, to 0·001 m, allowing 1 m for anchoring at either end.   (*See* VII, **8–12**.)

(c) What was the index error of the theodolite used?
    (*See* VI, **23**.)

7. (a) Copy out and complete the following abstract from a level field book, using the rise and fall method. Show all arithmetical checks on the working. If the reduced level of BM2 should be 244·440 m A.O.D., distribute the misclosure.

BS	IS	FS	Rise	Fall	R.L.	
1·234					247·643	BM1
0·890		2·345				
0·762		3·176				
	4·013					
3·769		2·876				
	0·006					
		1·467				BM2

                                           (*See* X, **34–35**.)

(b) Copy out and complete the following traverse computation:

	dY	dX		Y	X
			A5	398·23	602·01
A5–T11	+118·10	+11·07			
84° 38′ 40″					
111·62					
			T11		
T11–T12	−32·24	−103·73			
197° 16′ 50″					
108·62					
			T12		
T12–B11	+117·88	−213·00			
151° 02′ 20″					
243·44					
			B11	601·89	296·45

                                             (*See* IX, (**29–45**.)

The following are from the papers for the C.N.A.A. degree of B.Sc. in Building, Economics and Estate Management from the Polytechnic of the South Bank (I.L.E.A. Brixton School of Building), first examination, 1969:

8. Describe briefly any *four* methods of determining the horizontal distance between two points which are at different levels and in excess of 50 m apart. Mention the instruments you would use and the measurements you would make in each case and explain the circumstances under which you consider the methods might be used.   (*See* II, **1**.)

9. Describe and discuss the significance of the following:

    (*a*) Reciprocal levelling.
    (*b*) The zero circle of a planimeter.
    (*c*) The stadia hairs in a theodolite.
                                   (*See* X, **38**, I, **18**, XII, **4**.)

10. "A vertical air photograph is not a map." Discuss.
                                              (*See* XVII, **27**.)

11. The co-ordinates of a survey station X are to be established by measuring the distance and bearing of X from a co-ordinated station A. To check the calculated position of X the measurements are continued to another co-ordinated point B. From the following data calculate the co-ordinates of X, adjusting any closing error to give their most probable value:

$$\begin{array}{ccc} & E & N \\ & \textit{(metres)} & \\ A: & 497{\cdot}62 & 386{\cdot}74 \\ B: & 253{\cdot}00 & 533{\cdot}60 \end{array}$$

A–X: Whole circle bearing $= 220° \; 21' \; 00''$
       Length $= 150{\cdot}00$ m
X–B: Whole circle bearing $= 330° \; 33' \; 00''$
       Length $= 300{\cdot}00$ m
                                              (*See* IV, **1–16**.)

12. A tilting level was first set up midway between two staff positions, A and B, 70 m apart, and the following readings were taken on to a metric staff:

On to staff held at A: 1·702
On to staff held at B: 1·402

The level was then moved to a second position X, 10 m from B and 60 m from A, and the following readings were taken:

On to staff held at A: 1·875
On to staff held at B: 1·590

(a) The level is out of adjustment. What is its percentage error?

(b) If the reduced level of A is 42·713 m above the Newlyn datum, what is the reduced level of the soffit of a bridge if the reading taken on to a staff held upside down at C under the bridge is 4·249? Assume that the level has *not* been moved from X and that the distance C–X is 33·3 m.

(c) Explain in detail how this level would be adjusted.

(d) If the level is not moved from the second position at X after adjustment, what reading would then be obtained on a staff held at the following places?

    (i) At A.
    (ii) At B.
    (iii) At C.   (*See* X, **18–29, 36**.)

13. Much of the information that used to be obtained by plane tabling is now supplied by aerial photography, but the plane table is still the most suitable means of providing information under certain conditions.

Explain briefly the four surveying techniques used in plane tabling and describe *three* situations in which you consider the plane table to be preferable to other methods of survey.

                                             (*See* VIII.)

The following are from the papers of the C.N.A.A. degree of B.Sc. in Building, second-year examination, 1970:

14. (a) Errors in linear measurements are either systematic, accidental or gross. Give two examples of each type, indicate their effect and explain how this may be minimised.

(b) You are undertaking a survey to a degree of accuracy of 1 : 5000. What is the maximum angle of slope which may be ignored while still maintaining this accuracy?   (*See* II, **9–21**.)

15. (a) Describe in detail how the position of a point in England may be defined on an Ordnance Survey map to the nearest 10 m.

(b) Show how the maps of the Ordnance Survey published on National Grid sheet lines are uniquely referenced in relation to their different scales.   (*See* V, **1–11**.)

16. (a) Describe two methods of obtaining the true level between two points using a level known to be in error without making any instrumental adjustments.

(b) In order to obtain the level difference between two points A and B on either side of a river, the method of reciprocal levelling was adopted. The following field observations resulted:

At instrument position 1, 5 m from A:
    Reading on to staff at A = 1·396
    Reading on to staff at B = 1·387

At instrument position 2, 5 m from B:

Reading on to staff at A = 1·837
Reading on to staff at B = 1·842

If the R.L. of A = 10·000 m, what is the R.L. of B?
(See X, **20, 38.***)*

17. A tacheometer, with a stadia constant of 100 and an additive constant of zero, was set up at Station A and the following observations were taken to a vertically held staff:

To station	Stadia	Horizontal circle	Vertical circle
	3·150		
B	2·440	316° 22′	+3° 30′
	1·730		
	1·570		
C	1·060	7° 00′	−2° 00′
	0·540		

Calculate the distance BC and the height difference between B and C.   *(See* XII, **13, 15.***)*

18. (*a*) What are the two principal factors governing the length of summit vertical curves?

(*b*) Calculate the setting out data for a simple parabolic summit curve 100 m long where a +4 per cent gradient meets a −1 per cent gradient, pegs being placed at each 10-m chainage. The R.L. of the beginning of the curve is 27·310 m.   *(See* XVI, **30–36.***)*

19. Discuss the applications of *four* of the following:

(*a*)	The optical square.	*(See* II, **36–39.***)*
(*b*)	The "Autoplumb."	*(See* XV, **23–25.***)*
(*c*)	The abney level.	*(See* II, **10.***)*
(*d*)	A travelling rod.	*(See* XV, **11–13, 40.***)*
(*e*)	The site square.	*(See* XV, **15.***)*
(*f*)	Profile boards.	*(See* XV, **16.***)*
(*g*)	Subtense bar.	*(See* XII, **19–25.***)*
(*h*)	Aerial photography.	*(See* XVII, **1, 25–31.***)*

The following are from the General section and Building Surveying paper of the Royal Institution of Chartered Surveyors, first examination, 1970:

20. The following notes of a levelling survey were made along the centre line of a proposed roadway. Transfer the details to your answer and complete the notes by the rise and fall method. Reduce the levels, given that the level of A is 100·21 m above datum.

Thereafter determine the gradient of a roadway constructed at a uniform gradient from A to B. Calculate the depth of cutting or the amount of filling at every 20 m to give a uniform gradient from A to B.

Staff readings are in metres.

B.S.	I.S.	F.S.	Distance (m)	Remarks
2·140			0	At A
	1·024		20	
2·403		0·820	40	
	1·740		60	
	2·061		80	
1·426		2·325	—	
	2·098		100	
2·954		2·258	120	
	2·291		140	
	1·124		160	
1·627		0·462	—	
	0·763		180	
		1·423	200	At B

(*See* XI, **12**.)

21. The angle between two "straights" of a road to be connected by a circular curve is 120°. It is necessary that the circular curve should have a radius of 150 m. The centre of the circle of which the curve is a part lies in the obtuse angle between the two straights.

Calculate the following:

(*a*) The tangent lengths.

(*b*) The length of the curve.

(*c*) The angle subtended at the centre of the circle by the chord to the whole of the curve.

Describe briefly a method of setting out the curve by the use of two theodolites. (*See* XVI, **2, 3, 16**.)

The final question is from the paper of the first examination, 1970, of the Institute of Quantity Surveyors (thirty minutes allowed):

22. (*a*) Calculate the cubic contents in a 25·00-m length of a cutting 12·00 m wide at the bottom, 5·00 m deep at one end and 4·00 m deep at the other end, with sides sloping 1 in 1.

(*b*) Calculate the area of covering in square metres which will be required for a conical roof 10·00 m high, if the area of the base is 38·50 m².

(*c*) Calculate the volume of a right prism on a triangular base, the sides of the base being 65 mm, 70 mm and 75 mm, and the height being 50 mm. (*See* XIV, **19**.)

ANSWERS TO
EXAMINATION QUESTIONS

1. (a)

To	Distance	R.L.
Fence	132·4 m	294·3 m
Stream	258·2 m	228·2 m
Road	82·5 m	280·2 m

2. (a) Simpson's rule: 2596 m².
Trapezoidal rule: 2571 m².

3. E6 to 1. 53° 30', 26·64 m.
E6 to 2. 120° 11', 15·48 m.

4.

Chainage	R.L.
0	78·46 m
25	78·61 m
50	78·56 m
75	78·31 m
100	77·86 m

Volume: 3400 m³.

5. T2: 194·362 Y, 716·468 X.

6. (a) 142° 10' 38", 77·664 m.
   (b) 80·027 m.
   (c) 09".

7. (a) 246·533
244·248
240·998
242·136
245·900

   (b)

	Y (E)	X (N)
T11	516·31	613·11
T12	484·05	509·40

11. X: 400·50 E, 272·40 N.

12. (*a*) 0·03 per cent.
    (*b*) 48·845 m.
    (*c*)   (*i*) 1·893.
            (*ii*) 1·593.
            (*iii*) 4·239.

16. (*b*) 10·002 m.

17.   Length *BC* = 110·2 m.
         Height difference = 10·86 m.

18.

Chainage	R.L.
0	27·31
10	27·68
20	28·01
30	28·28
40	28·51
50	28·68
60	28·81
70	28·88
80 high point	28·91
90	28·88
100	28·81

20.   *AE* = 160° 29′ 20″, 914·44 m.

20.

Chainage	Cut	Fill
0	—	—
20	0·790	—
40	0·668	—
60	1·004	—
80	0·357	—
100	—	0·905
120	—	1·391
140	—	1·054
160	—	0·214
180	0·986	—
200	—	—

21. (*a*) 86·60 m.
    (*b*) 157·08 m.
    (*c*) 60°.

22. (a) 1862·5 m³ (*end areas*), 1858·3 m³ (*prismoidal*).
    (b) 116·50 m²
        (Curved surface area of a cone = π × Base radius × Slant height.)
    (c) 105 000 mm³.

ANSWERS TO
PROGRESS TEST QUESTIONS

Progress Test 1

13. (a) 189·75 m².
    (b) 191·58 m².

15. 5·923 ha.
16. 284·6 m² or 0·028 ha.

Progress Test 2

9.   20·015 m.
10. 3·167 ha.
11. 1 in 39 or 1° 29′.

13. 0·25 m.
14. 1·15 m.

Progress Test 3

9.   19·3 m at 347¾°.

10. AB: 20½°; BC: 117°;
     CD: 197°; DA: 273°;
     62·5 m at 8½°.

Progress Test 4

7.   S 88° 22′ 20″ E; S 74° 21′ 20″ W; N 5° 38′ 40″ W;
     N 89° 00′ 00″ E; N 88° 22′ 20″ W; S 89° 00′ 00″ W.

9. B: 270·0 E, 755·7 N.

10. AB = 454·9 m at
     307° 47′ 40″.

11. C: 144·33 E, 251·65 N;
     AC = 526·36 m.

12. (a) D: 1507·0 E,
         128·0 N.
     (b) CD = 1295·7 m at
         191° 26′ 20″.
     (c) Angle ACD
         = 40° 09′ 50″.

Progress Test 5

9.   227°; 28·3 km.

Progress Test 6

5.   77·8 mm.

447

Progress Test 7

6.   70·5439 m.

7. Adjusted angles, seconds only:

$A1$ 32·1; $A2$ 40·3; $A3$ 28·1; $A4$ 01·8;
$B1$ 24·0; $B2$ 27·7; $B3$ 02·4; $B4$ 23·6.

8. Adjusted angles, seconds only:

$A1$ 09·4; $B1$ 53·6; $C1$ 57·0.
$A2$ 39·4; $B2$ 18·6; $C2$ 02·0.
$A3$ 49·4; $B3$ 04·6; $C3$ 06·0.
$A4$ 27·4; $B4$ 49·6; $C4$ 43·0.
$A5$ 09·4; $B5$ 09·6; $C5$ 41·0.
$A6$ 44·4; $B6$ 44·6; $C6$ 31·0.

10.   84·37 m.

11.   40·02 m.

12.   95·6 m.

13.   −11·21 m.

14.   408·35 m.

Progress Test 9

16. A: 537·34 E, 285·30 N.
         B: 671·71 E, 321·19 N.
         C: 747·46 E, 403·09 N.

17.   Error = +0·09 E, −0·04 N.   18.   20° at Station B.
         Accuracy = 1/5281.   19. AB: 30 m too long.

Progress Test 10

17.   25·071, 22·575, 24·881, 20·421, 21·347, 19·305, 19·205, 16·167.

19. (a)   No.
     (b)   50·000 m.

Progress Test 11

8.   Chainage 42·0 m, level 111·30 m.
         Chainage 64·2 m, level 111·38 m.
         Chainage 69·5 m, level 111·49 m.
         Chainage 99·4 m, level 112·09 m.

9. (a)   37·30, 35·39, 35·87, 35·13, 32·57, 32·30, 34·49, 37·32.
     (b)   5 per cent.
     (c)   20 m, fill 0·91 m; 40 m, cut 0·57 m; 60 m, cut 0·83 m; 80 m, fill 0·73 m.
     (d)   Chainage 32·3 m, level 35·69 m.
         Chainage 70·6 m, level 33·77 m.

10. (a)   5·00 m.
       (b)   7·50 m.
       (c)   1400 m, 73·51 m.

Progress Test 12

8. B: 8·885 m; C: 9·494 m;
       $BC = 47·0$ m.
12.   (5)   56·93 m, 40·72 m.
       (6)   132·64 m, 31·40 m.

Progress Test 14

2.   2742 m² or 0·274 ha.
3.   221·7 m².
4.   0·699 ha.
5.   6985·6 m².
6. $AX = 83·14$; $XY = 125·76$; $YB = 113·02$.
7.   248·0 m.
8. $CX = 204·9$ m, $BX = 399·7$ m.
9.   10·14 m.
10.   28·3 m².
11.   5706·7 m³.
12.   2526 m³

Progress Test 15

10. (a) 1·370 m, 0·485 m.
    (b) 14·560 m.
18. (a) 0·497 m.
    (b) 0·19 m.

Progress Test 16

3. $\delta = 1°$ 30′ 00″
            3   00   00
            4   30   00
            6   00   00
            7   09   00
4. $B.C. = 9 + 73·66$ m; $E.C. = 11 + 72·92$ m.
       $\delta = 0°$ 10′ 54″
            0   45   17
            1   19   39
            1   54   02
            2   28   25
            3   02   47
            3   37   10
            4   11   33
            4   45   55
            5   20   18
            5   42   30
5. (a) 879·81 m.
   (b) $B.C. = 5 + 25·05$.
        $E.C. = 9 + 39·65$.

 (c) 0° 48′ 44″; 0° 48′ 50″; 0° 28′ 37″.
 (d) 24·95 m, 14·65 m.
9. 2·93 m, 0·43 m.
13. 0° 21′ 36″, 0·670 m.
14. (a) 260·82 m.
  (b)   0° 02′ 17″
      0 09 10
      0 20 38
      0 36 40
      0 57 18
  (c) 315·39 m.
17. Chainage   0 m, level 26·85 m.
   Chainage 25 m, level 26·08 m.
   Chainage 50 m, level 25·45 m.
   Chainage 75 m, level 24·98 m.
   Chainage 100 m, level 24·65 m.
   Chainage 125 m, level 24·48 m.
   Chainage 141·67 m, level 24·44 m.
   Chainage 150 m, level 24·45 m.
   Chainage 175 m, level 24·58 m.
   Chainage 200 m, level 24·85 m.
   Chainage 225 m, level 25·28 m.
   Chainage 250 m, level 25·85 m.

Progress Test 17

15. 66·1 m.
16. 441·6 m.

APPENDIX V

SITE SURVEY PLAN

Many students are required to undertake site surveys and submit plans and field notes for assessment. Presentation is all important and reference must be made to the text for the manner of plotting and presentation of survey work. The plan on pp. 452–53, produced by courtesy of Engineering Surveys Ltd., is an example of professional practice. It illustrates a form of plan layout used for traverse surveys. It may be adapted in minor details for chain surveys or any particular requirements of examining bodies.

Points to note with regard to the presentation of this survey are as follows:

 (a) It is important that the information should be presented in the clearest possible manner. No unnecessary lines are therefore included which might confuse detail. For example, the co-ordinate grid lines do not extend right across the survey, but

may be established if required from the surrounding grid outline. In students' presentation work the grid would usually be
wholly drawn in blue ink. Also, the trees are simply shown
without confusing detail by drawing in the foliage outline.
This is usual for engineering works, though for architectural
and students' practical work the foliage outline is often desirable.
Tree details are recorded in a separate schedule on the drawing.
Note that tree numbering is normally in sequence. In this plan
example trees surveyed have been omitted to save unnecessary
repetition. The traverse lines are not shown, only the survey
station positions. In students' presentation work, lines and
stations would normally be shown in red ink. Occasionally the
traverse layout of lines is shown as an inset with a record of all
final co-ordinates, lengths and bearings of lines and reduced
levels of stations. This would be useful for setting-out purposes
later, but is only supplied for clients with the knowledge to use
such information.

(b) The contours are shown with the contour heights recorded
reading up the slope, which is normal Ordnance Survey practice.
On developed sites contours are frequently omitted, only the
spot levels to 0·01 m being recorded. On very rough, broken
ground spot levels may be recorded to 0·1 m, as on this plan.
More usually levels are shown to two places, though the second
decimal place is imprecise, except on hard surfaces. On smaller
scales the spot height values are generally omitted in favour of
contours only, except at salient points.

(c) Levels to two decimal places are shown on adjacent roads
and always include back of pavement levels, top and bottom
of kerbs and centre line levels to allow for the proper design of
new access roads.

(d) Overall site dimensions are included as they are usually
required by the designer. They may be obtained as a result of
direct measurement or may be calculated from co-ordinated and
checked points.

(e) All available services are surveyed as far as possible, *e.g.*
manholes. No information shown is assumed to be correct without absolute verification.

(f) A T.B.M. is always established adjacent to the site unless
an existing O.B.M. is sufficiently close, as in this case.

(g) Explanatory notes and a legend of symbols are always
included.

(h) The layout of the survey is always such that the North
point points as nearly as possible to the top of the sheet.

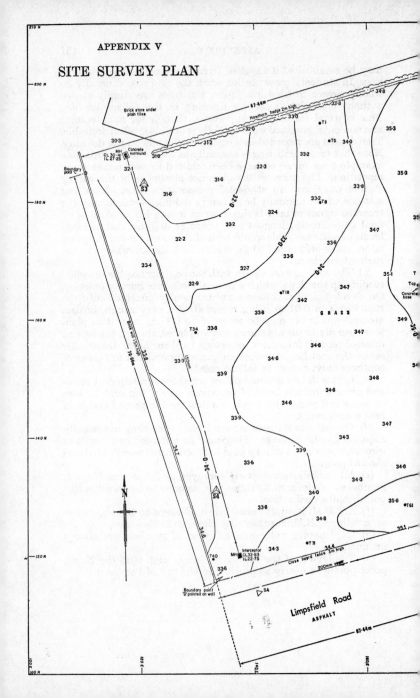

APPENDIX V

SITE SURVEY PLAN

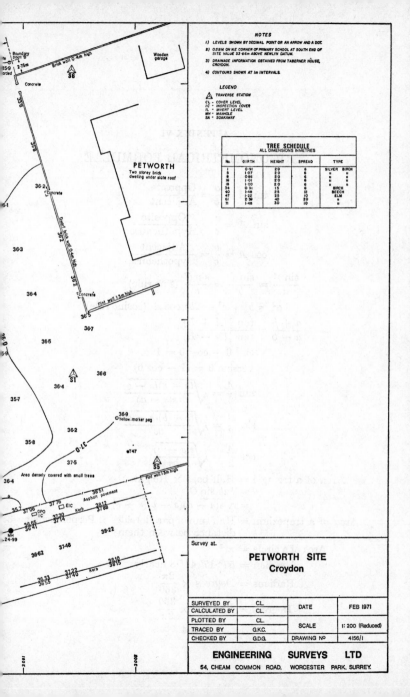

TRIGONOMETRICAL FORMULAE

$$\tan A = \frac{a}{b} = \frac{\text{Opposite}}{\text{Adjacent}}$$

$$\sin A = \frac{a}{c} = \frac{\text{Opposite}}{\text{Hypothenuse}}$$

$$\cos A = \frac{b}{c} = \frac{\text{Adjacent}}{\text{Hypothenuse}}$$

$$\frac{\sin A}{a} = \frac{\sin B}{b} = \frac{\sin C}{c} \quad \text{(sine rule)}$$

$$a^2 = b^2 + c^2 - 2bc \cos A \quad \text{(cosine rule)}$$

$$\frac{a+b}{a-b} = \frac{\tan \frac{1}{2}(A+B)}{\tan \frac{1}{2}(A-B)}$$

$$\sin^2 \theta + \cos^2 \theta = 1$$

$$\text{versine } \theta = (1 - \cos \theta)$$

$$\tan \frac{A}{2} = \sqrt{\frac{(s-b)(s-c)}{s(s-a)}}$$

$$\sin \frac{A}{2} = \sqrt{\frac{(s-b)(s-c)}{bc}}$$

$$\cos \frac{A}{2} = \sqrt{\frac{s(s-a)}{bc}}$$

$$
\begin{aligned}
\text{Area of a triangle} &= \text{Half base} \times \text{Height} \\
&= \tfrac{1}{2}ab \sin C \\
&= \sqrt{s(s-a)(s-b)(s-c)}
\end{aligned}
$$

Area of a trapezium = Half sum of parallel sides × Perpendicular distance between them

Area of a circle = πr^2

A radian = $57° \ 17' \ 44'' \cdot 8$ nearly

$$\text{Radians} = \text{Degrees} \times \frac{2\pi}{360}$$

$$\text{Degrees} = \text{Radians} \times \frac{360}{2\pi}$$

One second of arc = 0·000 004 848 radians

Log

$$\sin 1'' = \frac{1}{\rho} = 0\text{·}000\ 004\ 848 \qquad \bar{6}\text{·}685\ 574\ 9$$

$$\rho = 206\ 265 \qquad\qquad 5\text{·}314\ 425\ 5$$

$$\pi = 3\text{·}141\ 592\ 65 \qquad\quad 0\text{·}497\ 149\ 9$$

Tangent formulae for calculating the co-ordinates of p *from points* a *and* b *at the intersection of bearings* α_a *and* α_b *from* a *and* b *respectively*

$$\Delta N_{ap} = \frac{\Delta E_{ab} - \Delta N_{ab} \tan \alpha_b}{\tan \alpha_a - \tan \alpha_b}$$

$$\Delta N_{bp} = \frac{\Delta E_{ab} - \Delta N_{ab} \tan \alpha_a}{\tan \alpha_a - \tan \alpha_b}$$

$$\Delta E_{ap} = \Delta N_{ap} \tan \alpha_a$$
$$\Delta E_{bp} = \Delta N_{bp} \tan \alpha_b$$
$$E_p = E_a + \Delta E_{ap} = E_b + \Delta E_{bp}$$
$$N_p = N_a + \Delta N_{ap} = N_b + \Delta N_{bp}$$

TACHY REDUCTION TABLE

θ	0°	1°	2°	3°	4°
0'	0·00	1·74	3·49	5·23	6·96
5'	0·15	1·89	3·63	5·37	7·10
10'	0·29	2·04	3·78	5·52	7·25
15'	0·44	2·18	3·92	5·66	7·39
20'	0·58	2·33	4·07	5·80	7·53
25'	0·73	2·47	4·21	5·95	7·68
30'	0·87	2·62	4·36	6·09	7·82
35'	1·02	2·76	4·50	6·24	7·97
40'	1·16	2·91	4·65	6·38	8·11
45'	1·31	3·05	4·79	6·53	8·25
50'	1·45	3·20	4·94	6·67	8·40
55'	1·60	3·34	5·08	6·81	8·54

$100(\frac{1}{2} \sin 2\theta)$

θ	5°	6°	7°	8°	9°
0'	8·68	10·40	12·10	13·78	15·45
5'	8·83	10·54	12·24	13·92	15·59
10'	8·97	10·68	12·38	14·06	15·73
15'	9·11	10·82	12·52	14·20	15·87
20'	9·25	10·96	12·66	14·34	16·00
25'	9·40	11·11	12·80	14·48	16·14
30'	9·54	11·25	12·94	14·62	16·28
35'	9·68	11·39	13·08	14·76	16·42
40'	9·83	11·53	13·22	14·90	16·55
45'	9·97	11·67	13·36	15·04	16·69
50'	10·11	11·81	13·50	15·17	16·83
55'	10·25	11·95	13·64	15·31	16·96

$100 \cos^2 \theta$

0°	100·00
0° 30'	99·99
1°	99·97
1° 30'	99·93
2°	99·88
2° 30'	99·81
3°	99·73
3° 30'	99·63
4°	99·51
4° 30'	99·38
5°	99·24
5° 30'	99·08
6°	98·91
6° 30'	98·72
7°	98·51
7° 30'	98·30
8°	98·06
8° 30'	97·82
9°	97·55
9° 30'	97·28
10°	96·98
10° 30'	96·68

$$100 \left(\tfrac{1}{2} \sin 2\theta\right)$$

θ	$10°$	$11°$	$12°$	$13°$	$14°$
$0'$	17·10	18·73	20·34	21·92	23·47
$5'$	17·24	18·87	20·47	22·05	23·60
$10'$	17·37	19·00	20·60	22·18	23·73
$15'$	17·51	19·13	20·73	22·31	23·86
$20'$	17·65	19·27	20·87	22·44	23·99
$25'$	17·78	19·40	21·00	22·57	24·11
$30'$	17·92	19·54	21·13	22·70	24·24
$35'$	18·05	19·67	21·26	22·83	24·37
$40'$	18·19	19·80	21·39	22·96	24·49
$45'$	18·33	19·94	21·53	23·09	24·62
$50'$	18·46	20·07	21·66	23·22	24·75
$55'$	18·60	20·20	21·79	23·35	24·87

$$100 \cos^2 \theta$$

$11°$	96·36
$11° \ 30'$	96·03
$12°$	95·68
$12° \ 30'$	95·32
$13°$	94·94
$13° \ 30'$	94·55
$14°$	94·15
$14° \ 30'$	93·73
$15°$	93·30

INDEX